D1318359

Introduction to
ATOMIC AND NUCLEAR PHYSICS

Introduction to
ATOMIC AND NUCLEAR PHYSICS

D. E. CARO
University of Melbourne

J. A. McDONELL
Monash University

B. M. SPICER
University of Melbourne

Foreword by
MELBA PHILLIPS
University of Chicago

ALDINE PUBLISHING COMPANY / Chicago

First published in the United States 1964 by
ALDINE PUBLISHING COMPANY
64 East Van Buren Street
Chicago 5, Illinois

Published in Great Britain by
Edward Arnold (Publishers) Ltd., London

Published in Australia by
F. W. Cheshire Pty. Ltd., Melbourne

Library of Congress Catalog Card Number 64-14909
Printed in the United States of America

Acknowledgments for permission to publish Figures

Figure 3·5 is redrawn, with permission from the paper by Lubersky and Prilezaev, *Zeitschrift für Physik*, **49,** p236 (1928); Julius Springer, Berlin.

Figures 8·1, 11·9 and 11·12 are reprinted, with permission, from Gentner, Maier-Leibnitz and Bothe, *An Atlas of Typical Expansion Chamber Photographs.* Copyright, 1954; Pergamon Press Ltd., London.

Figure 11·7 is redrawn, with permission, from data for the 6342A tube supplied by the Radio Corporation of America.

Figure 11·10 is reprinted, with permission, from Wilson, *Proceedings of the Royal Society of London,* **A104,** p192 (1923).

Figure 12·4 is reprinted, with permission, from Blackett and Lees, *Proceedings of the Royal Society of London,* **A136,** p325 (1932).

Figure 17·4 is reprinted, with permission, from Anderson, *Physical Review,* **43,** p491 (1933).

Figure 17·5 is reprinted, with permission, from Fowler, Gaerttner and Lauritsen, *Physical Review,* **53,** p628 (1938).

Figure 17·6 is reprinted, with permission, from Thomson, *Physical Review,* **74,** p490 (1948).

Figures 17·1, 17·2, 17·3, 17·7, 17·8 and 17·9 have been reproduced from photographs kindly supplied by Dr. V. D. Hopper, University of Melbourne.

FOREWORD

Science, as a continuing endeavor, cannot be properly understood in ignorance of how its concepts and theories arose in relation to experimental discoveries, and how, in turn, great experiments have been suggested by theory. This is particularly true of modern physics, and a somewhat historical approach is especially important for those students who may not continue their education in physics to include more highly mathematical accounts of modern physical concepts. It is in this context that the publication of this book is most welcome.

In their own preface the authors make clear their reasons for preparing this introduction to atomic and nuclear physics, and indicate its role in a system of physics education patterned after the British model. The school and college system of the United States is less standardized than that for their home audience, and the utility for us of a treatment of atomic physics at this level is likely to be much more varied and thus less easily defined. Its use as a basic textbook is probably limited to a third term course, following the study of more classical aspects of physics. In addition, this book may be even more extensively useful as supplementary reading for students completing conventional freshman courses in physics or physical science, for it traces the origins of our knowledge of atomic structure more fully than is ordinarily possible in standard elementary texts. Moreover, the treatment is sufficiently clear and engaging to interest the nonacademic reader, whether he works in a scientific field or not. In sum, this slender volume should prove a valuable addition to the literature which traces the rise of modern atomic concepts.

MELBA PHILLIPS
University of Chicago

PREFACE

Some years ago it was quite common for many University students to receive their introduction to physics in the first year of their University course. This has now become quite exceptional in the University of Melbourne, where we find that nearly all students taking first-year physics – and this includes those doing such courses as Medicine, Dentistry and Agricultural Science – have had one or two years' physics at school. This situation is, we believe, common to many Universities. This being the case, there is room, in such first-year courses, for quite an appreciable amount of atomic and nuclear physics, and it is in an attempt to meet the specific needs of these courses that this book has been written.

The standard aimed at has been deliberately made higher than one would normally expect a student to reach after about three years' study of physics as a separate subject. Thus the book should provide a considerable amount of reading material extending beyond the immediate requirements of most conceivable introductory courses in atomic and nuclear physics.

While the material covered has been determined principally by the needs of first-year University students, we have tried to make the book useful and readable for students in their last school year. Some chapters, particularly in the early part of the book, should be completely within the range of such students. In nearly all other chapters, the development is such that these students should be able to follow the early sections without difficulty and without any need to refer back to more difficult sections of preceding chapters. Certainly the subject matter goes, in matters of detail, a long way further than any syllabus which we envisage as being appropriate to a secondary school course in physics. However, a good student embarking on such a course might, we hope, be encouraged to explore the subject beyond his immediate requirements for examination purposes.

In the belief that students should understand *how* a theory was developed as well as *what* the theory is, we have adopted an historical approach to the material presented. Nuclear and atomic physics is a living subject and a study of its growth can be an exciting experience. Furthermore, in studying the way new concepts evolve, the student gains an understanding of the methods employed by scientists to unravel the problems confronting them. We are aware that some students resent being taught 'history' in a physics course. However, we believe that most of them enjoy the subject if it is taught as a 'detective story', showing the way in which contributions from apparently unrelated investigations are brought together to build up a coherent picture of a new field of science.

The standard of presentation varies quite considerably – and intentionally – throughout the book. For example, in Chapter 9 we have gone further in discussing the electron structure of atoms than is usual in texts of this nature. We have done so because the modern teaching of chemistry demands a relatively detailed knowledge of electron states. It seems to us to be questionable that students should be asked to use this material before some justification has been provided for its physical basis. Again, in the chapters devoted to nuclear reactions and nuclear structure, we have provided more material than is customary in an introductory course. It has been our experience that the good student wishes to learn something about nuclear structure at an early stage.

We have not hesitated to use calculus when it seemed to provide the easiest method of deriving a particular relation. However, there are few places in the book where it appears and these derivations can be omitted, if necessary, without weakening the discussion at any point. In most cases an elementary knowledge of algebra is sufficient. It has been assumed that the reader has some knowledge of the elements of mechanics, electricity and magnetism, but no deep experience is demanded. The M.K.S.A. system of units has been used throughout.

In the text we have provided references to original papers describing significant experiments and new theoretical concepts. Exceptions have been made where a new theoretical idea has been couched in mathematical language which is too sophisticated for the young student.

We would like to acknowledge permission to publish material drawn from many sources. Individual acknowledgments have been made at appropriate points elsewhere in the book. Our first-year students have unwittingly played no small part in the production of this book. We have taught from it and the reactions of students have helped us to appreciate their problems, so that perhaps the path of future students may be strewn with rather fewer difficulties.

Finally we wish to express our appreciation of the assistance of Mrs. P. George who has been able to decipher the manuscript and from it prepare an excellent typescript. Our thanks are due to Mr. L. McBride, who has produced the line drawings, to Mr. J. Smith, for assistance in the reproduction of photographs, to Miss J. Filshie, for considerable secretarial assistance, and to our publishers, who have shown great patience and co-operation.

D. E. Caro

J. A. McDonell

B. M. Spicer

CONTENTS

Chapter 15 Radioactivity and Nuclear Structure

Chapter 16 Nuclear Energy

Chapter 17 More Fundamental Particles Are Discovered

Introduction to
ATOMIC AND NUCLEAR PHYSICS

The Atomic Theory of Matter

Most of this book is concerned with the behaviour of atoms and the particles of which they are composed. Nobody has ever seen, or is ever likely to see an atom, if by 'seeing' we mean the usual methods of visual observation, assisted perhaps by optical magnification. But if 'seeing' atoms is taken to mean the observation of effects which can readily be explained in terms of an atomic theory of matter and are difficult to account for in any other way, then seeing atoms and sub-atomic particles has become almost a commonplace experience for a great many people. Look at the luminous figures on a clock through a magnifying glass — in the dark, the faint glow of light will then appear as a host of tiny flashes. Listen to a Geiger counter of the type used in geological survey-ing — each click records a separate event. These flashes and clicks are each the result of the detection, or 'seeing' of an individual particle from the atomic world.

But does this atomic world really exist? Is it reasonable to regard atoms as actual physical objects even though they can never really be seen or handled? These are very reasonable questions to ask and until about fifty years ago there were still some eminent scientists who found themselves unhappy about accepting the atomic theory as giving a true picture of the nature of matter. They felt that a theory based on such completely intangible entities, as atoms then appeared to be, was hardly acceptable as a really firm basis on which to build a complete picture of the universe. With the passage of time, however, the atomic theory has come to be universally accepted. Such an enormous variety of phenomena, ranging from the evolution of stars to the structure of the minute constituents of living organisms and including such vast fields as chemistry and electronics are capable of description in terms of the behaviour of atoms and their components. It is hardly surprising, then, that we are now quite happy to believe in the reality of atoms.

1

CHAPTER 1

The Growth of Atomic Concepts

1·1 Early Ideas about the Structure of Matter

The Greek philosophers, Democritus and Leucippus, about 2400 years ago, were the first to suggest in their writings that matter might not be infinitely divisible, but might in fact consist ultimately of particles which cannot be further subdivided. From the Greek word *atomos*, meaning 'indivisible', they proposed the name *atom* for these 'fundamental' particles. Less than a century later, however, Aristotle was at the height of his powers and was proposing an entirely different picture of the constituents of matter. In his view, all matter in the world in which we live is made up of mixtures, in various proportions, of the four elements, Fire, Air, Water and Earth. Each of these elements was supposed to have its 'natural place' and 'natural movement', Fire having the greatest tendency to rise and Earth having the greatest tendency to fall. In this way one could readily explain, for example, why gases, being largely composed of the element Air, rise through liquids; while solids, in which Earth is the predominant element, fall through both liquids and gases. In addition, Aristotle proposed a fifth element, the Quintessence, from which all heavenly bodies are formed, this element having its natural place in circular orbits around the earth.

Now while this five-element theory may seem fanciful to us today, it did provide an explanation of sorts for a large number of phenomena and this, after all, is one criterion by which any scientific theory must be judged. Science, at the time, was a subject for philosophy rather than for experimentation, and verification of the few quantitative predictions made by Aristotle was largely neglected. The prestige of Aristotle, who had made important contributions to many fields of learning, resulted in the acceptance of his views as authoritative for about 2000 years. Various authors had questioned these theories during this period, but no-one had presented arguments of sufficient weight to overthrow them until Galileo was able to do so. He, by consistent use of experimental investigation, showed that Aristotle's pronouncements on the laws governing the motion of falling bodies were untenable and that, as Copernicus and Kepler had proposed, the earth was in motion around the sun, in contradiction to the Aristotelian view that the earth constituted the centre of the universe. The way was now cleared for a revision of other physical theories, in particular the 'five-element' picture of the structure of matter.

1·2 The Rise of Atomic Theory in Chemistry

One of the first steps forward was taken by the Englishman, Robert Boyle, the 'Father of Chemistry'. In his book, *The Sceptical Chymist*, which appeared in 1661, he introduced for the first time the concept of chemical elements as distinct from mixtures and compounds. Boyle put forward this idea with considerable clarity:

And to prevent mistakes I must advertize you, that I now mean by elements, . . . certain primitive and simple, or perfectly unmingled bodies; which not being made of any other bodies, or of one another, are the ingredients of which all those call'd perfectly mixed bodies are immediately compounded, and into which they are ultimately resolved: . . .

In the light of these principles the identification of elements and the understanding of the ways in which they combine to produce chemical compounds was carried forward with considerable success by the chemists of the eighteenth century, outstanding amongst whom were such men as Joseph Black, the Scottish physician, the Yorkshireman Joseph Priestley and the greatest of them all, the French chemist, Antoine Lavoisier. From this study of chemical compounds, two significant facts emerged. Lavoisier was careful to measure the amounts of the reacting substances which took part in various reactions and, generalising his results, proposed as '. . . an incontestable axiom . . .' the principle that *the total mass of an isolated reacting system remains constant.* In addition, Proust put forward his *law of definite proportions,* in which he pointed out that *the proportions by weight of the elements present in any chemical compound are entirely independent of the manner in which the compound is prepared.* With these laws and the concepts of the existence of elements and of their combinations with one another firmly established, the stage was set for the appearance of the atomic theory, as proposed by the Englishman, John Dalton.

The main points of Dalton's theory, as expounded in his book *A New System of Chemical Philosophy,* which was completed in 1810, may be summarised as follows:

(a) *Matter consists of indivisible particles, which Dalton referred to as atoms, and each element consists of identical atoms of a type characteristic of that particular element. Atoms themselves are completely unchangeable.*

These concepts were entirely consistent with the established picture of elements as substances which were the basic components of all chemical compounds and which could not be transformed from one to another.

(b) *When elements combine to form compounds, their atoms are not created or destroyed, but group together in simple combinations which constitute the smallest component particles (or, as we now call them, molecules) of these compounds. Then, reactions between compounds or between elements and compounds simply result in the rearrangement of the atoms into new molecules.*

This description of the fundamental processes occurring in chemical combinations clearly gave a satisfactory explanation of Lavoisier's law of conservation of mass and of Proust's law of definite proportions.

Dalton also put forward two rules governing the possible ways in which compounds could be formed. In an endeavour to give some concrete form to his ideas as to how atoms combined into molecules he suggested his *rule of simplicity* which states that, *when only one combination of two elements can be obtained it should be assumed to be a simple binary one,* that is, one atom of each element combining to form a molecule of two atoms. The next simplest combination, if a second compound of the same two elements is known, would be a three-atom molecule.

The other of Dalton's laws was his *law of multiple proportions,* in which he proposed that, *if two elements A and B combine to form various compounds and if the weight of element A in each compound is kept constant, then the weights of element B present in these compounds will be in the ratios of small integers.* This law was well substantiated by a mass of information which had been accumulated before Dalton's time, but which had never been analysed in such a way as to bring out this particularly simple relationship. It is, of course, in complete accord with the concept of atoms combining in fixed proportions for every compound.

Perhaps Dalton's most important contribution was towards the determination of the relative weights of atoms. Although many of the results he obtained are incorrect, he must be credited with the enormous step forward of assigning some measurable quantity to an atom — its weight — and using this quantity as a reliable guide in the identification of elements and the analysis of compounds. In order to find the relative atomic weights of two elements A and B, the first step is to determine their proportions in a compound.

If the weights of the atoms of A and B are m_A and m_B respectively, and if there are a atoms of A and b atoms of B in each molecule of the compound, then

$$R = \frac{Weight\ of\ element\ A\ in\ the\ compound}{Weight\ of\ element\ B\ in\ the\ compound}$$
$$= \frac{Weight\ of\ the\ atoms\ of\ A\ in\ the\ molecule}{Weight\ of\ the\ atoms\ of\ B\ in\ the\ molecule}$$
$$= \frac{a \cdot m_A}{b \cdot m_B}$$

Now the ratio R is determined experimentally, but the ratio $\frac{a}{b}$ must, at this stage, be assumed; and this is the point at which Dalton used the rule of simplicity. By calculations of this sort, extended to many compounds, Dalton was able to draw up a list of what he considered to be the most reasonable values of atomic weights. These he referred to the lightest atom, hydrogen, whose weight he took to be his unit of atomic weight.

However, there was one step in Dalton's argument which proved to be untenable, namely his rule of simplicity. In the case of water, for example, he assumed that the molecule consisted of one atom of hydrogen together with one of oxygen, so that $\frac{a}{b} = 1$, and the oxygen atom is then taken to be 8 times heavier than the hydrogen atom, since oxygen and hydrogen combine in the ratio 8 : 1 by weight to form water. Despite errors of this kind, however, Dalton must be given the credit for compiling the first table of atomic weights and for drawing attention to the importance of these quantities.

At almost the same time, the French chemist Joseph Gay-Lussac, an exceedingly careful and capable experimenter, showed that, in reactions between gases under conditions of constant temperature and pressure, *the volumes of the reacting gases and of the product gas were always expressible in simple ratios.* Such a result once again suggested, qualitatively, a simple combination between atoms and molecules, in accord with Dalton's fundamental ideas. But in matters of detail,

Dalton found it hard to accept Gay-Lussac's result. For example, he was unable to reconcile the combination of two volumes of hydrogen with one of oxygen to form two volumes of water vapour with his own rule of simplicity, in which one atom of hydrogen combined with one of oxygen to form one water vapour molecule. Furthermore, since he believed that different atoms occupied different volumes, he was unable to understand how, in other cases, the quantities of the reacting gases which combined, and which must then have had equal numbers of atoms, could have equal volumes.

This conflict was resolved by the Italian physicist Amedeo Avogadro who, guided by Gay-Lussac's law, put forward the hypothesis that *the number of molecules in a given volume of a gas is the same for all gases.* Then if, in a particular case, one volume of gas A combined with three volumes of gas B to form two volumes of gas C, in accordance with Gay-Lussac's law of simple ratios, Avogadro's interpretation of such a reaction would be that each molecule of gas A was combining with three molecules of gas B to form two molecules of gas C. This, of course, implied that the molecules were divisible, each consisting of more than one atom. Let us consider once again the combination of hydrogen and oxygen to form water vapour. In terms of our modern notation, Avogadro replaced the concept of hydrogen and oxygen combining according to the equation

$$H + O = HO$$

with the proposition that the reaction was more correctly described by

$$2H_2 + O_2 = 2H_2O \ ,$$

thus retaining all of the important features of Dalton's theory and incorporating the results of Gay-Lussac's precise measurements.

Unfortunately, Avogadro's paper in which he set forth these ideas was, in places, rather obscurely worded; in particular, the distinction in meaning between the terms 'integral molecule' and 'solitary elementary molecule', which he used to describe the particles which we now refer to as 'molecules' and 'atoms' respectively, was not always as clear as it might have been. Partly for this reason and partly because of the esteem in which Dalton's work was held, Avogadro's paper was largely ignored. In addition, there was one particularly weighty objection which was quite validly raised. If two similar atoms tend to stick together to form a molecule, why do not *all* of the similar atoms in a gas cling together, so that the gas condenses? It is only within the last forty years that we have been able to provide a satisfactory answer to this question.

As a result of this neglect of Avogadro's ideas, attempts to product a consistent set of atomic weights — the values of which, as we have seen, depend on a knowledge of the atomic composition of molecules — resulted in confusion which worsened and persisted for a period of nearly fifty years. Ultimately, however, in 1858 Cannizzaro, a fellow-countryman of Avogadro, was responsible for 'reviving' Avogadro's paper and clarifying once and for all the relationship between molecule and atom.

Once this stage had been reached, the determination of atomic and molecular weights could be carried out in an orderly manner. It soon became apparent that, if the scale of atomic weights was based on that of hydrogen being taken as unity, all atomic weights were almost integers. However, if oxygen was chosen instead as the standard and its atomic weight assigned to be exactly 16, the atomic weights of the other elements came, on the average, to be closer still to integers. So this scale was adopted and has been used ever since. Now if the molecular weights of two gases are M_A and M_B, equal volumes of these two gases, since they contain equal numbers of molecules, will have masses in the ratio $M_A : M_B$. Conversely, amounts of these two gases weighing M_A kgm and M_B kgm respectively will occupy the same volume and contain the same number of molecules. In general then, the number of molecules in M kgm (one kilogramme-mole) of a gas whose molecular weight is M is a constant. This constant, for which we use the symbol N_0, is known as Avogadro's number, and turns out to be of fundamental importance in physics.

If it can be determined, the actual masses of atoms can then be found, as distinct from their atomic weights which are only ratios. For the molecular weight of oxygen is 32, so that there are N_0 oxygen molecules, or $2N_0$ oxygen atoms in 32 kgm of that gas. Thus the mass of the oxygen atom is just $\dfrac{16}{N_0}$ kgm, and the masses of other atoms are similarly determined — hence the significance of the measurement of N_0. It should be noted that, while N_0 has been defined in terms of a discussion of molecules, it is equally true that there are N_0 *atoms* of any element of atomic weight W in W kgm of that element (one kilogramme-atom).

N_0 is, in fact, an exceedingly large number — $6 \cdot 02 \times 10^{26}$ molecules per kilogramme-mole. The first determination of Avogadro's number with any claim to precision was not made until almost 100 years after the appearance of Avogadro's paper, and the measurement was based, not on any chemical properties at all, but on physical phenomena described by the *Kinetic Theory of Gases*.

1.3 Physical Evidence for the Atomic Theory

The Swiss physicist Daniel Bernoulli was apparently the first to suggest, in 1738, that a gas should be thought of as consisting of a vast number of particles, all in rapid motion. In his view, these particles should be regarded as perfectly elastic, so that no energy is lost by collisions between them. Then the pressure on the walls of the containing vessel would be provided by the enormous number of impacts of these tiny particles, a process which would go on continuously. Bernoulli went so far as to show that this model would result in the product of the pressure and volume of a gas at constant temperature being constant, in accordance with Boyle's law. Strangely enough this was another case of an important idea which was not followed up for a long time.

It was not until 1847 that the Kinetic Theory was brought back into prominence by James Joule, who had studied under Dalton.

In the meantime, however, there had been several developments which very much strengthened its basic assumptions. In the first place the chemists, led by Dalton, had provided solid support for the atomicity of matter. Then there was the important contribution by Count Rumford, confirmed by a whole series of experiments by Joule himself, in which heat and motion were shown to be only different forms of the same quantity — energy. Lastly, there was the law proposed by the German doctor, Julius Mayer, which has become one of the foundations of physical thought — the *law of conservation of energy*. Thus the ground was well prepared for the acceptance of the Kinetic Theory of gases, which was to be remarkably successful in accounting for a wide range of physical phenomena.

The principal assumptions of the Kinetic Theory as put forward by Joule are:

(a) *A gas consists of a large number of molecules, all of which are in rapid and random motion.*

(b) *These molecules are very small compared with the average distance between them, and have no influence on one another, except when they happen to collide.*

(c) *Collisions between molecules are perfectly elastic, that is, no energy losses occur when such collisions take place.*

(d) *The temperature of the gas is directly proportional to the average kinetic energy of its molecules; thus, when a gas is heated at constant volume, the energies of its molecules are increased and its temperature rises.*

We shall not describe in any detail the way in which these assumptions (and further refinements which were added by Maxwell, Boltzmann and others in the latter half of the nineteenth century) can be used to derive a remarkable range of quantitative results about the behaviour of gases. It is sufficient for our purpose to realise that the theory is able to predict such apparently diverse results as the laws of Boyle and Charles which govern the relationships between the pressure, volume and temperature of a gas, the absence of an atmosphere around the moon, the fact that the viscosity of a gas is largely independent of its pressure and density, the rates at which gases diffuse through one another, the specific heats of gases and many other experimentally verifiable relationships between physical quantities.

These impressive successes of the Kinetic Theory, together with the rapid and consistent growth of chemistry and chemical theory appeared to provide overwhelming evidence for the basic assumption in each case — the existence of atoms and molecules. Nevertheless there remained a few quite eminent sceptics who were unable to believe in the reality of particles which no-one had ever seen. They felt that *direct* evidence for the existence of atoms was still lacking. These final doubts were removed in 1912 by the experiments of the French chemist Jean Perrin. Perrin undertook the first quantitative study of a phenomenon which had been discovered by the botanist, Robert Brown, as far back as 1827, the so-called Brownian motion. When tiny grains of a substance such as pollen are suspended in water and observed through a microscope, they are found to be in constant motion.

The peculiar thing about this motion is that it is quite random — the particles move in tiny rapid jerks, the direction of each little movement being entirely unrelated to the previous path of the particle. It had been suggested that this movement was really due to the incessant bombardment of the particle by water molecules, and Perrin took this suggestion one step further. It seemed to him that this collection of small particles could themselves be regarded as behaving like very large molecules and that they should then move and distribute themselves like the molecules of one gas in thermal equilibrium with another. This idea was supported by the observation that the particles did not all sink to the bottom of the container, but ultimately reached a 'sedimentation equilibrium' in which the density of particles increased in a regular manner from the top of the column of liquid to the bottom.

Now this type of behaviour is just what is

predicted by the Kinetic Theory. Since the molecules of a gas have weight, one expects the action of gravity on a vertical column of gas to produce a higher density of molecules at the bottom than at the top, with a corresponding increase in pressure from top to bottom. Equilibrium will be reached when, for a thin 'slice' of gas at any height, the weight of the gas molecules in the 'slice' is equal to the difference between the pressure force on the underside of the 'slice' and the pressure force on the upper side where the pressure, due to the slightly lower density, is a little less. The Kinetic Theory enables us to express these ideas in mathematical form and thus to predict the exact manner in which the number of particles per unit volume increases down the column. The expression obtained in this way for the ratio of the numbers per unit volume at two particular heights turns out to depend on the mass of each particle, the difference in heights, the temperature of the gas and, significantly, on Avogadro's number.

By means of very careful measurements using suspensions of gamboge in which the particles were very uniform in size and mass, with diameters between 10^{-4} and 10^{-5} cm,

Perrin found that the distribution of particles through the column of water was exactly as predicted by the Kinetic Theory, so that the proposition that they behaved just like large molecules in constant collision with the water molecules was entirely justified. At last there was direct and quantitative evidence of the action of molecules. Not only this, but Perrin's measurements made it possible to obtain the first reliable estimate of Avogadro's number, since all of the other quantities which affected the distribution of the particles could be measured. Lastly, Perrin was able to observe the average displacements per unit time of individual particles as they wandered through the liquid. Here also a comparison with the Kinetic Theory was possible, since the solution of this problem of the 'random walk' of a gas molecule had been achieved by Einstein and Smoluchowski. Once again Perrin's measurements substantiated the molecular origin of the Brownian motion.

From this time onward, the atomic theory of matter has never been questioned, and we have no hesitation at all in believing in the 'reality' and 'existence' of the atoms which we never see with our eyes but which we 'see' in so many other ways.

The Turn of the Century: Some Momentous Advances in Physics

In the latter part of the nineteenth century, it seemed that the basic structure of physics was all but complete. Newton's laws of motion and the law of gravitation had provided a solid foundation on which the science of dynamics had been raised to impressive heights. Virtually all of the complicated motion of the planets of the solar system could be predicted with extreme accuracy in terms of the gravitational attraction of the sun and of the planets on one another. Indeed, slight variations which were observed in the motion of Uranus from its calculated orbit had resulted in the discovery of another planet — Neptune. The laws of thermodynamics and the Kinetic Theory gave a satisfactory account of heat transfer and the behaviour of gases. Electrical and electromagnetic phenomena could apparently be completely understood in terms of the work of such men as Ampère and Faraday, all of which was finally gathered together as a unified picture in the monumental Electromagnetic Theory of Maxwell. The crowning achievement of this theory was the emergence from it of a complete account of all optical phenomena, resulting from the description which it gave of light as an electromagnetic wave.

However, some unsolved problems remained. Some of these were cases in which no-one seemed to have hit on the right way to tackle their interpretation in terms of existing theories — for example, no satisfactory explanation of the origin of permanent magnetism had been found. Some of them, however, were problems of disagreement between theory and experiment. The orbit of the planet Mercury could not quite be accounted for; the spectrum of light emitted from an incandescent solid was not the same as that predicted by the Electromagnetic Theory. The ten years from 1895 to 1905 saw the discovery of a whole series of new phenomena, mostly concerned with the physics of atomic particles. Some of these also could not be fitted into the elegant structure of 'classical' physics and so the time had come for this structure to be modified, and even for parts of it to be completely replaced with new theoretical concepts.

In the next five chapters we shall survey some of the new fields of experiment and thought which were opened up in that exciting decade, and see something of how these lines of investigation developed.

CHAPTER 2

The Identification of the Electron

2·1 The Conduction of Electricity in Gases

Under normal conditions a gas is a poor conductor of electricity. If, however, a high potential difference is applied between two electrodes which are sealed into a tube, and the pressure is then reduced sufficiently, a transport of electricity takes place across the gas. This transport can be detected by the flow of an electric current in the external circuit.

It is probable that the first electrical discharge in an exhausted vessel was produced by the French scientist Picard, about 1670. He reported that when the mercury column of a barometer was shaken up and down vigor-ously, a bluish phosphorescence could be observed in the Torricellian vacuum. Hanks-bee in England (1705) showed that the effect observed by Picard was due to the production of charges of electricity on the glass by friction between the mercury and the walls of the tube.

In 1836, Faraday recorded that he studied 'sparks, brushes, glows, etc.' in different gases. In the course of these experiments he discovered the gap in the glow discharge which today bears his name — the *Faraday dark space*. The apparatus he used consisted of a glass globe which could be evacuated through a stopcock. Brass electrodes were inserted into the vacuum vessel and their separation could

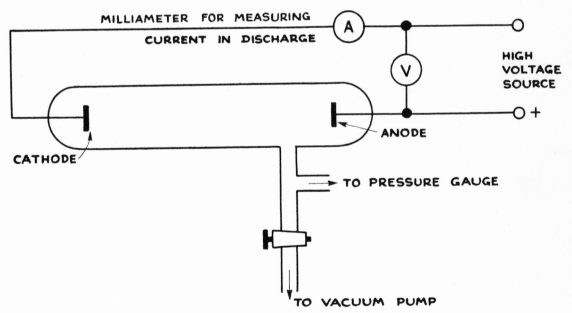

Fig. 2·1—*Typical apparatus for the study of discharges in gases*

be varied. Faraday described his discovery of the dark space in these words:

> . . . at the moment of separation of the rods a glow of light came over the end of the negative wire, the positive being dark. As the distance increased, a purple stream or haze went right out from the end of the positive wire towards the negative wire; this elongated as the distance increased, but there was always a dark space between the end of it and the haze in the negative wire. The space was nearly invariable in its width . . . the dark space is probably an important point to understand.

The invention of a mercury pump by Geissler in 1855 made lower pressures possible and the simpler discharges at these lower pressures led to increased efforts to understand the phenomenon. The work of the thirty years following 1855 culminated in three major discoveries: the electron, X-rays and positive rays.

A tube suitable for the study of the change of form of the discharge with pressure is shown in Figure 2·1. It is connected via a side tube to a pump capable of producing pressures less than 0·01 mm of mercury. The potential difference between the electrodes is supplied by a unidirectional high voltage source. This type of high voltage supply is preferred since the appearance of the discharge may be influenced considerably by variations in this potential difference, and by variations in the current through the tube. In the most careful work, the tube current is maintained constant.

Figure 2·2 shows the changing appearance of the discharge as the pressure is reduced. The illustrated data were taken with a tube current of two milliampere. No glow discharge appears until the air pressure has been reduced to less than 10 mm of mercury when it first appears as a streamer of brilliant blue light which flickers to and fro down the length of the tube. When the pressure is reduced further, the streamer broadens and becomes paler in colour until, at a pressure of about 1 mm of mercury, the discharge is a broad, luminous, pale mauve band which fills the tube except for the Faraday dark space near the *cathode*, or negative electrode. This luminous band is called the *positive column*. Further decrease of pressure results in an increase in the length of the Faraday dark space (with a corresponding decrease in the length of the positive column) and in the appearance of a luminous region at the cathode. This is the *negative glow*.

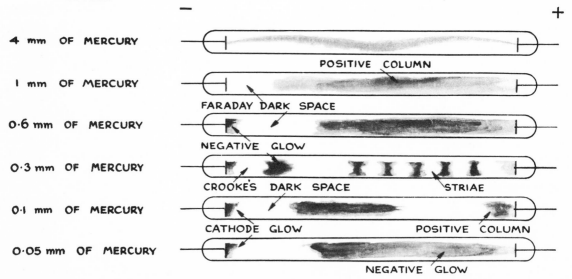

Fig. 2·2—*The variation of the appearance of a gas discharge as the gas pressure is reduced. The potential difference across the tube is varied so as to maintain a constant current of 2 milliampere*

At pressures less than 0·5 mm of mercury, the discharge assumes a different structure and this also is shown in Figure 2·2 The cathode is now covered with a soft reddish glow, the *cathode glow*, and a new dark region, *Crookes' dark space*, separates the cathode glow from the negative glow. The Faraday dark space still separates the negative glow from the positive column. This column is now broken up into a number of discs (striae) of relatively high luminosity. The conditions of formation of striae are not well understood, but factors such as gas impurity, current density and gas pressure are known to influence them to some extent.

As the gas pressure is reduced below 0·1 mm of mercury, the width of the Crookes' dark space increases and the negative glow becomes brighter and expands towards the anode. At the same time the positive column shrinks and eventually disappears so that the negative glow then fills the tube.

Further reduction in the pressure results in the expansion of Crookes' dark space and the shrinkage of the negative glow. For pressures less than 0·01 mm of mercury, Crookes' dark space nearly fills the tube, the cathode glow fades, and a bright fluorescence is observed on the wall of the tube near the anode. The colour of this fluorescence is determined by the chemical composition of the glass, and is not influenced by the nature of the gas in the tube.

2·2 Early Observations of Cathode Rays

The fluorescence observed in the wall of the glass tube opposite the cathode was first observed by Plücker in 1858 while he was making investigations into the negative glow in low pressure discharge tubes. As well as observing the fluorescence, he found that it could be moved about with a magnet held close to the cathode. This led him to ascribe the fluorescence to currents of electricity flowing from the cathode.

Later Hittorf showed that if an opaque object was placed in the path of these 'rays', a well-defined shadow was produced within the fluorescent area, indicating that the 'rays'

travel in straight lines from the cathode. A significant extension of this idea was made when Goldstein in 1876 showed that the sharply-defined shadows were produced even if the cathode was an extended surface. When he communicated this idea to the Berlin Royal Academy of Sciences, Goldstein used the word 'Kathodenstrahlen' — *cathode rays* — for the first time. Goldstein's conclusion was that the cathode rays were principally emitted in a direction normal to the cathode surface. However, he believed that the cathode rays were some form of disturbance in the aether;* that is, he used the word 'ray' in the literal sense.

Quite the opposite view was suggested by Varley and later by Crookes. Both of these scientists constructed discharge tubes which contained a light paddle-wheel balanced on a pair of horizontal rails. This was mounted in front of the cathode and the rays emanating from that electrode were directed against the upper and lower vanes in turn, control of the direction of the cathode rays being achieved by means of a magnetic field. It was found that the vane struck by the rays always turned away from the cathode and Varley was the first to suggest that this was due to the impact of '. . . attenuated particles of matter set free from the negative pole by electricity'. Crookes was able to move the paddle-wheel backwards and forwards along the tube by reversing the polarity of the electrodes. This led him to conclude that the cathode rays were particles which possessed momentum, and therefore mass and velocity.

It was shown later by J. J. Thomson and Starke that the rotation of the paddle-wheel was almost entirely an effect due to the heating of only one side of the vanes by the cathode rays. Thus a correct conclusion about the nature of the rays had been reached, even though the interpretation of the experiment which led to this conclusion was quite erroneous.

The solution of the problem of the identity of the cathode rays was provided by a series

---

* The aether was considered to be an all-pervading medium responsible for the propagation of light. Its properties are discussed more fully in Section 6·2.

of experiments carried out by J. J. Thomson in the years immediately preceding 1897.

2·3   The Charge and Mass of Cathode Rays

Thomson's experiment[1] to determine the sign of the charge carried by cathode rays was a repetition of an earlier one by Perrin.[2]   A discharge tube of special design was used. The cathode rays were collimated into a narrow beam, and at the end of the tube struck a metal strip painted with zinc sulphide.   The impact of the cathode rays on the zinc sulphide caused it to fluoresce, thereby defining the path of the cathode rays. When a horse-shoe magnet was placed centrally over the outside of the discharge tube the fluorescent spot shifted, indicating that the beam of cathode rays had been deflected in the magnetic field.   When the direction of the magnetic field was reversed, the spot shifted in the opposite direction. From the direction of the deflection, Thomson deduced that the sign of the charge carried by the cathode rays was negative, thus confirming Perrin's conclusion.

The first attempts to observe the deflection of cathode rays in an electric field were made by Hertz.   They were unsuccessful, and this negative result was interpreted as evidence against the proposition that cathode rays were particles.   Thomson also repeated this experiment, and found that the cathode rays were deflected.   He pointed out that Hertz's lack of success was due to having had too high a pressure in the discharge tube.

All the evidence presented thus far is best accounted for by the hypothesis that cathode rays are small particles carrying a negative charge of electricity.   However, these rather qualitative results gave no indication of the size of this negative charge, or of the masses of the particles.   On the other hand, the fact that a well-defined beam of cathode rays was apparently deflected by a fixed amount in passing through an electric or a magnetic field

[1] The experiments discussed in this section are described in Thomson's book *Conduction of Electricity Through Gases* (Cambridge University Press, 1906).

[2] Perrin, *Comptes Rendus*, **121**, p1130 (1895).

suggested that these particles were possibly all of the same mass and carrying the same amount of charge.   If this were not so and they were ions having a range of charges and masses they would exhibit a variety of deflections, as may be deduced from the calculations which follow.   Now the force on a charged particle of mass m in either an electric or a magnetic field is proportional to its charge, e; hence the acceleration of the particle, which determines its displacement as it passes through such a field depends on the ratio $\frac{e}{m}$.   If it could be shown, by measuring such displacements, that the value of this *specific charge*, $\frac{e}{m}$, was constant for the cathode rays, it would then be tempting to suppose that they really did consist of identical particles, each having the same charge and mass.

Before discussing Thomson's crucial experiment of 1897 in which he investigated quantitatively the specific charge of the cathode rays, the dynamics of a charged particle moving in an electric or a magnetic field should be considered.

From the definition of electric field strength, the force on a particle carrying charge e in a field of strength E is given by

$$F_E = eE. \qquad (2\cdot1)$$

The direction of this force is in the direction of the electric field, and is independent of the direction of motion of the particle.

If, on the other hand, the same particle, moving with velocity v, enters a magnetic field of flux density B, it experiences a force, F_M, which is at all times perpendicular to the plane containing both of the vectors v and B. For the case in which v is perpendicular to B, the magnitude of F_M is given by

$$F_M = evB. \qquad (2\cdot2)$$

Thomson's method of measuring the charge-to-mass ratio of cathode rays involved the use of 'crossed' electric and magnetic fields.   That is, the rays passed through a region of space within which the two fields were established at right angles to one another.   A schematic diagram of the apparatus is shown in Figure

2·3. The cathode rays, after leaving the cathode C, passed through two slits S_1 and S_2. A potential difference was maintained between S_1 and the cathode so that the particles were accelerated and passed through S_1 to slit S_2. Beyond S_2 the particles could be deflected by either an electric or a magnetic field.

If neither field was established, the cathode rays passed straight through and caused a fluorescent spot on the wall of the tube. The electric field was obtained by applying a potential difference between the plates P_1 and P_2, and the resulting deflection d of the fluorescent spot was measured. Let the dimension of the plates in the direction of travel of the rays be l, and suppose that the speed of the cathode rays is v. Since the force on a particle of charge e is Ee directed perpendicular to the plates, the acceleration is Ee/m. The field is assumed to be uniform, and so the particles experience a constant transverse acceleration. Thus the transverse velocity, on emergence from the electric field, is

$$v' = \frac{Ee}{m}\frac{l}{v}\cdot ,$$

since l/v is the time spent under the action of the field. The tangent of the angle of deflection θ is v'/v, and assuming that this angle is small, it can be written

$$\theta = \frac{eEl}{mv^2}. \qquad (2\cdot3)$$

Having measured this deflection, the fluorescent spot was brought back to its original position by applying a second deflecting force which acted in the opposite direction to that produced by the electric field. This second deflecting force was due to a magnetic field, which was produced by placing outside the tube two coils whose diameter was equal to the length of the plates. The coils were placed so that they covered the space occupied by the plates, and the distance between the coils was equal to the coil radius. The current through the coils was increased until the magnetic deflection was equal and opposite to the electric deflection. The net zero deflection meant that there was zero resultant force acting on the particles as they travelled through the two deflecting fields. That is,

$$evB = eE,$$

or

$$v = E/B. \qquad (2\cdot4)$$

Substituting this value for v in equation (2·3) leads to

$$\frac{e}{m} = \frac{E\theta}{B^2l}. \qquad (2\cdot5)$$

E and B can be measured and the angle θ, which in the small angle approximation equals $\tan\theta$, is given by the linear deflection divided by the distance xy (see Figure 2·3).

Thomson found that the value of the specific charge which he obtained was constant, within the accuracy of his measurements, for quite a variety of experimental conditions. The use of different gases in the discharge tube and of different metals for the electrodes of that tube produced no appreciable change in this property of the cathode rays. Thus it was reasonable to conclude

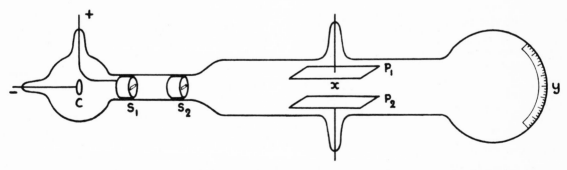

Fig. 2·3—*Thomson's apparatus for the measurement of the specific charge of the electron*

Table 2·1 — *Early values of specific charge*

Cathode rays (Thomson's first measurement)		$0·8 \times 10^{11}$ coulomb kgm^{-1}
Cathode rays (other workers)	from $1·0$ to	$1·9 \times 10^{11}$ coulomb kgm^{-1}
Negative ions from thermionic emission		$0·9 \times 10^{11}$ coulomb kgm^{-1}
Negative ions from photoelectric effect		$1·2 \times 10^{11}$ coulomb kgm^{-1}

that these particles were not characteristic of any of the chemical elements which played some part in their formation, but were some fundamental constituent of matter. This view was supported by measurements of other workers who used different methods to measure $\frac{e}{m}$ for cathode rays. They all arrived at about the same value for this specific charge as did Thomson.

Strong reinforcement for this conclusion about these new particles came from other sources. It was known that negative ions of some sort were emitted both when a wire was heated to a high temperature (*thermionic emission*) and also when light of short wavelength was allowed to fall on certain metallic surfaces (the *photoelectric effect*). Methods were devised for measuring the specific charges of these ions and in both cases, the value found was almost the same as that for cathode rays. Table 2·1 shows some typical results obtained by about 1900. The fundamental nature of these particles was quite apparent.

2·4 The Electron

A significant feature of the specific charges found in this way was that their magnitude was thousands of times greater than the specific charges of ions in electrolytes. These latter were quite well known following Faraday's work with electrolytes in 1833.

Faraday showed that during electrolysis the mass of any substance deposited from any electrolyte by the passage of electricity is proportional to the charge passing through the solution. The mass of any element deposited by the same quantity of electricity is proportional to its *chemical equivalent*, that

is, the ratio of its atomic weight to its valency. These facts concerning electrolysis can be summarised in the one relation for the mass M kgm of material deposited during electrolysis,

$$M = \frac{AQ}{Fv},$$

where A is the atomic weight of the substance, v the valency of the ion, Q coulomb the quantity of electricity transported through the electrolyte and F is a universal constant known as the faraday. It has a value of $9·65 \times 10^7$ coulomb (kgm-mole)$^{-1}$.

The ratio of the total charge transported to the total mass deposited is $Q/M = Fv/A$. Now Stoney had suggested in 1874 that if the atomic theory is correct, each ion must have a charge q and a mass m, and the ratio q/m for a single ion must equal the ratio Q/M for the large number of ions involved in electrolysis. Hence the specific charge on an ion is

$$q/m = Fv/A .$$

By measuring the mass of a given substance deposited by a known electrical charge, the value of the specific charge of the ion can be obtained.

The largest specific charge known prior to Thomson's experiment was that of the hydrogen ion which has both valency and atomic weight equal to one. Its specific charge is therefore $9·65 \times 10^7$ coulomb kgm^{-1}. From the values in Table 2·1, we see that the new fundamental particles had a specific charge about 1000 times greater. This showed conclusively that they were particles of a type which had not previously been encountered. It was some years before these particles were universally referred to as *electrons*, a name originally used by Stoney in his description of electrolytic conduction.

The next important point to investigate was the reason for this large value of specific charge. Was the charge of the electron 1000 times greater than that of the hydrogen ion, was its mass 1000 times smaller, or were both its charge and mass different from those of any known particle? The easiest way to settle this question was to find a method of measuring the electronic charge.

Before discussing the methods used to measure this charge, we should consider the information which was available in Thomson's time concerning the magnitude of the charge carried by the hydrogen ion. Since 9.65×10^7 coulomb of charge is carried by the N_0 ions in one kilogramme-atom of any monovalent substance, the charge on each such ion was known to be $9.65 \times 10^7/N_0$ coulomb. But N_0 had never been measured. The best that could be done was to rely on arguments, based principally on the Kinetic Theory of gases, which showed that N_0 should lie between the limits 4×10^{26} per kilogramme-atom and 2×10^{27} per kilogramme-atom. Thus the charge of the hydrogen ion was known to lie between about 2.5×10^{-19} coulomb and 0.5×10^{-19} coulomb.

About 1900 there were several partly successful attempts to measure the value of the electronic charge. In 1897, C. T. R. Wilson reported his discovery that gaseous ions act as nuclei for the condensation of clouds. If a volume of air saturated with water vapour is ionised by X-rays and then suddenly expanded, a cloud is formed. By accurate control of the expansion conditions, it is possible to arrange that condensation takes place only on negative ions.

Thomson[1] reasoned that these negative ions were in fact electrons. He produced such a cloud and was able to measure the total charge which it carried. He was able to calculate the mass of water in the cloud, the average mass of a drop and hence the number of drops in the cloud. From this number and the total measured charge he obtained a value of the electronic charge. In view of the

assumptions necessary to arrive at this result, it is not to be expected that any great accuracy would be achieved and it is perhaps remarkable that Thomson's result differed by only about 30% from the presently accepted value. However, the significant point is not the accuracy of the result which was obtained but rather the order of magnitude of the electronic charge which was so deduced. Thomson's value of about 1.1×10^{-19} coulomb fell within the limits which could at that time be placed on the charge of the hydrogen ion.

Since the charge of the electron was now shown to be of about the same size as that of the hydrogen ion, it became apparent that the electron itself was an entirely new particle with a mass about a thousand times less than that of the lightest atom. We now know that the electronic mass is even smaller; the ratio of the masses of the hydrogen ion and the electron is 1836.

2·5 The Accurate Measurement of the Charge of the Electron

The year 1909 marked the start of a series of investigations by Millikan,[2] the results of which, together with his work on the photoelectric effect, were destined to win for him the Nobel Prize for Physics in 1923.

The experimental technique used by Millikan to measure the charge of the electron was a refinement of that used earlier by Thomson. Droplets of oil were sprayed from an atomiser and in the process acquired charges due to friction. After the spraying the droplets did not necessarily retain their original charges, changes occurring because of collisions with stray ions in the air. The use of a relatively non-volatile oil meant that evaporation of the droplets, which was one of the chief sources of error in Thomson's measurement, was minimised.

A schematic diagram of Millikan's apparatus is shown in Figure 2·4. The whole of

[1] J. J. Thomson, *Philosophical Magazine*, **46**, p528 (1898); **48**, p547 (1899); **5**, p346 (1903).

[2] Millikan, *Electrons (+ and —), Protons, Photons, Neutrons, Mesotrons and Cosmic Rays* (University of Chicago Press, 1947).

the apparatus was kept in a constant temperature enclosure. The spray of oil droplets was formed just above a hole in the upper of two parallel metal plates. A drop which fell through the hole and into the region between the plates could be selected and observed with the aid of a short focus telescope. From the observations on a particular droplet, the charge on that droplet could be determined. This again was an improvement as the averaging process used in Thomson's experiment was eliminated.

The procedure used involved the following observations. First, with no potential difference applied between the plates, the fall of the droplet under gravity was observed and its terminal velocity measured. This velocity is related to the size of the droplet by Stokes' law, which gives the following relation between the resistance R to the motion of a sphere of radius a, moving with velocity v, through a medium whose coefficient of viscosity η, is

$$R = 6\pi\eta a v.$$

A terminal velocity v_0 is reached when the resistance to the motion exactly equals the effective weight of the sphere, buoyancy being taken into account. This effective weight w

is given by

$$w = \frac{4}{3}\pi a^3(\rho - \sigma)g, \qquad (2 \cdot 6)$$

where ρ is the density of the sphere and σ that of the medium. When R equals w, the terminal velocity is given by

$$6\pi\eta a v_0 = w, \qquad (2 \cdot 7)$$

whence

$$v_0 = \frac{2}{9\eta}a^2(\rho - \sigma)g. \qquad (2 \cdot 8)$$

From the measured value of v_0, a can be obtained from equation $(2 \cdot 8)$ and hence w from equation $(2 \cdot 6)$.

Next, a potential difference was established between the plates, with the polarity such that the droplet could be caused to move upwards against gravity. In this case, when a steady upward velocity v_1 was reached, the Stokes' law resistance could be equated to the difference between the electrostatic force and the effective weight. Since the plates are parallel, the value of the electrostatic field is V/d, where V is the potential difference between the plates and d is the distance between them, so that

$$6\pi\eta a v_1 = \frac{V}{d}q - w, \qquad (2 \cdot 9)$$

where q is the charge on the droplet.

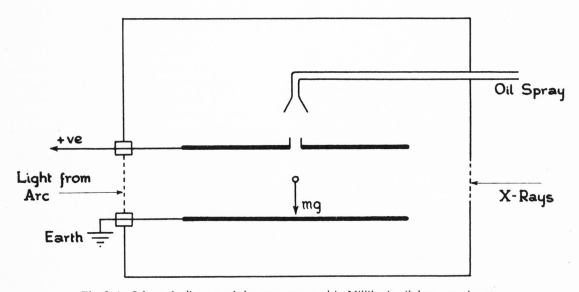

Fig. 2·4—*Schematic diagram of the apparatus used in Millikan's oil-drop experiment*

Combining this with equation (2·7) gives

$$\frac{v_1}{v_0} = \left(\frac{V}{u} q - w \right) / w .$$

This may be rearranged to give q explicitly, thus:

$$q = \frac{dw}{V} \left(1 + \frac{v_1}{v_0} \right) \qquad (2·10)$$

Since w has been deduced from the first observation, the magnitude of q may be calculated. Note that equation (2·10) does not involve the viscosity of the air explicitly; it occurs in equations (2·7) and (2·8) which are involved in the calculation of w.

It should be emphasised here that q gives simply the magnitude of the charge of the droplet; there is no assumption made that the droplet carries a single electronic charge, or even that q is an integral multiple of that quantity.

From observations on a large number of droplets, Millikan obtained a great number of different values for the charges carried by each of them. However, the really striking result was that Millikan did not observe a charge smaller than $1·591 \times 10^{-19}$ coulomb, and all other charges computed were integral multiples of that value. This demonstrated conclusively the atomic character of electricity, and at the same time the magnitude of the fundamental unit was determined.

In an accurate determination of the fundamental unit, there were a number of corrections which had to be made to what was apparently already a precise experiment. These considerations illustrate the point that, even in a well-performed investigation, the experimenter must appreciate the limiting conditions upon all of the 'laws' of physics that he uses. In Millikan's case the relevant corrections are:

(a) The condition of validity of Stokes' law assumes that the dimensions of the droplet are very great compared to the mean free path of gas molecules. Thus, for very small droplets or low pressures, the expression given for this law is no longer exact. Millikan determined by experiment the required correction factor.

(b) Stokes' law also assumes an infinite expanse of gas, and this is far from true. The effect of this appears as an extra retardation on the droplet over and above that given by the simple form of this law. When a droplet approaches a wall, the compression waves which are sent out while it is moving are reflected at the wall. These reflected compression waves provide the additional resistance to motion.

(c) Due to the hole in the upper plate, the lines of force of the electric field in its vicinity are not all exactly parallel, so that the droplet does not move in a uniform electric field.

(d) The greatest source of error in the whole experiment is due to the uncertainty in the coefficient of viscosity of the air. Since η is used in equation (2·6) for the determination of the droplet weight w, its value must be precisely known. The required measurement was made with high precision by Bearden,[1] who obtained the following values: at 20°C, η is $1·81920 \times 10^{-5}$ newton sec metre^{-2}, while at 23°C, the value is $1·83412 \times 10^{-5}$ newton sec metre^{-2}. This result indicates the need for extremely good temperature control during the experiment, and this need was met by Millikan with the use of the constant temperature enclosure.

The values of η given by Bearden were higher than those used by Millikan and, if applied to his experimental results, would increase the value of the electronic charge from $(1·591 \pm 0·002) \times 10^{-19}$ coulomb to $1·601 \times 10^{-19}$ coulomb. It thus caused a change greater than the quoted experimental error.

Hopper[2] has given a careful review of the effect of variations in the value of the viscosity

[1] Bearden, *Physical Review*, **56**, p1023 (1939).

[2] Hopper, *Australian Journal of Scientific Research*, **1**, p369 (1948).

of air used in the computation of the electronic charge. He concludes that the best value of η is $(1 \cdot 8265 \pm 0 \cdot 0006) \times 10^{-5}$ newton sec metre^{-2} at 23°C.

A modification of the Millikan oil-drop technique was used by Laby and Hopper.[1] They used vertical rather than horizontal plates, and introduced an acceleration perpendicular to that of gravity instead of one antiparallel to it. They photographed the droplet under observation at $\frac{1}{25}$ second intervals and thus obtained a continuous record of the position of the drop from which its velocity could be calculated. Using the value of $1 \cdot 830 \times 10^{-5}$ newton sec metre^{-2} for the viscosity of air at 23°C, Laby and Hopper arrived at the value $(1 \cdot 6007 \pm 0 \cdot 0004) \times 10^{-19}$ coulomb for the electronic charge.

The currently accepted value of the electronic charge is $1 \cdot 60206 \times 10^{-19}$ coulomb. This value is taken from a review of fundamental constants by Cohen, DuMond, Layton and Rollett.[2]

It should be pointed out that the oil drop method is not the only one which is capable of giving a precise value for the electronic charge.

The study of the diffraction of X-rays enables the spacings between atoms in crystals to be deduced. If the crystal is assumed to have a simple cubic structure this information leads immediately to the number of atoms per unit volume. Now the number of atoms per unit volume can also be calculated from Avogadro's number, the atomic weight and the density of the substance. Thus, knowing the atomic weight and density, Avogadro's number may be computed from the X-ray data with great accuracy.

Now, the quantity of electric charge, the faraday, F, is related to Avogadro's number and the electronic charge by the equation

$$F = N_0 e \, .$$

Since F is also capable of measurement with considerable accuracy, a precise value of e can be found.

Indeed, it was because of a discrepancy between these two methods of determining the electronic charge that Bearden and others undertook investigations of the viscosity of air. There is no longer any disagreement between the two methods.[3]

2·6 The Accurate Measurement of the Specific Charge of the Electron

The mass of the electron is determined by combining accurate measurements of the electronic charge and of e/m. One of the best measurements of specific charge was made by Dunnington.[4] His method makes use of the fact that a magnetic field will select a unique electron velocity if a particular radius of curvature of the electron path is specified. The apparatus is shown schematically in Figure 2·5. The system is contained in a vacuum chamber, which is pumped out to a pressure of 10^{-5} mm of mercury, or less.

The path of the electrons is selected by the slit system S_1 to S_4, and thus a radius of curvature for the orbit of the electrons is specified. In the magnetic field, the force on the electron is evB and for the circular path this equals the centripetal force mv^2/r. Thus

$$eBr = mv \qquad (2 \cdot 11)$$

is the equation which gives the velocity of those electrons which can pass through all four slits.

The source of electrons is a heated filament, and the electrons are accelerated by means of a potential difference between the filament and slit S_1. The potential difference used is an alternating one, which has a time variation given by

$$V = V_0 \, \sin 2\pi f t \, ,$$

where V_0 is the maximum value of the

[1] Laby and Hopper, *Nature*, **145**, p932 (1940).

[2] Cohen, DuMond, Layton and Rollett, *Reviews of Modern Physics*, **27**, p363 (1955).

[3] For a full discussion of the various methods of determining e, see Stranathan, *The 'Particles' of Modern Physics*, Chapter 2 (The Blakiston Company, 1942).

[4] Dunnington, *Physical Review*, **43**, p404 (1933). See also Chapter 3 of Stranathan, *loc. cit.*

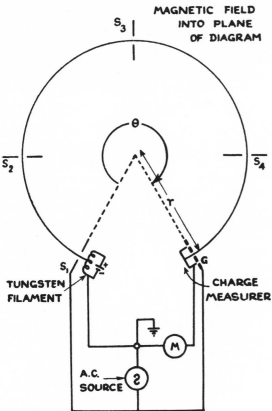

MAGNETIC FIELD INTO PLANE OF DIAGRAM

S_3

S_2

S_4

θ

r

S_1

TUNGSTEN FILAMENT

G

CHARGE MEASURER

M

A.C. SOURCE

Fig. 2·5—*Illustration of the essentials of Dunnington's apparatus*

potential difference and f is its frequency. This alternating potential difference will thus produce a beam which contains electrons with a wide range of velocities. The actual velocity of any electron depends on the phase of the potential difference as the particular particle passes through slit S_1. Those electrons with the appropriate velocity pass around through the slit system. All others are stopped.

After moving around the circle of radius r, the electrons reach a grid G, behind which is a Faraday cage. This cage measures the current passing through the grid. The same high frequency alternating potential difference which is applied between the filament and S_1 is also applied between G and the Faraday cage. The filament is at every instant of time at the same potential as the Faraday cage, and likewise G and S_1 are always at the same potential. Thus, what happens to an electron at G depends on the time taken to reach there. If an electron, drawn through S_1 by the attracting field takes exactly one cycle of the alternating potential difference to reach the grid, it will experience at the grid a repulsive field of exactly the same magnitude as the accelerating field. It is assumed that the filament is very close to S_1 and G is very close to the Faraday cage. This means that the transit times from the filament to S_1 and from G to the Faraday cage can be neglected. The electron will thus lose its energy and in general will not reach the Faraday cage. The current recorded will thus be a minimum.

If, however, the electrons take only one-half of a cycle of the alternating voltage to travel the circular path, then they will experience an attraction at G, and will be drawn into the Faraday cage. In this case a maximum current is recorded.

The experimental procedure is to alter either the flux density B of the magnetic field or the frequency f of the alternating voltage until the current recorded is a minimum. This corresponds to exactly one cycle of the alternating voltage occurring during the electron transit.

In this case, the velocity of the electrons is given by

$$v = \frac{r\theta}{T} = r\theta f, \qquad (2·12)$$

where T and f are the period and frequency respectively of the alternating potential difference applied, and θ is the angle subtended at the centre of the circle by the electron path between S_1 and G. Then, eliminating v between equations (2·11) and (2·12), we obtain

$$\frac{e}{m} Br = r\theta f,$$

or $\qquad e/m = \theta f/B.$

Thus, to determine e/m, this method requires measurement of an angle, a frequency, and a magnetic flux density.

Dunnington's final value for e/m was
$(1 \cdot 7597 \pm 0 \cdot 0004) \times 10^{11}$ coulomb kgm^{-1}.

The currently accepted values for the electron charge and mass are given in the paper of Cohen, DuMond, Layton and Rollett.* These are

$$e/m_0 = (1 \cdot 75890 \pm 0 \cdot 00002) \times 10^{11} \text{ coulomb kgm}^{-1},$$

* See reference on page 18.

$$e = (1 \cdot 60206 \pm 0 \cdot 00003) \times 10^{-19}$$
coulomb, and thus
$$m_0 = (9 \cdot 1083 \pm 0 \cdot 0003) \times 10^{-31} \text{ kgm.}$$

m_0 is written here for the electron rest mass, to take cognisance of the increase of electron mass with velocity as predicted by the theory of relativity (see Section 6·3). It may be pointed out here that relativity theory has been fully verified on this point

CHAPTER 3

The Photoelectric Effect

3·1 The Early Observations of Hertz and Others

In 1887, Hertz[1] was conducting a series of experiments on the production of electromagnetic waves by oscillating charges. The oscillations were initiated by a spark jumping across a gap between metal electrodes which were connected to a circuit containing inductance and capacitance. The detector in his apparatus consisted of a second gap in another resonant electrical circuit. The transmission of electromagnetic waves was indicated by the presence of a spark across the detector gap when a spark occurred at the transmitter gap. Under normal conditions, an increase in the detector gap width beyond a certain limit resulted in the extinction of the spark. However, in the course of his experiments, Hertz made the accidental discovery that the detector gap length could be increased without preventing a spark from occurring, provided the transmitter spark was visible from the detector gap. This totally unexpected result seemed at the time to be quite inexplicable and Hertz proceeded to carry out a systematic investigation of its cause. He discovered that it was ultra-violet light from the transmitter gap which was effective in permitting a lengthening of the detector gap.

In 1888, Hallwachs[2] made the important observation that ultra-violet light falling on a charged plate caused it, under some circumstances, to lose its charge. The principle of the experiment performed by Hallwachs is illustrated in Figure 3·1. If the electroscope and the zinc plate are charged *negatively*, it is found that the gold leaf of the electroscope falls when the zinc plate is illuminated by the arc. If the plate is *positively* charged, the electroscope is not discharged. Hallwachs concluded, quite correctly, that the discharge was due to the liberation of negative charges from the body. Thus, if the plate were negative, the electric charges would be repelled, while if the plate were positive, the liberated negative charges would be attracted back to it so that no discharge would occur. These results are now known to be due to the *photoelectric effect*. Furthermore, Hallwachs showed that if a glass plate is interposed between the arc and the zinc, no discharge occurs for either polarity of charge on the plate. Since glass is opaque to ultra-violet radiation, these results show that the photoelectric effect occurs in zinc only for radiation wavelengths shorter than those contained in the visible region of the spectrum.

In the following few years, a number of physicists investigated the photoelectric effect, perhaps the most notable contribution being made by Elster and Geitel.[3] They found that, for the alkali metals (for example, lithium, sodium and potassium), light in the visible region produced the photoelectric effect, while for most other metals the effect occurred only for ultra-violet illumination. In 1899, J. J. Thomson[4] and Lenard[5] showed indepen-

[1] H. Hertz, *Electric Waves*. D. E. Jones, Translator (Macmillan, 1893), pp68-69.

[2] Hallwachs, *Annalen der Physik und Chemie*, **33**, p301 (1888).

[3] Elster and Geitel, *Annalen der Physik und Chemie*, **38**, pp40, 497 (1889).

[4] J. J. Thomson, *Philosophical Magazine*, **48**, p547 (1899).

Lenard, *Annalen der Physik*, **2**, p359 (1900).

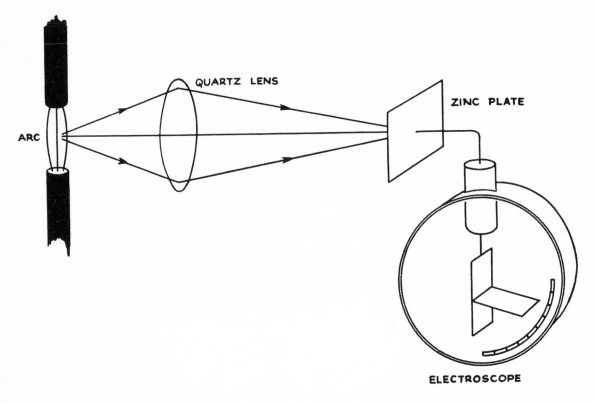

Fig. 3·1—*Experimental arrangement for demonstrating the photoelectric effect*

dently that the negative ions liberated by the photoelectric effect had the same charge-to-mass ratio as *cathode rays*. Thus these ions are, in fact, electrons and although they differ in no way from electrons produced by other means, it is usual to identify their method of liberation by using the name *photoelectron*.

In 1902, Lenard made a study of the velocities of the photoelectrons. He found that, while there was a distribution of velocities from zero to a definite maximum value, this distribution was entirely unaffected by variations in the intensity of the incident radiation. The number of photoelectrons emitted per second was found to be directly proportional to the *intensity* of the incident light, while the electron velocities were found to depend on its frequency.

3·2   Theoretical Difficulties

Lenard's discoveries were, at the time, both unexpected and inexplicable. By 1902 the following facts were beyond dispute.

(i) Electrons are emitted when light falls on a metal surface,

(ii) the number of electrons emitted in unit time depends linearly on the light intensity,

(iii) the velocity of the electrons is independent of the light intensity but depends on its frequency, and

(iv) below a certain frequency of the incident radiation no electrons are emitted at all.

These facts are in direct conflict with the wave theory of radiation as developed by Maxwell. This *classical* theory of radiation assumes that the production, absorption and transmission of light may all be described in terms of the properties of continuous waves. If this were so, radiant energy should be distributed continuously and uniformly over the wave front and all the electrons near the surface of the photoelectric emitter should share the energy delivered to the surface by the radiation. It will be shown that the consequences of this theory are inconsistent with the experimental facts of photoelectric emission.

The number of atoms in a kilogramme-mole of a substance is given by Avogadro's number N_0. In one cubic metre of a substance with density ρ, and atomic weight A, there will be n atoms given by

$$n = \frac{N_0 \rho}{A} . \qquad (3 \cdot 1)$$

If these atoms are assumed to be arranged in regular layers throughout the cube, the number of atoms along one edge will be $n^{1/3}$ and the number of atoms in a single layer one atom thick will be $n^{2/3}$. Taking sodium as an example, $A = 23$, $\rho = 970$ kgm m^{-3}, while $N_0 = 6 \times 10^{26}$ for any substance. These values give $n^{2/3} = 8 \cdot 6 \times 10^{18}$ atoms per layer per square metre of surface. Suppose now that one electron per atom in each of the 10 layers of atoms nearest the surface is involved in the photoelectric effect. Then the number of electrons involved per square metre of surface is about 10^{20}.

Now suppose that the absorbed light intensity is about 10^{-2} watt per square metre, a quite moderate value. If, as the classical theory of radiation requires, the incident energy is shared equally among all the electrons under consideration, the rate of gain of energy by one electron will be about 10^{-22} joule per second. It is known that emitted electrons have energies of the order of 10^{-19} joule. For the assumed incident intensity, the classical theory thus predicts a time delay of about 1000 second before an electron can be emitted. However, measurements show that electrons are emitted within 10^{-9} second of the time of arrival of the incident radiation. To obtain time delays of the order of 10^{-9} second from the classical theory, it would be necessary to assume that only about 10,000 electrons per

square centimetre were involved in the photoelectric effect. This assumption is not supported by the fact that measured electron currents correspond to the emission of hundreds of millions of electrons per square centimetre every second.

The classical theory of radiation also predicts that photoelectric emission should occur provided sufficient energy has been transferred to the electrons in the metal surface by the light wave. This transfer of energy depends only on the intensity of the wave and not on its frequency. Therefore no explanation can be given for the absence of photoelectrons when the frequency of the light falls below a certain value.

3·3 Einstein's Predictions and the Quantum Theory

At about the same period it became apparent that another aspect of the behaviour of electromagnetic radiation could not be satisfactorily explained by classical theory. When a body is heated, the radiation which it emits has a well-defined spectrum, as shown in Figure 3·2. Attempts to account for this spectrum were made, using different sets of assumptions, by Wien in 1896 and by Ray-

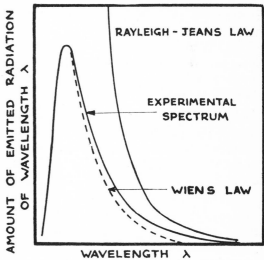

Fig. 3·2—*Spectrum of the radiation emitted from a hot body*

leigh and Jeans in 1900 and 1905. Neither of these two attempts was successful. Wien's law gave a good fit at the short wavelength end of the spectrum but failed at long wavelengths, while the reverse was true of the Rayleigh-Jeans law, as Figure 3·2 shows.

In 1901, Max Planck[1] put forward a radical new hypothesis in an attempt to explain these discrepancies. He suggested that the emission of light might not be a continuous process as had been believed previously. Instead, he supposed light to be emitted and absorbed in packets or *quanta*, each *quantum* carrying a definite amount of energy. It was not necessary, however, for the success of his theory, to make any assumptions about the way in which light *travelled* through space. At the time of publication of this hypothesis, physicists found Planck's ideas rather too radical since they appeared to be in direct conflict with Maxwell's wave theory of radiation, which had been outstandingly successful in describing so many other phenomena. In consequence, little attention was paid to Planck's hypothesis although it did lead to a satisfactory expression for the radiation spectrum from incandescent bodies.

It might have been a long time before the quantum picture of radiation re-emerged had it not been for Albert Einstein, one of the greatest theoretical physicists of all time. In 1905[2] he proposed an explanation of the puzzling photoelectric effect, in which he extended Planck's suggestion. Einstein postulated that not only was light emitted and absorbed in discrete amounts but that it also travelled in quanta, each of which was closely concentrated in space. Each quantum then carried a definite energy $h\nu$, where ν is the frequency of the radiation and h is a universal constant known as Planck's constant of action, or more simply as *Planck's constant*. The expression for the energy of a quantum was just that which had been used by Planck. Einstein added to this the postulate that in the photoelectric effect, a light quantum, or *photon* as it is often called, gives up the whole

of its energy to just one electron in the metal. He allowed no half measures for this process; a photon cannot give up a part of its energy, but must transfer its full energy to the photoelectron which it produces. It must be remembered, however, that only a small fraction of the photons which give up this energy to the metal do so by this photoelectric process.

To this new concept must be added the statement that a certain minimum amount of energy W, called the *work function*, is required to remove an electron from the metal. Electrons do not normally leave a metal of their own accord; energy has to be supplied to remove them. Thus if a photon gives energy $h\nu$ to an electron, an amount of energy at least as great as W is used up before the electron emerges from the metal. The remainder is available as kinetic energy of the photoelectron. This reasoning led Einstein to propose the following relation for the *maximum* kinetic energy of the emitted photoelectrons:

$$(\tfrac{1}{2}mv^2)_{max} = h\nu - W. \qquad (3.2)$$

This relation is called Einstein's equation for the photoelectric effect. Most of the photoelectrons have, in practice, kinetic energies less than the maximum value, since they lose energy by collisions in escaping from the metal.

It will be seen that this prediction received overwhelming experimental support and for his contribution to the understanding of this phenomenon, Einstein received the Nobel Prize for Physics in 1921.

It will be noticed from equation (3·2) that if $h\nu = W$, the maximum kinetic energy of the electrons is zero. The whole of the quantum energy is used in removing the electron in this case and no energy is available to give it a velocity at emission. The frequency

$$\nu_0 = W/h \qquad (3.3)$$

is called the *threshold frequency* for the particular metal surface concerned. Radiation with frequencies less than ν_0, and therefore quantum energies below $h\nu_0$, cannot produce emission since a *minimum* energy $h\nu_0$ is

[1] Planck, *Annalen der Physik*, **4**, p553 (1901).
[2] Einstein, *Annalen der Physik*, **17**, p132 (1905).

needed to extract the electrons from the metal. With this notation, equation (3·2) becomes

$$(\tfrac{1}{2}mv^2)_{max} = h(\nu - \nu_0)'. \qquad (3·4)$$

The wavelength of light λ, and its frequency ν, are related to the velocity c, by the equation

$$\lambda\nu = c . \qquad (3·5)$$

corresponding to threshold frequency ν_0, there is a threshold wavelength λ_0, given from equations (3·3) and (3·5) by

$$\lambda_0 = \frac{hc}{W} . \qquad (3·6)$$

3·4   The Electron Volt

In the specification of the energies involved in the interaction of radiation and matter it is convenient to introduce a new unit of energy called the electron volt. Suppose that an electron, whose charge is e coulomb, is moved from one point to another. If the difference in electrostatic potential between these two points is V volt, the work done on the electron is Ve joule. Further, if the electron is initially at rest, it will, after passing through this potential difference, have a kinetic energy

$$W = \tfrac{1}{2}mv^2 = eV \quad \text{joule}, \qquad (3·7)$$

where m is the electron mass and v its velocity, both in m.k.s. units.

Thus, if the electron is accelerated through a potential difference V, it is convenient to say that it has an energy of V *electron volt*. Since the magnitude of the energy of the electron, when the joule is used as the unit of energy is eV, and the magnitude of the same quantity, measured in electron-volts is V, the conversion factor between these two units of energy is

1 electron-volt = $1·6 \times 10^{-19}$ joule.

The factor $1·6 \times 10^{-19}$ is the *magnitude* of the electronic charge. The electron-volt is thus a very small unit of energy. Nevertheless it is a convenient unit for the energies involved in the photoelectric effect.

The electron-volt is usually abbreviated as eV. In many nuclear processes, the energies

involved are several millions of electron-volts and the abbreviation MeV is used to signify 10^6 electron-volt.

The photoelectric work function W is often expressed in electron-volt rather than in joule. It is well to remember that in any physical equation a consistent system of units must be used. In an equation such as the Einstein equation (3·2) the kinetic energy of the electron may be expressed either in joule or electron-volt provided that the same unit is used for both terms on the right-hand side of that equation. On the other hand, the threshold frequency and wavelength given by equations (3·3) and (3·6) will be obtained in the units of cycle sec^{-1} and metre respectively, *only* if the work function W is expressed in joule.

3·5   The Experimental Verification of Einstein's Predictions

The first experimental tests of the Einstein photoelectric equation were made independently in 1912 by Hughes and by Richardson and Compton.[1] The work of Richardson and Compton is of particular significance as they obtained a strictly linear dependence of maximum photoelectron energy on frequency, as required by the Einstein equation. In 1916 Elster and Geitel[2] were able to show that the number of emitted electrons was directly proportional to the incident radiation intensity even when the light intensities were varied by a factor of 10^8.

In 1916 Millikan[3] carried out an elegant set of experiments which not only showed the Einstein relation to be correct in every detail but also produced an accurate value for Planck's constant h. In order to determine the value of Planck's constant from a study of the photoelectric effect, it is necessary to be able to measure the maximum kinetic energy of the photoelectrons and the frequency of the incident radiation. The principal parts of

[1] Compton, *Philosophical Magazine*, **23**, p579 (1912); Richardson and Compton, *Philosophical Magazine*, **24**, p575 (1912).

[2] Elster and Geitel, *Physicalische Zeitschrift*, **14**, p741 (1913); **15**, p610 (1914); **17**, p268 (1916).

[3] Millikan, *Physical Review*, **7**, pp18, 355 (1916).

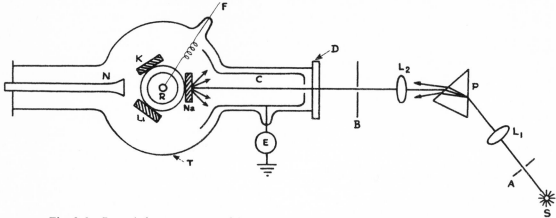

Fig. 3·3—*Part of the apparatus used by Millikan for the determination of Planck's constant*

the apparatus used by Millikan for these measurements are shown in Figure 3·3.

A source of light, produced by an electric arc at S was passed through a slit system A which was at the principal focus of a quartz lens L_1, quartz being used since this material is transparent to both visible and ultra-violet light. The parallel beam of light leaving L_1 and containing a wide range of frequencies was passed through a quartz prism P which produced dispersion, that is deviation of the different frequency components by different amounts. The quartz lens L_2 then focused these different frequencies at different points on the screen B. A small aperture in B allowed light in a narrow frequency range to pass through to the quartz window D and thence into the evacuated tube T where it fell on a surface of sodium, lithium or potassium. The surface under investigation could be swung into position by rotation of the wheel R. In the Millikan apparatus this wheel could be rotated without allowing the pressure in the evacuated tube to rise.

In the photoelectric experiments performed prior to Millikan's work it had been found that the condition of the surface of the photoelectric emitter had a profound effect on the velocities of the emitted electrons. To ensure absolute cleanliness of the surfaces, Millikan included a knife N inside the vacuum tube. This knife could be pushed in and out of the tube without admitting air to the system and by rotating R, a shaving could be taken off any one of the three surfaces immediately prior to bringing it into position for a set of readings.

When the selected surface was illuminated, photoelectrons were emitted and these were collected by the electrode C and the emitted charge measured by the electrometer E, which was maintained at zero potential. By applying a positive potential to the rotor R via the electrode F, a retarding field could be set up to prevent the less energetic electrons from reaching the collector.

Millikan made a careful study of the electron current to the collector for various values of the retarding potential applied to F and determined the minimum potential necessary to prevent any electrons from reaching the collector. This limiting potential, called the *stopping potential*, is then related to the maximum kinetic energy of the electrons. If V_s is the stopping potential,

$$(\tfrac{1}{2}mv^2)_{max} = eV_s . \qquad (3·8)$$

By this means, Millikan was able to obtain an accurate measure of the maximum kinetic energy of the electrons emitted by incident light of any one frequency.

He repeated this measurement for a number of different frequencies of the incident light and for all three emitting surfaces. From the results he was able to produce, for any one surface, a graph of the maximum kinetic

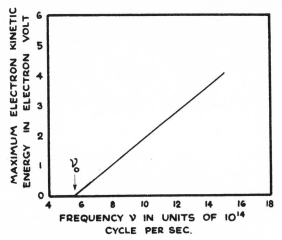

Fig. 3·4—*Relation between the maximum kinetic energy of emitted photoelectrons and the frequency of the incident radiation*

energy of the photoelectrons as a function of the frequency of the incident radiation. A typical graph is shown in Figure 3·4.

Millikan found that the experimental points for any one material lay on a straight line which intercepted the frequency axis at some frequency ν_0. Radiation with frequencies less than ν_0 was incapable of producing any photoelectrons at all. The equation for the straight line in Figure 3·4 is of the form

$$(\tfrac{1}{2}mv^2)_{max} = \text{const.} \, (\nu - \nu_0). \qquad (3\cdot9)$$

Millikan found that no matter what material formed the photo-emissive surface, the slope of this straight line was always exactly the same, although the threshold frequency ν_0 differed from material to material. Thus these experimental results were in complete agreement with the predictions of the Einstein theory as expressed in the equation

$$(\tfrac{1}{2}mv^2)_{max} = h(\nu - \nu_0). \qquad (3\cdot4)$$

Comparison of the experimental result (3·9) with this equation shows that the slope of the straight-line graph relating maximum energy and frequency can be equated to Planck's constant, h. In this way, Millikan made the first accurate determination of h. His value of $6·56 \times 10^{-34}$ joule sec is remarkably close to the best present day value of $6·625 \times 10^{-34}$ joule sec.

The identification of Millikan's experimental result with equation (3·4) is complete if $h\nu_0$ is equated to the work function of the surface. Thus the work function can be determined from the intercept of the straight line with the frequency axis as shown in Figure 3·4.

For each photo-emissive surface and for each frequency of the incident radiation, Millikan measured the current to the collector as a function of the stopping potential. For any one stopping potential V_s, only electrons with kinetic energy greater than eV_s joule could reach the collector. By analysis of curves of current against stopping potential, Millikan was able to determine the complete energy distribution of the photoelectrons. Typical distributions found in this way are shown in Figure 3·5.

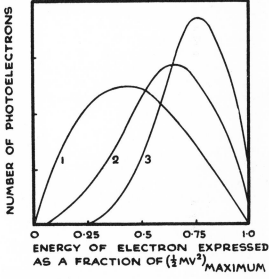

Fig. 3·5—*Energy distribution of photoelectrons from thin films of silver on glass. 1: Thick layer. 2: Film 3×10^{-6} cm thick. 3: Film 10^{-6} cm thick*

3·6 Variation of Photoelectric Emission with Intensity

While Millikan's experiment verified the predictions of Einstein concerning the dependence of the photoelectron *energies* on the frequency of the incident radiation, another aspect of the photoelectric effect which should be discussed is the variation in the *number* of electrons emitted per second as a function of intensity and frequency. It had been shown experimentally that the number of electrons emitted per second was directly proportional to the incident intensity, provided the spectral distribution of the light remained constant. It was also found that for constant intensity there was a variation of electron current with wavelength. The shape of the current-wavelength curve depended very much on the material concerned, and on the method of preparation of the surface. A typical curve is shown in Figure 3·6.

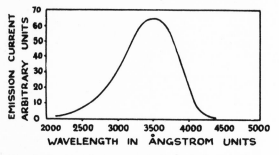

Fig. 3·6—*A typical curve of the variation of photo-electron current with wavelength. The light intensity is constant over the wavelength range*

Curves such as the one shown in **Figure 3·6** are called *colour sensitivity curves* since they indicate the relative response of a particular surface to different wavelengths in the spectrum. The incident intensity of radiation I, is defined as the energy falling on unit area of the emitting surface per second. If each quantum of radiation has an energy $h\nu$, there will be $I/h\nu$ quanta falling on unit area each second. Then if each quantum of the incident radiation produces α electrons, where α must be less than one, the number emitted per second is $\alpha I/h\nu$ and since each photoelectron carries a charge e, the photoelectric current is

$$i = \alpha \frac{Ie}{h\nu}. \qquad (3\cdot10)$$

It must be remembered that if ν is less than the threshold frequency ν_0 no emission can occur. The coefficient α is called the *quantum efficiency* of the surface. Equation (3·10)

can be rewritten in terms of wavelength by using the relation $\lambda\nu = c$. This gives the emitted current as

$$i = \alpha\lambda \frac{Ie}{hc}. \qquad (3\cdot11)$$

If the quantum efficiency α were constant, equation (3·11) implies that i is directly proportional to λ, so that the colour sensitivity curve would be of the form shown in Figure 3·7. The emission would be a maximum near the threshold wavelength λ_0, falling abruptly to zero for wavelengths slightly greater than λ_0. In the same figure, the experimental curve of Figure 3·6 is reproduced, and it is seen that this simple theory is quite wrong. It must be concluded that the quantum efficiency α in equation (3·11) is itself a function of wavelength.

This variation of α is not easily accounted for, but is certainly due to the fact that photoelectric emission is basically a phenomenon associated with the surface layer of the material. The behaviour of electrons in such surface layers can be very complicated, and it is not surprising that the simple picture of a constant quantum efficiency proves to be inadequate. This view is strongly supported by the fact that the work function and the form of the colour sensitivity curve are profoundly affected by the treatment to which the surface is subjected.

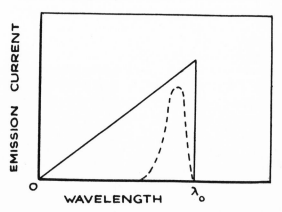

Fig. 3·7—*The variation of photoelectron current with wavelength for constant intensity and quantum efficiency, as predicted by equation (3·11). The dotted curve is that of Figure 3·6 plotted on the same wavelength scale*

3.7 Radiation — Waves or Particles?

We have seen in the preceding sections that the quantum picture of radiation accounts for the photoelectric effect while the classical wave picture fails to do so. Yet the classical theory provides the basis for a complete explanation of other phenomena such as diffraction, interference and polarisation of light, while the quantum theory, at least at first sight, presents difficulties in these fields. In the diffraction at a slit, for example, light passing through the slit is found to emerge at some angles but to be entirely absent at others. From the quantum point of view, how do the photons know where they can go and where they cannot go? It seems that the wave picture of radiation gives an explanation of some effects produced by light while the quantum picture explains others. It seems

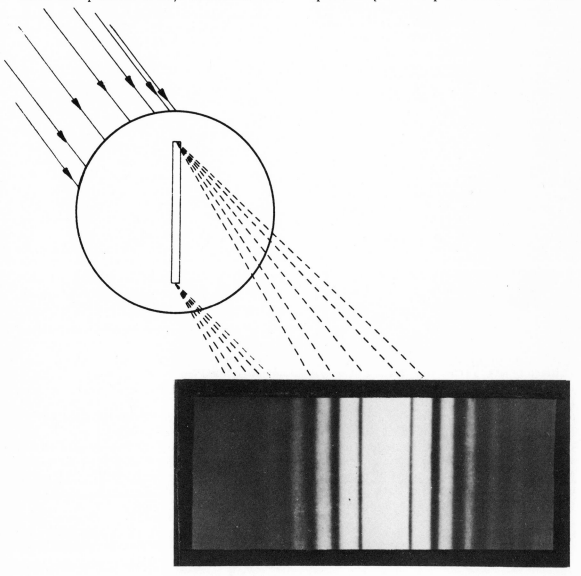

Fig. 3·8—*Diffraction of light by a rectangular slit*

reasonable to suppose that there should be no actual change in the nature of light from one phenomenon to another. Thus the wave viewpoint and the quantum viewpoint must be two incomplete pictures of the same thing.

For some time after the development of the quantum theory with its outstanding initial success in describing the photoelectric effect and subsequent triumph in explaining the production of electromagnetic radiation by atoms, it was necessary to view the two theories, wave and quantum, as distinct entities, the one or the other picture being used according to the problem involved. Thus in 1920 there was irrefutable evidence from diffraction, polarisation and interference phenomena that light must behave as waves. On the other hand there was equally strong evidence from the photoelectric effect that light must consist of packets of energy. It seemed that light was emitted and absorbed as quanta but travelled as waves. This point of view cannot be challenged experimentally but it is philosophically objectionable to have to think of one quantity as appearing in two different forms.

The reason for the difficulty lies in trying to form mechanical pictures of a phenomenon which can only be observed by its effects. We never see light, only the effects it produces. Thus quantum and wave pictures of radiation are each only one aspect of the full picture. Both are needed to explain all the observed facts. There is a link between the two apparently divergent viewpoints, and the most satisfactory way to clarify the relation between the two pictures is to think in terms of a specific situation, illustrated in Figure 3·8. Suppose that a parallel beam of light passes through a narrow slit and then falls on a screen. It is found that if the pattern on the screen is closely examined it is not exactly a well-defined rectangular patch as might be expected. Instead, a series of dark and light bands are found on either side of the central illuminated region, these bands being parallel to the long edges of the slit. This phenomenon is known as a *diffraction pattern*, and the location of the dark and light bands can be predicted by a wave theory calculation. In doing this the amplitude of the light waves arriving at various points of the screen is calculated and points at which the amplitude is a minimum are interpreted as corresponding to the dark bands, while the light bands occur at points of maximum amplitude.

The same pattern can now be described in terms of a quantum picture by identifying the intensity at a point on the screen with the probability that a given photon passing through the slit will ultimately reach that particular point. This identification is made plausible by a consideration of the energy carried by a beam of light. In wave theory, the square of the amplitude of a wave is proportional to its intensity, that is to the energy passing through unit area per second. However, on the quantum theory, the number of photons passing through unit area per second is also proportional to the intensity. This means that when quantum ideas are used, the history of an individual photon is traced, while when wave ideas are used, the problem concerns the distribution of a large number of quanta throughout the region under consideration. The quantum theory applies to the individual event, the wave theory to a statistical average over vast numbers of quanta.

The quantum theory of radiation as advanced by Planck and Einstein passed its first major test in the explanation of the photoelectric effect. It will be seen later that the quantum theory of the interaction of matter and radiation plays an essential part in the understanding of the behaviour of atoms and therefore of the whole of the world we live in. The quantum theory must take its place as one of the most far-reaching theories of modern physics.

CHAPTER 4

X-Rays

4·1 The Discovery of X-Rays

Scientific interest in cathode rays was considerable in the latter half of the nineteenth century and investigations of the properties of these rays by Hittorf, Goldstein, Crookes and others had led to a lively speculation concerning their nature. Most British physicists believed the cathode rays to be charged particles, but German workers, on the other hand, took the view that they were some sort of aether wave. In 1892, Hertz succeeded in passing the cathode rays through a thin metal foil, and in 1893, Lenard extracted the rays from a discharge tube through a thin aluminium window. These experiments lent support to the aether wave theory, since it was considered unlikely that charged particles could penetrate a metal foil. It was not until 1897, when J. J. Thomson proved that cathode rays *were* charged particles, that the aether theory was finally rejected.

Late in October 1895, Wilhelm Röntgen, Professor of the Physical Institute of the University of Würzburg, decided to repeat the experiments of Hertz and Lenard with the definite purpose of searching further for evidence of aether waves emitted from a low pressure discharge tube. The current for this tube was supplied by a large, high voltage induction coil. Röntgen had covered this tube with black cardboard to absorb any visible or ultra-violet light produced by the discharge. Late in the evening of the 8th of November, 1895, when Röntgen was working alone in his darkened laboratory, he noticed a bright fluorescence in a paper sheet coated with barium platinocyanide. He found that the fluorescence occurred only when the dis-charge tube was operating and persisted even when the paper screen was placed as far away as two metres from the apparatus. Since the cathode rays were known to travel far less than two metres through air, Röntgen immediately realised that he had discovered some hitherto unknown radiation, which he called 'X-rays'.

Shortly after this discovery, Röntgen is reported to have told a friend that he had found something interesting, but except for this remark apparently he talked to no one about his work and not even his research assistants were aware of the important discovery. Instead, Röntgen spent the next seven weeks carrying out a series of painstaking experiments which elucidated most of the important properties of the new radiation. On December 28, 1895, he handed the manuscript of his preliminary report 'On a New Kind of Rays' to the President of the Physical Medical Society of Würzburg and it was printed as a 'preliminary communication' in the Annals of the Society. It was immediately translated into several languages and was republished between January and March 1896 in England, France and the United States of America.*

4.2 Röntgen's Preliminary Communication

Röntgen's experiments, as reported in his preliminary communication, repay some study because they are beautiful illustrations of the painstaking application of scientific method. His paper starts with a description of his

* Röntgen, *Nature*, **53**, p274 (1896); *Science*, **3**, p227 (1896); *Journal de Physique*, **5**, p101 (1896).

discovery of fluorescence in barium platino-cyanide and the observation that the new rays passed through materials which are opaque to visible and ultra-violet light.

Following this observation, he proceeded to place various objects between the discharge tube and the fluorescent screen and observed the change in intensity of the fluorescence. He found that all bodies were transparent to a degree, the absorption depending on the thickness of the material and on its density. In the course of this series of experiments he showed that the X-rays would pass through 'a bound book of about 1000 pages', a double pack of cards, several sheets of tinfoil, pinewood boards 2 or 3 centimetre thick and sheets of hard rubber. A 15 mm aluminium plate '. . . though it enfeebled the action seriously, did not cause the fluorescence to disappear entirely.' He obtained a shadow image of the bone structure of his own hand, an event which produced enormous public interest and which attracted the immediate attention of the medical profession.

Röntgen observed that glass plates containing lead were much more highly absorbing than ordinary glass and this observation led him to test the transmission of X-rays through plates of copper, silver, lead, gold and platinum. He deduced that '. . . the transparency of different substances, assumed to be of equal thickness, is essentially conditional upon their density.' He then proceeded to experiment with different substances having approximately equal densities and was able to show, for example, that calcite was noticeably less transparent than glass, aluminium and quartz. Thus density is not the only factor influencing the absorption.

Since neither density alone nor thickness alone governed the degree of absorption, Röntgen next sought a factor which was some combination of these two. Such a factor is mass per unit area, the product of thickness and density. To investigate this possibility, '. . . sheets of platinum, lead, zinc and aluminium were rolled of such thickness that all appeared nearly equally transparent.' These sheets were found not to have the same mass per unit area, so that this factor was not the one determining the transparency of the material to X-rays. For example, he found that the X-rays were equally absorbed by a given mass per unit area of platinum and nearly twenty-five times that mass per unit area of aluminium. Thus while he found more dense and thicker materials to be generally better absorbers of X-rays, he deduced that the absorption did not depend only on these two physical quantities.

Röntgen showed that X-rays produced fluorescence in uranium, glass, calcite, rock salt and some calcium compounds, and he found that they affected a photographic plate so that it was possible to record the observed phenomena permanently.

Röntgen attempted to refract X-rays by passing them through prisms of water, carbon disulphide, hard rubber and aluminium. No definite refraction was found and he deduced that the refractive index of all these materials for X-rays was less than $1 \cdot 05$. He then passed X-rays through powdered materials, reasoning that refraction or regular reflection would result in considerable scattering if such processes actually occurred. Again the experiments were negative. From shadow photographs, Röntgen was able to demonstrate the rectilinear propagation of X-rays and he showed that they could not be deflected by magnetic fields. His final conclusion was that X-rays were longitudinal vibrations in the aether. This seems to be one of the few deductions that he made which has not stood the test of time. Even so, seventeen years were to pass before the true nature of X-rays was established — they are electromagnetic radiation of very short wavelength.

In addition to this investigation of the properties of the X-rays, Röntgen made a careful study of the conditions under which they were produced. He deduced that they were emitted whenever the cathode rays struck any material in the discharge tube. Thus the X-rays are not associated with the passage of the cathode rays through the tube, but arise from their interaction with matter.

4·3 Röntgen's Second and Third Papers

Röntgen published a further paper in March, 1896. This was again translated widely.* In this paper he described experiments which proved that X-rays cause gases to become conducting. He made a zinc box of sufficient size to hold himself and his experimental apparatus. This box was hermetically sealed and was equipped with a thin aluminium window to allow the X-rays to enter. In this way he ensured that any effects on the air inside the box were due to X-rays and not to discharges in the vicinity of the induction coil outside the box. Röntgen was able to show that electrified bodies were discharged when exposed to X-rays inside the box. He deduced that the air was rendered conducting and proved this point by drawing air, previously exposed to X-rays, past a charged conductor which was shielded from the X-rays. He found that the conductor was discharged, proving that the air had lost its insulating properties.

In this second paper, Röntgen described a greatly improved tube for the generation of X-rays. The principle features of this tube are shown in Figure 4·1. The cathode was made concave so that the electrons leaving it normal to the surface were focused on a small

* Röntgen, *Science*, **3**, p726 (1896); *Journal de Physique*, **5**, p189 (1896).

area of the anode. The anode was made of platinum and set at 45° to the axis of the electron beam. The X-rays, generated by electron collisions with the platinum target, were emitted through the side of the tube. Röntgen showed, by photographs taken with a pin-hole camera, that the X-rays did in fact originate from the region of the anode struck by the electrons.

In a third communication in 1897, Röntgen reported the observation that bodies irradiated by X-rays from the discharge tube may themselves re-emit X-rays, although he was unable to make any statement about the quality of these secondary X-rays. He also made a study of the penetrating power of X-rays as a function of the degree of vacuum in the discharge tube. 'Hard' tubes, that is ones which were highly evacuated, produced more penetrating X-rays than 'soft' tubes. Since highly evacuated tubes required a higher voltage to maintain the discharge producing cathode rays, he deduced that the quality of the X-rays was determined by the potential difference across the discharge tube. Even today the terms 'hard' and 'soft' are still used to distinguish between highly penetrating and less penetrating X-rays. Röntgen also showed that while the current through the discharge tube affected the X-ray intensity, it had no

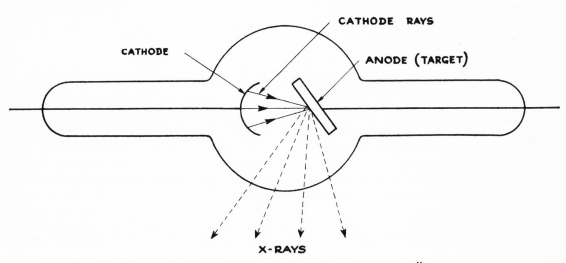

Fig 4·1—*An early form of X-ray tube of a type used by Röntgen*

Table 4·1 — *Wavelengths of electromagnetic radiation*

Type of Radiation	Approximate wavelength in metre
Radio	$3 \times 10^4 - 10^{-3}$
Infra-red	$10^{-3} - 10^{-6}$
Visible light	$7 \times 10^{-7} - 3·5 \times 10^{-7}$
Ultra-violet	$3·5 \times 10^{-7} - 5 \times 10^{-9}$
X-rays	$5 \times 10^{-9} - 10^{-15}$
soft X-rays	approx. 10^{-9}
X-rays produced in commercial tubes for medical or industrial use	approx. 10^{-11}
very hard X-rays produced by a betatron	approx. 10^{-13} to 10^{-15}

effect on the 'hardness', that is the penetrating property, of the X-rays.

The question which most exercised Röntgen's mind at this stage was the nature of the X-rays. He felt that they must have a character similar to light rays but none of his experiments was conclusive in this respect.

4·4 Summary of the Properties of X-Rays

By 1897, Röntgen and other workers had uncovered most of the properties of the new radiation. Indeed, the majority of this information was contained in Röntgen's first two papers in 1896. It is desirable at this stage to summarise the most important properties possessed by X-rays.

1. X-rays are produced when cathode rays (electrons) strike any solid body.

2. All substances are more or less transparent to X-rays. The thicker or the denser the material, the greater, in general, is the absorption of X-rays.

3. X-rays produce fluorescence in a number of materials such as barium platino-cyanide, phosphorescent calcium salts, glass, calcite and rock salt.

4. X-rays affect photographic emulsions in much the same way as ordinary light, so that X-ray photography is possible.

5. X-rays cannot be deflected at all by magnetic or electric fields and therefore cannot be charged particles.

6. X-rays travel in straight lines and cannot easily be reflected or refracted.

7. X-rays discharge electrified bodies, whether the electrification is positive or negative.

It will be seen later that decisive experiments in 1912 showed that under special conditions X-rays can be diffracted and that in fact they are electromagnetic in nature with wave lengths very much less than the wavelengths of visible light. Table 4·1 compares X-ray wavelengths with the wavelengths of other types of electromagnetic radiation.

4·5 The Coolidge Tube

Before continuing the story of the experiments which led to an understanding of the nature of X-rays, it is desirable to study the development of devices for the generation of X-rays and for their detection. Early X-ray tubes very soon became standardized along the lines suggested by Röntgen in his second paper, and as illustrated in Figure 4·1. These tubes were evacuated to a pressure of the order of 10^{-3} mm of mercury. When the voltage was applied to the tube, some electrons and positive ions were produced in the residual gas. The positive ions were accelerated towards the cathode by the electric field and on hitting the cathode released electrons. The electrons, being negatively charged, were accelerated towards the anode where, on impact, they produced X-rays. In this type of tube, known as the 'gas' tube, the current through the tube, the potential difference across it, and the gas pressure inside it were all more or less interdependent and satisfactory operation could only be obtained over a narrow range of gas pressures. If the gas pressure was too low it was not possible to obtain sufficiently high voltages to initiate the discharge, while if the pressure was too high the discharge took place at a low voltage and the X-rays produced were rather 'soft'. Various ingenious devices were invented to control the gas pressure, but it was not until 1913 that a really satisfactory X-ray tube was produced by Coolidge.

In 1912, Gaede and Langmuir developed the diffusion type of vacuum pump which made possible the production of much better vacua. Langmuir showed that in a good vacuum pure tungsten filaments emitted electrons when heated to high temperatures. Encouraged by Langmuir's results, Coolidge, of the General Electric Company of America, designed the X-ray tube* shown in Figure 4·2. The tube is highly evacuated and contains a metal anode A, and a filament C which is heated by the passage of an electric current from the battery E. Thermionic emission takes place at the hot filament and the emitted electrons are accelerated to the anode in the electric field produced by a potential difference of some thousands of volts applied

* Coolidge, *Physical Review*, **2**, p409 (1913).

between it and the filament. A hood H surrounding the filament is found to assist in focusing the electrons on to the anode. The face of the anode or target block is set at 45° to the incident electron stream so that the X-rays, which are emitted predominantly at right angles to the electron beam, pass out through the side wall of the tube. If desired, a thin window can be inserted in the tube wall in the region through which the X-rays emerge.

In operation, the anode becomes very hot due to the dissipation of the kinetic energy of the electrons on impact. The target is usually formed of a small button B of a high melting point metal such as tungsten, let into a copper block A. This block is mounted on a thick copper stem sealed through the glass wall of the tube so that there is good thermal conduction from the target to the cooling fins F, mounted on the copper support rod. The heat conducted from the target is dissipated by radiation and convection from the cooling fins. In X-ray tubes designed for very high X-ray outputs, cooling is often achieved by circulating oil through the target block. Modern X-ray tubes differ little from the original design produced by Coolidge.

In the Coolidge tube, the intensity of the X-rays is proportional to the number of electron collisions with the anode. This, in turn, is determined by the filament temperature, which can be controlled by the heating current. Also, the 'hardness' or penetrating

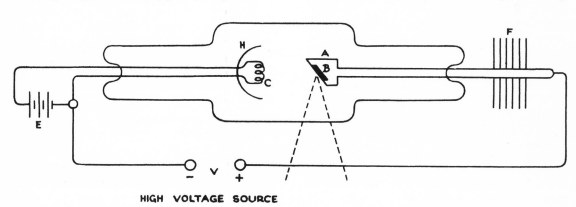

HIGH VOLTAGE SOURCE

Fig. 4·2—*The Coolidge X-ray tube*

power of the X-rays is found to be dependent on the energy of each electron on impact with the anode. This energy is determined by the potential difference between the cathode and anode. Thus in the Coolidge tube, independent control of intensity and hardness is possible, while in the earlier gas tubes independent control could not be obtained.

The Coolidge type tube is used in most medical and industrial X-ray equipment to-day. Voltages as high as two to three hundred thousand volt are applied between anode and filament, and very penetrating X-rays are produced. However, for some purposes, even more penetrating X-rays are required and breakdown of insulation under much higher voltages prohibits the use of a Coolidge tube. In this case, therefore, some alternative source of very high energy electrons must be used to generate X-rays. Linear accelerators, in which electrons are accelerated by a radiofrequency electromagnetic wave, have been used to produce electrons with an energy of several hundred million electron-volt. Other devices, such as the betatron and synchrotron which accelerate electrons travelling in a circular orbit, can also produce electron energies from a few million electron-volt up to one thousand million electron-volt.

4·6 The Detection of X-Rays

Röntgen showed that X-rays could be detected by the fluorescence they produce in certain materials and by their action on photographic plates. While it is possible to make quantitative intensity measurements by determining the blackening produced in a photographic plate, such measurements are time-consuming and not particularly accurate. It will be remembered that Röntgen found that X-rays discharge electrified bodies, an observation made independently by J. J. Thomson. Thomson pointed out that this phenomenon provided a much more delicate and expeditious method of studying X-ray intensities than the photographic plate or the fluorescent screen.

The discharging effect of X-rays was soon traced to the ionisation of air molecules. The effect was studied more carefully by Thomson and Rutherford, in the Cavendish Laboratory. They found that when the air between the plates A and B of the apparatus shown in Figure 4·3 was exposed to X-rays, a small

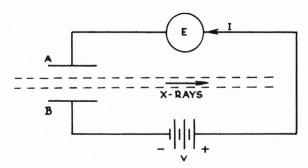

Fig. 4·3—*Ionisation of air by X-rays*

current passed between the plates, the current being measured by the electrometer E. When the applied potential difference V was increased the current varied as shown in Figure 4·4. The maximum constant value, I_s, obtained at high voltages, was called the saturation current. The existence of this saturation effect was explained by assuming that at high voltages both the positive and negative ions produced by the X-rays were all swept over to the plates before any of them could recombine to form neutral molecules. Hence the saturation current was a measure

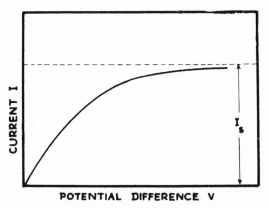

Fig. 4·4—*Curve of ionisation current as a function of potential difference*

of the total ionisation produced and thus of the intensity of the X-rays. This ionisation chamber method is still used to measure X-ray intensities although nowadays the electrometer is often replaced by a vacuum-tube amplifier and galvanometer. Ionisation chambers can take various forms but commonly they are made with one electrode in the shape of a cylinder entirely enclosing the second electrode. For the measurement of very low X-ray intensities, a Geiger counter (see Section 11·3) may be used in place of the ionisation chamber.

4·7 Diffraction of X-Rays by Crystals

In the period up to 1912 many attempts were made to diffract X-rays, using slit systems similar to those with which diffraction effects could easily be produced with light rays. No recognisable diffraction patterns were observed. It was pointed out that the absence of measurable diffraction would be accounted for if the X-rays had wavelengths much shorter than that of visible light. However, some effects were observed which could possibly have been due to diffraction and by 1912, most workers in the X-ray field were convinced that X-rays were electromagnetic radiations with a wavelength of the order of 10^{-10} metre. In order to be sure of this hypothesis, it was necessary to find a way of producing some phenomenon characteristic of waves of this nature.

The crucial experiment came in 1912 when the German theoretical physicist Max von Laue suggested that a narrow beam of X-rays should give a definite diffraction pattern after passing through a crystal. He reasoned that the atomic spacing in a crystal was of the same order as the probable wavelength of X-rays, and that the atoms, arranged in equally spaced layers, would act like a diffraction grating. Two of von Laue's colleagues, Friedrich and Knipping,* undertook to test the prediction experimentally. The apparatus they used is shown in Figure 4·5. X-rays from the target T were collimated by pinholes

* Friedrich, Knipping and von Laue, *Le Radium*, **10**, p47 (1913).

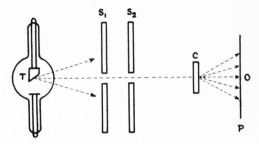

Fig. 4·5—*Diagram of apparatus used to produce Laue diffraction pattern*

in the two lead screens S_1 and S_2 and the resulting narrow pencil of X-rays passed through the thin crystal C onto a photographic plate P. After an exposure of many hours, Friedrich and Knipping developed the plate. They found that, in addition to the central image at O where the main X-ray beam struck the plate, there were many fainter spots present on the plate. These 'Laue spots' as they are now called were arranged in a regular pattern around the central point O. Figure 4·6 shows a typical

Fig. 4·6—*Symmetrical Laue diffraction pattern of an iron crystal*

pattern obtained when X-rays are diffracted by a thin crystal. Friedrich, Knipping and von Laue analysed a series of photographs of diffraction patterns from a crystal of zinc sulphide orientated at several angles to the incident beam. They concluded that the X-rays they were using contained a distribution of wavelengths within the range $1\cdot3 \times 10^{-11}$ metre to $4\cdot8 \times 10^{-11}$ metre. The results demonstrated without any doubt firstly that X-rays are electromagnetic waves with very short wavelengths, and secondly that the atoms in a crystal are arranged in a regular three-dimensional array.

These simple but very elegant experiments paved the way for the measurement of X-ray wavelengths, for the production of monochromatic X-rays and for the development of X-ray crystallography, the technique used very widely to determine the type of structure in crystals. The importance of von Laue's suggestion was recognised by the award to him of the Nobel Prize for Physics in 1914.

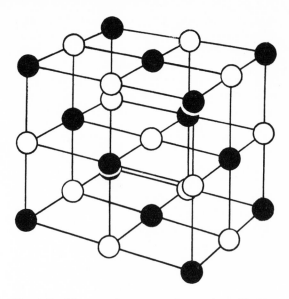

Fig. 4·7—*The crystal structure of potassium chloride. Black dots represent potassium atoms, white dots chlorine atoms*

4·8 The Bragg X-Ray Spectrometer

W. H. Bragg in England* devised a simple way of looking at the process of diffraction in a crystal. He made use of the assumption that in any crystal the atoms are arranged in a regular fashion. Figure 4·7 shows the arrangement for a potassium chloride crystal. Consider a single line of atoms as shown in Figure 4·8. A small fraction of the incident X-rays is scattered by each atom. Each atom can be imagined to be emitting a very weak wavelet. These scattered wavelets reinforce only in the direction for which the angle of incidence is equal to the angle of 'reflection'. Thus while the process is really one of diffraction, it *appears* as if reflection takes place. If a single complete plane of atoms in the crystal is considered, the same type of behaviour occurs. It appears therefore as if a fraction of the incident X-rays is reflected by the plane. While this process is often referred to as X-ray

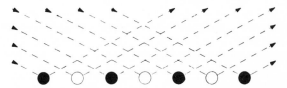

Fig. 4·8—*Diffraction from a single line of atoms.*

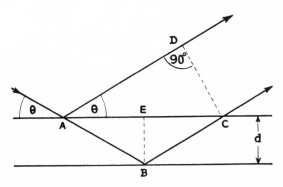

Fig. 4·9—*Interference between X-rays diffracted at successive crystal planes*

* W. H. Bragg, *Proceedings of the Cambridge Philosophical Society*, **17**, p43 (1912).

reflection, it should be stressed that the phenomenon is really one of diffraction.

Consider now two consecutive atomic planes in the crystal as illustrated in Figure 4·9. A part of the incident X-ray beam is diffracted by the top crystal plane and follows the path AD. A further part of the incident beam is diffracted by the lower crystal plane and follows path BC. The parallel diffracted beams interfere at some distance from the crystal, the result of this interference depending on the difference between their paths. From Figure 4·9, the second beam travels further than the first by the length (ABC − AD). But

$$ABC = 2AB = 2d/\sin \theta,$$

where d is the spacing between the crystal planes. Also

$$AD = AC \cos \theta = 2AE \cos \theta = 2d \cot \theta \cos \theta.$$

Thus the path difference is

$$\frac{2d}{\sin \theta} - \frac{2d \cos^2 \theta}{\sin \theta} = 2d \sin \theta.$$

Constructive interference takes place and a strong 'reflection' occurs when the path difference is equal to an integral number of wavelengths of the incident radiation. Thus the condition for strong reflection is

$$n\lambda = 2d \sin \theta,$$

where λ is the X-ray wavelength and n is any integer. This relation is known as Bragg's law. It gives the glancing angles θ, at which strong reflections occur. It should be noticed that for one incident wavelength, there may be several angles giving strong reflection. The smallest angle, corresponding to $n = 1$, represents the direction for *first order reflection*. The next smallest, corresponding to $n = 2$, represents the direction for *second order reflection* and so on. Since $\sin \theta$ can never be greater than one, the number of maxima produced must be such that

$$n_{max} < \frac{2d}{\lambda},$$

where n_{max} is the integer representing the highest possible order reflection.

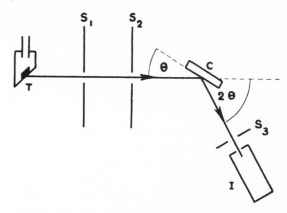

Fig. 4·10—*The principle of the Bragg X-ray spectro-meter*

W. H. Bragg and his son W. L. Bragg made a thorough study of the diffraction of X-rays in crystals and developed the X-ray spectrometer for the measurement of X-ray wavelengths or crystal lattice spacing.[*]

The principle of the Bragg spectrometer is illustrated in Figure 4·10. X-rays from the target T of an X-ray tube are collimated by narrow slits, S_1 and S_2, a few hundredths or tenths of a millimetre wide. The slits are formed from lead plates or other material which absorbs X-rays strongly. The ribbon X-ray beam so formed falls on the crystal C at an angle θ to the crystal face. The reflected X-rays are deflected through an angle 2θ and enter the ionisation chamber I after passing through the slit S_3 in a third lead plate. The ionisation current produced by the X-rays in the ionisation chamber gives a measure of the intensity of those rays which are diffracted through the angle 2θ. Using the Bragg law, the X-ray wavelength corresponding to the angle θ can be determined if the crystal lattice spacing is known. Alternatively, if the X-ray wavelength is known, the crystal lattice spacing can be calculated. It should be noted that when the crystal is rotated so that the angle θ is changed, the ionisation chamber must be simultaneously rotated so that the beam entering it still makes an angle 2θ with

[*] W. L. Bragg, *Nature*, **90**, p410 (1912); W. H. Bragg and W. L. Bragg, *Proceedings of the Royal Society*, **88**, p428 (1913); W. H. Bragg, *Nature*, **91**, p477 (1913).

the incident beam. By measuring the ionisation current as a function of the angular setting, a spectrum of the X-ray wavelengths produced by the source of X-rays may be obtained.

4·9 X-Ray Spectra

The first experiments with the Bragg spectrometer were performed with a rock salt crystal and a platinum target in the X-ray tube. Bragg plotted the ionisation current against glancing angle θ, and obtained a curve of the form shown in Figure 4·11. The group of three peaks a_1, b_1 and c_1 was found at glancing angles 9·9°, 11·6° and 13·6° respectively. A second group a_2, b_2 and c_2 was found at greater glancing angles, the structure of this second group being very like that of the first. Assuming a crystal lattice spacing of 2·184 Ångström units,* Bragg calculated the wavelengths for the a_1, b_1 and c_1 peaks using the law

$$n\lambda = 2d \sin \theta$$

with $n = 1$. He obtained wavelengths of 0·97, 1·13 and 1·32 Å for the three peaks. The

* 1 Ångström unit (Å) = 10^{-8} cm. Another length unit commonly used to express X-ray wavelengths is the X-unit. 1 X.U. = 10^{-11} cm.

second set of peaks he considered to be due to second order reflection with $n = 2$. The wavelengths computed on this assumption checked well with those for the first set of peaks. It seemed, therefore, that the X-rays from platinum possessed a *line emission* spectrum giving rise to the peaks, superimposed on the *continuous* spectrum shown dotted in Figure 4·11.

To show whether the peaks were produced by the X-ray tube target or by the crystal in his spectrometer, Bragg tried several other crystals. These all showed the same three lines, the only difference being a shift in the glancing angles due to the different lattice spacing d of the various crystals. As a final check, Bragg used different X-ray targets and found that the wavelengths of the lines changed while the continuous background radiation remained the same.

Since Bragg's experiments, many different types of X-ray spectrometers (using ionisation chamber detection), and spectrographs (with photographic plate detection) have been developed. A very large number of the precision determinations of X-ray wavelengths has come from M. Siegbahn's laboratory in Sweden and a detailed account of the spectrometers developed by him and by other

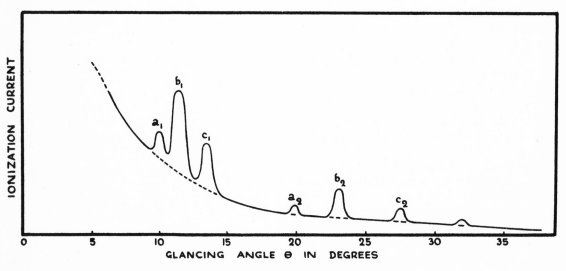

Fig. 4·11—*Bragg's curve for the X-ray spectrum from a platinum target*

workers is given in his book.* From Bragg's work, and from later measurements, it is apparent that two types of radiation are produced in an X-ray tube:

   (i) a line spectrum characteristic of the target material, arising from the *characteristic radiation* and

   (ii) a continuous spectrum which does not depend on the target material.

4·10 The Continuous Spectrum

The *intensities* of both the line spectrum and the continuous spectrum for X-rays depend on the current passing through the X-ray tube. The *type* of spectrum obtained depends on the potential difference between the cathode and the target of the X-ray tube. For low applied voltages, only the continuous radiation is produced. As the tube voltage is increased, well-defined groups of spectral lines, the *M*-series, the *L*-series and finally the *K*-series successively appear. Each series is found to appear as a whole at a particular threshold voltage for the target element concerned. A description of the origin and characteristics of these spectral series is deferred to Section 9·13, where they are considered in the context of a discussion of the electronic structure of atoms.

The continuous spectrum varies with tube voltage in the manner indicated in Figure 4·12. It should be noted that for any given voltage between the electrodes of the X-ray tube there is a definite minimum wavelength, the cut-off being quite sharp. This state of affairs is somewhat reminiscent of the cut-off in emitted electron energies for the photoelectric effect. Just as the quantum theory was found to explain the photoelectric emission of electrons by electromagnetic radiation, so it also serves to explain the emission of continuous X-rays from a target bombarded by high speed electrons.

It is postulated that when an electron loses energy in collision with an atom of the target, all or part of this lost energy may appear as a quantum of radiation. Thus each quantum emitted from the target originates in the

* Siegbahn, *The Spectroscopy of X-Rays* (Oxford University Press, 1925).

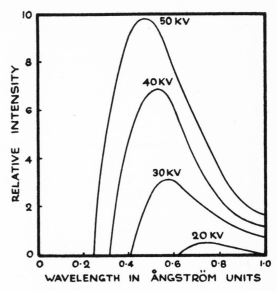

Fig. 4·12—*Variation of X-ray intensity with wavelength*

slowing-down of just one electron. It follows therefore, that the *maximum* energy of an X-ray quantum is equal to the kinetic energy of the electron producing it. According to the quantum theory, the energy of a radiation quantum, or photon, is given by $h\nu$ where h is Planck's constant and ν is the frequency of the radiation. Thus if all the kinetic energy of an electron is converted to a single photon when the electron hits the X-ray tube target,

$$h\nu = \tfrac{1}{2}mv^2, \qquad (4\cdot1)$$

where m is the mass of the electron and v is its velocity.

If the potential difference between the target and cathode in the X-ray tube is V volt, an electron with charge e coulomb will gain Ve joule of kinetic energy in being accelerated from cathode to anode. It follows that

$$\tfrac{1}{2}mv^2 = Ve. \qquad (4\cdot2)$$

Combining (4·1) and (4·2) gives

$$h\nu = Ve. \qquad (4\cdot3)$$

Thus the value of ν given by this relation is the maximum frequency of the X-radiation produced in a tube with a potential difference of V volt. Since the wavelength λ, the frequency ν and the velocity of propagation c of the X-rays are connected by the relation $\lambda\nu = c$, the value of the *shortest wavelength* of the X-rays which can be produced by a potential difference V volt is given by

$$\lambda_{min} = \frac{c}{\nu} = \frac{hc}{Ve}. \qquad (4\cdot4)$$

The wavelength determined by this relation will be in metre if V is in volt, e in coulomb, c in metre per second and h in joule-second. If the wavelength is measured in Ångström units, substitution of the appropriate numerical values in (4·4) yields

$$\lambda_{min} = \frac{12,400}{V} \text{ A}, \qquad (4\cdot5)$$

where V is expressed in volt. It should be noted that the higher the potential difference between the electrodes of the X-ray tube, the shorter is the minimum wavelength of the X-rays, the higher is the maximum frequency and the more penetrating is the radiation produced.

Actually it is relatively rare for an electron to give up all of its energy in one impact within the target. Generally the electron loses energy in a number of collisions with target atoms and consequently much of the X-radiation produced is of longer wavelength than that given by equation (4·5). In addition to the possibility of one electron producing several photons of energy less than the maximum possible, there is a high probability of the electron being slowed down without the production of X-rays. In this case the electron ionises atoms in the target and its kinetic energy is eventually converted into heat. In fact, in a typical Coolidge tube 99·8 per cent. of the energy carried by the electron stream appears as heat and only 0·2 per cent. as X-rays. For this reason cooling of the X-ray tube target presents a problem.

Examination of Figure 4·12 shows that the continuous X-ray spectra display the sharp cut-off on the short wavelength side as demanded by the quantum theory. It will be noted that for any one potential difference between the X-ray tube electrodes, there is a definite wavelength which is most copiously emitted, this wavelength becoming shorter at higher tube voltages. An explanation of the shape of the spectral curves is beyond the scope of this book.

The cut-off wavelengths in the X-ray spectrum can be measured with considerable precision using a crystal spectrometer. From these measured values of λ_{min} at known tube voltages, the ratio h/e can be determined from equation (4·4). Knowing the electronic charge e, a very accurate value of Planck's constant h may be computed. This provides an alternative method for the determination of this constant to that discussed in connection with the photoelectric effect (Section 3·5).

Since the distribution of wavelengths in the continuous spectrum is determined solely by the kinetic energy of the bombarding electrons, it is customary to specify the nature of this radiation merely by quoting the operating potential of the X-ray tube. Thus, reference to a beam of 100-kV X-rays implies that the X-rays concerned are those produced in a tube where the potential difference between the electrodes is 100,000 volt.

To specify an X-ray beam completely, it is also necessary to state its intensity, that is, the energy transported per second through unit area normal to the direction of propagation. A commonly used unit for measuring the *quantity* of X-ray energy is the Röntgen. It is defined as that quantity of X-radiation which produces, in one cubic centimetre of air at normal temperature and pressure, ions of either sign carrying a total of one electrostatic unit ($\frac{1}{3} \times 10^{-9}$ coulomb) of charge. A unit of intensity is therefore the Röntgen per second.

4·11 The Absorption of X-Rays

It has been seen that the radiation from an X-ray tube contains a wide distribution of wavelengths. For some X-ray experiments it is desirable to have a homogeneous beam of X-rays, that is one which has, ideally, one single wavelength. This ideal cannot be achieved in practice but it is possible to pro-

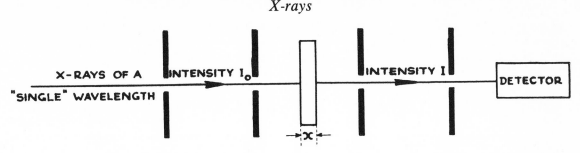

Fig. 4·13—*Reduction of X-ray intensity in passing through an absorber*

duce beams of X-rays with a small distribution of wavelengths by using a crystal spectrometer (Figure 4·10) to analyse a heterogeneous beam. At a particular setting of the spectrometer only paths within a very small angular range, determined by the finite widths of the slits, are accepted by the slit system. Hence at one glancing angle only a narrow range of wavelengths diffract in such a way as to reinforce and pass through slit S_3 of Figure 4·10.

If a homogeneous X-ray beam passes through successive equal thicknesses of any material, it is found that an equal fractional reduction in intensity occurs in each layer. Consider a homogeneous beam of X-rays of intensity I_0, incident on some absorbing material of thickness x as depicted in Figure 4·13. In traversing this layer there is a decrease in intensity such that the intensity I of the emergent beam is given by

$$I = I_0 e^{-\mu x}, \qquad (4·6)$$

where e is the base of natural logarithms. The quantity μ in this equation is called the *linear absorption coefficient* and is the fractional reduction in the intensity of the beam per unit path length in the absorbing substance. Its value depends on the material through which the X-rays pass and on the wavelengths of the X-rays.

Equation (4·6) may be established as follows. In traversing a thin layer of width dx there is a decrease in intensity dI such that

$$\frac{dI}{I} = -\mu dx. \qquad (4·7)$$

To find the total loss of intensity in traversing the whole absorber it is necessary to inte-grate equation (4·7). This gives

$$\ln I = -\mu x + \ln C, \qquad (4·8)$$

where C is a constant of integration. To find the value of this constant, the intensity at $x = 0$ is set equal to I_0. From (4·8), $C = I_0$ and therefore

$$\ln(I/I_0) = -\mu x,$$

or, taking antilogarithms,

$$I = I_0 e^{-\mu x}.$$

The absorption coefficient μ, varies with wavelength, the longer wavelengths being more strongly absorbed than the shorter wavelengths. In consequence, a heterogenous X-ray beam 'hardens' on passing through an absorber, the outgoing beam containing less X-rays of longer wavelengths.

The process which is mainly responsible for the absorption of X-rays is one of ionisation of the atoms within the absorber. In some cases an X-ray photon may 'bounce off' an electron, being deflected in the process. As far as an experimental arrangement such as that of Figure 4·13 is concerned, such a photon may be regarded as having been absorbed. Alternatively, a photon may transfer all of its energy to an electron which is thereby removed from the parent atom. This process is, in principle, identical with photoelectric emission and is referred to as photoelectric absorption of X-rays. When the mechanism underlying these two processes is understood it is possible to account for the way in which the absorption coefficient varies with the wavelength of the X-rays and the material of the absorber.

CHAPTER 5

The Discovery of Radioactivity

5·1 Becquerel's Experiments

Following Röntgen's discovery of X-rays, many scientists began their own investigations of this penetrating radiation. Some were interested in the properties of the X-rays themselves while others concentrated on experiments which, they hoped, would provide some information about the processes involved in the production of the rays. One of the lines of attack was this: Röntgen had reported that the X-rays were emitted from that part of his discharge tube opposite the cathode, where a strong fluorescence was observed on the inner wall of the tube. Thus, there seemed to be a possible connection between X-rays and fluorescence, and a logical move was to see if any of the many substances which were known to be fluorescent or phosphorescent also emitted X-rays.

This, then, is how Professor Henri Becquerel came to be wrapping photographic plates in layers of black paper, placing uranium compounds in contact with the package and exposing the whole thing to the sun for several hours.

Many years earlier Becquerel had found that uranium salts phosphoresced after exposure to sunlight. In these later experiments, any X-rays which were emitted by the phosphorescent salts would penetrate the light-tight wrappings and produce blackening of the photographic emulsion. Becquerel had tried this technique with a number of phosphorescent minerals, always without success. But he continued in his systematic search and with uranium salts obtained the first positive results. It seemed that his research had reached a very satisfactory conclusion; he had

searched for a suspected phenomenon and had, apparently, found it.

However, Becquerel, being an experienced physicist, went on to investigate a number of aspects of his experiment. The procedure he used was one which has proved so successful in all science — to vary systematically the conditions of the experiment and to observe the effect of each variation on the result. Firstly, he placed a metal screen with holes in it between the uranium salt and the black paper and found that the blackening on the negative was a silhouette of the perforated screen. Thus radiations were more strongly absorbed by metal than by paper, as X-rays were known to be. Next, a sheet of glass was placed between the uranium salt and the package, so that vapours, which might be given off when the salt was heated in the sunlight and which might produce the blackening of the emulsion by a chemical action, could not reach the photographic plate. Again, the negative was blackened, so that this possibility was eliminated. Everything seemed to point to the emission of X-rays accompanying phosphorescence as the explanation of the results. However, Becquerel varied another of his experimental conditions, namely the degree of exposure to sunlight. One package with its uranium salt had been exposed to sunlight only intermittently on two cloudy days and had then been put in a drawer, where it had stayed for several sunless days. Becquerel decided to develop this plate, expecting that only a feeble blackening of the negative would appear. Instead, the blackening was intense! Here was a situation such as every scientist experiences many times in his research. A series of experiments is going nicely, the results look interesting and internally consistent and suddenly an unexpected result crops up. Why? It frequently happens that a fault in the apparatus or an inaccurate observation can be traced and is sufficient to explain the anomaly, so that the temptation to ignore it is strong. It is the mark of a good scientist that he is never satisfied to leave the abnormal result unexplained, and it is from further investigation of such anomalies that many of the most fundamental discoveries in science have been made. So it was with Becquerel. He found that the uranium salt spontaneously emitted something which could penetrate paper and even thicker objects; this property was quite independent of any exposure of the salt to sunlight. Moreover, the same radiation was emitted by all compounds of uranium (including those known not to be phosphorescent) and by the element itself. The intensity of the radiation from samples of the same weight was proportional to the fractional weight of uranium present in each sample.

All of these results* pointed to the discovery of a new phenomenon which was later to be named 'radioactivity' by Marie Curie. In the sense that Becquerel found something other than the effect he set out to look for, the discovery could perhaps be called 'accidental'. But to do so would be doing Becquerel an injustice. He didn't 'just happen to' wrap a photographic plate in black paper, put some uranium next to it, put it away in a drawer and later develop the negative. What he did do was to exploit to the full an unexpected result which arose during an investigation.

5·2 The First Radio-Chemists

In just the same way as Becquerel had searched for phosphorescent minerals which gave off X-rays, a search began for other substances exhibiting radioactivity. One of the most active and most successful searchers was Madame Marie Curie, the wife of one of Becquerel's colleagues, Pierre Curie. She used

* Becquerel, *Comptes Rendus*, **122**, pp420, 501, 559, 689, 762 and 1086 (1896).

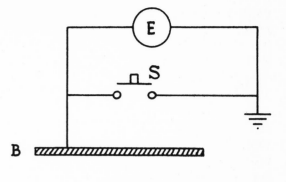

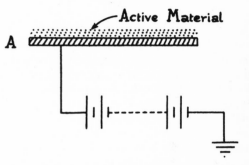

Fig. 5·1—*Electrical method for detecting radiations. The electrometer E is a device for measuring very small currents. Initially the switch S is closed. When S is opened, the reading of E gives a measure of the ionisation current produced between the plates A and B*

an electrical method of detecting the radiations. This method was developed from Becquerel's observation that these radiations, like X-rays, were capable of discharging a gold leaf electroscope. It should be remembered, however, that the intensities of the radiations observed in these early experiments were only a few thousandths of the X-ray intensities which were available at the time.

Mme. Curie's apparatus, a forerunner of the ionisation chamber, consisted of two parallel plates 8 cm in diameter and 3 cm apart (Figure 5·1) with one plate covered with a powdered layer of the substance under investigation. In terms of more recent ideas of the ionisation of gases, it is known that the air between the plates was ionised by the radiations from the sample. The rate of ionisation was proportional to the rate of emission of the radiations, that is to the 'activity' of the sample. The continual migration of the positive ions to the negatively charged plate and the negative ions to the positively charged plate constituted a current, proportional to the activity, which was measured by an electrometer.

In 1898, Schmidt, working in Germany, and Mme. Curie, in Paris, independently discovered that thorium and its compounds are also radioactive. Then Mme. Curie examined various minerals containing compounds of uranium and thorium. Some of her results are shown in Table 5·1.

Clearly, the activity in some of the naturally-occurring samples was more than could be explained by their uranium content, and it seemed a reasonable inference that this high activity was due to the presence of some radioactive substance other than uranium or thorium. However, in the case of pitchblende, which is about 80% uranium oxide, all the other elements such as barium and bismuth, which it was known to contain, had been found not to be radioactive. This meant that this other unknown substance must be present to a very small extent, since it had escaped detection by ordinary chemical methods. Further, it must be exceedingly radioactive if a very small quantity was to give such a marked increase in the activity of the pitchblende.

And so the Curies, husband and wife, began the laborious search for this unknown substance. The technique was simply to follow the well-known principles of chemical analysis and separation. At each separation the two substances thus separated were tested to see which carried the radioactivity with it. The inactive material was then discarded and further separation of the active residue was carried out. In practice, it was not a simple procedure at all. Because of the very low concentration of the unknown substance, it was obviously necessary to start with a very large amount of pitchblende in order to finish with a recognisable quantity of the radioactive material. In addition, pitchblende is

Table 5·1 — *Ionisation currents measured by Mme. Curie for some naturally occurring minerals and laboratory prepared compounds.*

Minerals	Current in micro-micro-ampere (10^{-12} amp)
Pitchblende from —	
Johanngeorgenstadt	83
Joachimsthal	70
Pzibran	65
Cornwall	16
Clevite	14
Chalcolite (phosphate of copper and uranium)	52
Autunite (phosphate of calcium and uranium)	27
Thorite	from 3 to 14
Orangite	20
Laboratory-prepared Samples —	
Uranium (containing a little carbon)	23
Black oxide of uranium	26
Green oxide of uranium	18
Phosphate of copper and uranium	9

by no means chemically pure; it contains small quantities of nearly all the known metals, so that the chemical separations were difficult and tedious.

However, the fact that the object of the search *was* radioactive meant that it could never be missed — they always knew *where* it was, even if they didn't know *what* it was! This was, literally, the birth of the techniques of radio-chemistry.

In their first attempt, the Curies did not start with a very large amount of pitchblende, so that they did not manage to separate out the unknown as a pure substance. Despite this, their search was highly successful in that they discovered not one unknown substance, but *two* new substances. The first one found was always chemically associated with the small amount of bismuth present in the ore. Bismuth itself and all the other chemically similar elements had been tested for radioactivity and are definitely not radioactive. Thus, this residual radioactivity of the bismuth fraction, about 400 times more intense than that of an equal weight of uranium, must belong to a new element, chemically similar to bismuth. This was named *polonium*,[1] in honour of Mme. Curie's native country, Poland.

The other activity found was always in the separated fraction containing barium. This was even more active, with an activity per unit mass 900 times that of uranium, and the presumed new element was named *radium*.[2] However, in order to confirm the existence of these elements it was necessary to isolate them by chemical methods, and so the Curies began the processing, not of grammes, or even of kilogrammes, but of *tons* of pitchblende. Although polonium was, in the first instance, identified prior to radium, there is about 5000 times more radium than polonium in pitchblende and so the separation of radium was made the initial aim. After four years of painstaking work, Mme. Curie achieved the separation of about one-tenth of a gramme of

pure radium chloride and was able to give a reasonably accurate value — 225 — for the atomic weight of radium. Later, in collaboration with Dr. Debierne, she was able to prepare metallic radium, a metal more than a million times more radioactive than uranium.

The number of known radioactive substances grew rapidly. By 1906, only ten years after Becquerel's discovery, about twenty such substances were known. Very few of these, however, had been identified as new elements. Indeed, radium was the only one of these substances (apart from the previously known elements uranium and thorium) of which more than a few microgrammes had been separated. How, then, had the differences between these substances been established? The answer came as the result of a study of the nature of the radiations given off by radioactive substances and of the rates at which they are emitted. It was only by detecting these radiations that the presence of the radioactive substances could be established. By studying the nature of the radiations, the particular substance emitting them could be identified. Radio-chemistry had become an indispensable tool of the scientist.

5·3 The Identification of the Three Types of Radiation

One of the first problems to be tackled in the study of radioactivity was the nature of the radiations. The obvious starting-point in finding out what the radiations *were* was to investigate their properties. One property, the ability to penetrate material substances, gave a clear lead for further measurements — to what extent did this penetration occur? There were many other questions to answer. Were the radiations from the different radioactive substances all of the same type? Were those emitted by one particular substance all the same? Could they be reflected and refracted? Did they behave like light, which was known to exhibit wave-like properties, or were they streams of particles?

In attempting to answer these and many other questions, two methods of distinguishing between the types of radiation and comparing

[1] P. and M. Curie, *Comptes Rendus*, **127**, p175 (1898).

[2] P. and M. Curie and Bémont, *Comptes Rendus*, **127**, p1215 (1898).

their properties were of major importance. They were:

(a) the measurement of the absorption of the rays by various thicknesses of solids and gases and

(b) the measurement of the extent to which they were deflected by magnetic and electric fields.

The first observations which showed that there was more than one type of radiation were made by Rutherford[1] in 1898 at the Cavendish Laboratory in Cambridge. He showed that much of the radiation emitted by uranium was not very penetrating, and could be stopped by a sheet of paper. The remainder of the radiation, however, was about 100 times more penetrating. Rutherford suggested that these two components of the radiation be termed the α-rays and the β-rays. Only the more penetrating β-rays could have been responsible for the blackening of Becquerel's photographic plates. It was soon shown that the radiations from thorium and radium also consisted of similar types of rays, while polonium gave off α-rays only. At about the same time, several experiments[2] showed that the radiations could be deflected by magnetic fields. Then Pierre Curie found that there was a component of the radiations for which the deflection, if it existed at all, was very small[3] indeed. At the same time he found that there was an appreciable difference between the ranges[4] in air of these 'deviable' and 'non-deviable' rays, the non-deviable rays being almost completely absorbed by 7 cm of air while the less intense deviable rays were much more penetrating. In the same year Villard[5] demonstrated the presence of a non-deviable component of the

radiation with a very long range. He allowed a narrow beam of rays to pass through a magnetic field and then strike a photographic plate placed at a considerable distance from the source. Thus the intense non-deviable component could not reach the plate. However, he found that two images were produced on it. One of these was deviated by the magnetic field and could also be completely removed by placing a lead absorber only 0·3 mm thick in the path of the rays. This absorber, however, produced only a slight reduction in the intensity of the image from the undeviated beam. In fact, this component of the radiation appeared to behave in exactly the same way as a beam of X-rays.

As a result of these observations, supported by various other measurements, it became possible to classify the radiations from radioactive substances as being of three distinct types, α-rays, β-rays and γ-rays.

α-rays are the least penetrating, having ranges of only a few centimetres in air or a few hundredths of a millimetre in metal foils. At the same time they are by far the most strongly ionising. They are deviated by magnetic fields, but the effect is quite small for moderate fields, and the strongly ionising 'non-deviable' rays observed by Curie were, in fact, α-rays.

β-rays are more penetrating, having ranges which are usually of the order of several tens of centimetres of air. They produce much less ionisation than the α-rays, and are markedly deviated by magnetic fields. These are the 'deviable' rays of Curie.

γ-rays can penetrate through considerable thicknesses of all materials, but are unaffected by magnetic fields. They are weakly ionising — indeed the relative amounts of ionisation produced by the α-, β-, and γ-rays of a thin layer of a radium compound in apparatus of the type shown in Figure 5·1 are roughly in the ratio 10,000 : 1000 : 1.

Before discussing the actual nature of these three types of radiation it should be pointed out that there is a significant difference, other than one of magnitude, between the effects of a magnetic field on the paths of α- and β-rays.

[1] Rutherford, *Philosophical Magazine*, **47**, p109 (1899).

[2] Giesel, *Annalen der Physik und Chemie*, **69**, p834 (1899). Meyer and Schweidler, *Physikalische Zeitschrift*, **1**, pp13, 90 (1899). Becquerel, *Comptes Rendus*, **129**, pp997, 1205 (1899).

[3] P. Curie, *Comptes Rendus*, **130**, p73 (1900).

[4] The 'range' in a particular material is the term used for the maximum thickness of that material which the rays are able to penetrate.

[5] Villard, *Comptes Rendus*, **130**, pp1010, 1178 (1900).

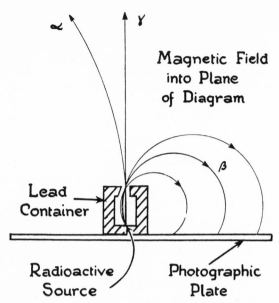

Fig. 5·2—Hypothetical experiment to show the difference in behaviour of α-, β- and γ-rays in a magnetic field

This difference is well illustrated by a hypothetical experiment described by Mme. Curie.[1] Suppose that a radioactive source is placed at the bottom of a lead container as shown in Figure 5·2. A narrow hole in this container will ensure that only a collimated beam, that is a beam essentially confined within a small angular range, emerges into the space above. The container rests on a photographic plate and a magnetic field is established perpendicular to the collimated beam and directed into the plane of the diagram. On development of the photographic plate it will be found that the only image present is that due to the β-rays, and that this will be on the side of the source shown in the diagram. From the direction of this deflection, it is immediately deduced that the charge carried by the β-rays must be *negative*. On the other hand, the trajectory followed by the α-rays is an arc of a circle of much greater radius, and on the opposite side of the container. Thus, the

[1] Marie Curie, Doctoral Thesis, University of Paris (1904). Reprinted in *Oeuvres de Marie Sklodowska Curie* (Polish Academy of Sciences, Warsaw, 1954), p139.

charge carried by the α-rays must be *positive*. Of course, the α-rays do not reach the photographic plate in this case, because they are soon absorbed after travelling only a short distance. The γ-rays are, as shown above, undeviated by the magnetic field. It should be pointed out that this is indeed, in this simple form, only a hypothetical experiment. In practice, the radii of curvature of the paths of the α- and β-rays are vastly dissimilar, and if the magnetic field were strong enough to separate the paths of the α-rays and the γ-rays, the paths of the β-rays would be circles of such small radii that they would never reach the photographic plate.

5·4   The α-Rays

The first definite evidence as to the nature of the α-rays came from experiments of considerable delicacy performed by Rutherford.[2] The apparatus which he used to show that they carry an electric charge is shown schematically in Figure 5·3. α-rays from a thin layer of radium salt in the bottom of the vessel were collimated by about twenty slits each of about 1 mm width. Thus the principal ionising effect measured in the electroscope by the rate of fall of the gold leaf was due to those α-rays from the radium which travelled in the right direction to pass through the slits. Now the apparatus was subjected to a strong magnetic field at right angles to the plane of the diagram. The rate of fall of the leaf was considerably reduced, showing that the α-rays had been deflected so that they struck the sides of the slit system. The immediate conclusion was that the α-rays could not be electromagnetic radiation, but must consist of charged particles. In order to discover the sign of this charge, Rutherford then half-covered the ends of the slits (remember they were only 1 mm wide!). Then the rate at which the ionisation measured in the electroscope was reduced as the magnetic field gradually increased depended on the direction of this field. As Figure 5·4 shows, reversal of the field has a marked effect on the number

[2] Rutherford, *Philosophical Magazine*, **5**, p177 (1903).

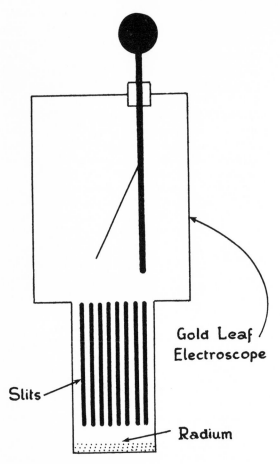

Fig. 5·3—*Apparatus used by Rutherford to show the magnetic deflection of α-rays*

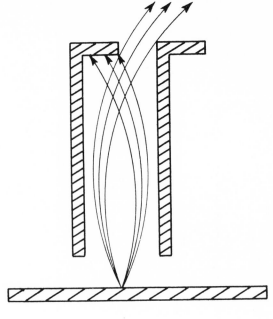

Fig. 5·4—*Effect of half-covering the slits in the apparatus of Figure 5·3 on reversal of the magnetic field*

of particles which are able to pass through the half-covered slits. A knowledge of the direction of the field which allowed the greater number to emerge into the electroscope enabled Rutherford to deduce the direction in which their tracks curved, and hence the sign of the charge carried by the α-rays. He found that this charge was positive.

The next step was to try to measure the specific charge (e/m) of the α-particles. This was done from quantitative measurements of their deflections in magnetic and electric fields.* The magnitudes of such deflections depend not only on the charges and masses of

* Rutherford, *Philosophical Magazine*, **12**, p348 (1906).

the particles, but also on their velocities. Early measurements soon showed that the α-particles given off by many radioactive substances did not all have the same velocities. Therefore it was necessary, in order to achieve any accuracy, to select only those sources which emitted homogeneous α-rays. Rutherford's apparatus for determining the magnetic deflection of the α-particles is shown schematically in Figure 5·5. The whole of the vessel V, evacuated so as not to slow down the α-particles, was placed in a magnetic field at right angles to the plane of the diagram. The strength of this field and the location of the narrow slit, S, fixed the one possible circular trajectory by which particles from a radium C source deposited on a thin wire at A could reach the photographic plate, P. Reversal of the field selected a similar trajectory of just the opposite curvature, and the photographic plate, when developed, showed two separate traces. If $2d$ is the separation of these traces, B the induction of the magnetic field, e the charge of the α-particle, m its mass, v its

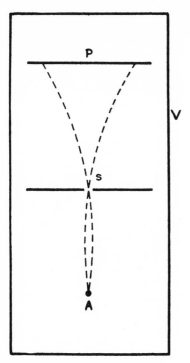

Fig. 5·5—*Rutherford's magnetic deflection apparatus used in the determination* e/m *for* α-*particles*

With his next piece of apparatus, Rutherford became the first to measure the tiny deflections of the α-particles by electrostatic fields. The principle of this device is shown in Figure 5·6. This time a pair of parallel plates, C, provided a uniform electric field and at the same time, acted as a slit system to select those particles which could reach the photographic plate, P. The plates, C, which were 4 cm long were carefully adjusted to be only 0·2 mm apart, thus producing quite an intense field. Those particles from the thin cylindrical source A which entered this electric field travelled in parabolic trajectories between the plates and, on leaving the field, kept going in straight lines to the photographic plate. Thus if one considers the extreme trajectories which could be accommodated between the plates, as shown in Figure 5·6, it turns out that the distance D, between

velocity, and a and b the distances of the plate and the source, respectively, from the slit, we find that

$$\frac{mv}{e} = \frac{Ba(a + b)}{2d}$$

to a good approximation, since d is quite small.

Apart from giving a value of the ratio $\frac{mv}{e}$, this particular experiment provided a significant piece of information about the α-particles emitted from this particular radioactive substance, namely that they were indeed of a single velocity. If they were not, the images on the photographic plate would not have been sharply defined. As the above equation shows, a range of velocities would have given rise to a range of values of d, that is, to a pair of blurred traces on the plate. In fact, it is found that even sources from which the α-particles are not monoenergetic emit these particles in discrete groups, each of which has a single, well-defined energy.

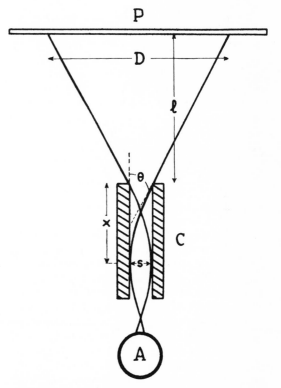

Fig. 5·6—*Rutherford's electric deflection technique used in the determination of* e/m *for* α-*particles. The size of the wire A is much exaggerated in the diagram*

the extreme edges of the two traces obtained by reversal of the voltage applied to the plates is quite well defined. The point at which the parabola grazes the plate is determined by the relation

$$s = \tfrac{1}{2}\left(\frac{eV}{sm}\right)\left(\frac{x}{v}\right)^2 ,$$

and its direction at the point of leaving the field is given by

$$\tan \theta = \frac{eV}{smv^2}x .$$

From these two relations and the geometry of the apparatus it is not difficult to show that

$$\frac{mv^2}{e} = \frac{8Vl^2}{(D-s)^2} ,$$

where m, v, and e have the same meanings as previously. V is the voltage applied to the parallel plates, s is their separation and l is the distance from their ends to the photographic plate.

Thus, from these two experiments, Rutherford obtained values of mv/e and mv^2/e. From these, he immediately found the velocity and specific charge for these α-particles. Further experiments with other sources soon showed that, no matter what the velocities of these particles, they all had the same specific charge, namely $5 \cdot 1 \times 10^7$ coulomb/kgm.[1] This led to the fairly obvious, but most important inference that the α-particles emitted from all radioactive substances are all identical.

Let us survey the information which had been accumulated at this stage. The α-rays had been shown to be positively charged particles, probably all identical in nature. They travelled with exceptionally high velocities, ranging from about 5% to 7% of the velocity of light. Their specific charge was 5×10^7 coulomb/kgm. This latter quantity was a vital piece of evidence, for this specific charge is almost exactly half that of the hydrogen ion. Now it had become fairly generally accepted that the charge of the hydrogen ion and the numerically equal negative charge of the electron were the basic unit charges. Thus the α-particle, assuming that it was a fairly

simple entity, had to be either a singly charged hydrogen molecule or the singly charged ion of a hitherto unknown atom of atomic weight 2, or a doubly charged atom of helium, whose atomic weight is 4. In order to decide between these alternatives, an obvious requirement was an independent measurement of the charge carried by each α-particle. Since this charge was expected to be very small the best way of determining it seemed to be to find some way of counting the number of α-particles given off by a particular source in a certain time interval and then to measure the total charge carried by these α-particles.

The apparatus devised by Rutherford and Geiger[2] to count individual α-particles was a direct predecessor of the Geiger counter. α-particles from a radium C source were allowed to enter a brass cylinder through a small aperture. This cylinder had a fine wire passing down its centre, the wire and the cylinder being insulated from each other. The cylinder was at a negative potential of about 1000 volt with respect to the wire and was filled with air or carbon dioxide at a pressure of a few centimetres of mercury. Under these conditions the gas multiplication of the ionisation produced by a single α-particle (see Chapter 11) gave a sufficient burst of charge arriving at the wire to produce a measurable ballistic deflection of an electrometer which was connected to it. With this arrangement the rate at which particles entered the counter had to be limited to about 5 per minute, but by knowing the size of the aperture through which the particles were admitted and its distance from the source, the total number of α-particles emitted per second from a known amount of radium C was determined. The other significant feature of this experiment was its verification of the fact that the α-rays did consist of individual particles.

Rutherford and Geiger then designed a piece of apparatus which enabled them to measure the total charge carried per second by the α-particles from a known quantity of

[1] The modern value is $4 \cdot 79 \times 10^7$ coulomb/kgm.

[2] Rutherford and Geiger, *Proceedings of the Royal Society*, **A 81**, p141 (1908).

radium C.[1] The source and a collecting plate were placed in a vacuum chamber and a magnetic field applied across the chamber so that no β-particles could reach the plate. Then the current collected by this plate was that due to the α-particles alone.

In this way, it was found that the charge carried by each α-particle was $3 \cdot 1 \times 10^{-19}$ coulomb, which was approximately twice the electronic charge. Thus it was concluded that the α-particle was probably a doubly ionised helium atom.

Final identification of the α-particle came from the elegant experiment of Rutherford and Royds.[2] Their apparatus is shown in Figure 5·7. A quantity of the radioactive gas, radon, was compressed into the fine glass tube, A. The walls of this tube, less than $\frac{1}{100}$ mm thick, were thin enough to allow α-particles to escape from the tube, but sufficiently robust to withstand a pressure difference of one atmosphere. The α-particles were stopped by the surrounding tube, T, which was evacuated, and by raising the level of the mercury, H, any gas which had accumulated in this tube could be compressed into the narrow discharge tube, V, where it could be examined spectroscopically. After six days the whole helium spectrum was clearly observed. In order to be sure that this helium was due to α-particles escaping from A and becoming neutral helium atoms on being brought to rest in T, the radon was pumped out of A and replaced by helium gas. No trace of helium was observed in the discharge tube after several days, so that the gas itself was shown to be incapable of diffusing through the walls of the capillary tube. Thus the nature of the α-particle was firmly established.

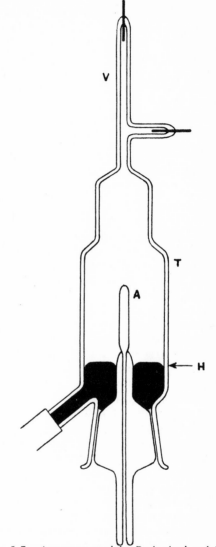

Fig. 5·7—*Apparatus used by Rutherford and Royds in the identification of the α-particle*

5·5 The β-Rays

In the early days of radioactivity these rays received rather more attention than the α- or γ-rays, principally because of their more 'spectacular' properties of penetration of

[1] Rutherford and Geiger, *Proceedings of the Royal Society*, **A 81**, p162 (1908).
[2] Rutherford and Royds, *Philosophical Magazine*, **17**, p281 (1909).

materials and deflection in magnetic fields. We have seen in Section 5·3, that several experimenters, at about the same time, observed the deflection of β-rays in magnetic fields. One of the most thorough series of measurements at this time was carried out by Becquerel. He used apparatus rather like that shown in Figure 5·2, but with sufficiently small magnetic fields for the β-rays to travel in circles of reasonable radii. The images produced on the photographic plate from an initially well-collimated beam would be sharply defined if the particles all had the same velocity and specific charge. In this case they would all travel along the same circle in the magnetic field and strike the same point of the plate. In fact the image on the photographic plate was diffuse and extended, showing that either the β-particles were not all identical, with a common value of specific charge, or they were emitted from the source with a range of velocities.

However, at least the direction of deflection was sufficient to establish that the charge carried by the β-particles is negative. This fact was confirmed by the Curies,[1] who used a modified form of the apparatus shown in Figure 5·1. No potential difference was applied between the plates and the upper plate was surrounded by an insulating material which excluded the α-rays and the ions produced in the surrounding air. However, this insulator was thin enough to allow the β-rays to reach the plate. It was found that the upper plate acquired a negative charge.

Becquerel was also one of the first to demonstrate the deflection of β-rays by an electric field.[2] By measuring separately the displacements of the image produced on a photographic plate by a narrow beam of β-rays when it passed through an electric and a magnetic field, he was able to make a rough estimate of the average velocity of the particles and their specific charge. Of course, only average values could be estimated, because the images of the beam were not only displaced, but spread out as well, due to the range of velocities present. However, despite their imperfections, these measurements gave the first indications of two very significant facts about the β-particles — their velocities, which were of the order of about one half of the velocity of light, and their specific charge, which was of the same order of magnitude as

that of the electron. The obvious conclusion was that the β-particles were probably identical with cathode rays, except for their considerably higher velocities.

The first successful attempt to measure the specific charge for β-particles and, in doing so, to deal with the complication of their non-uniform velocities, was made by Kaufmann.[3] His apparatus made use of the same technique of parallel electric and magnetic fields as was used by Thomson in his determination of the specific charges of 'positive rays' (see Chapter 10 and Figure 10·2). In this the electric field produces a deflection of the beam proportional to e/mv^2, while the deflection due to the magnetic field is proportional to e/mv. Thus, by measuring both these component deflections at various points of the trace produced on the photographic plate which records the resultant deflections of the beam, a succession of corresponding pairs of values of e/m and v can be obtained.

Kaufmann's results clearly showed a definite dependence of the value of e/m on v, with the specific charge decreasing with increasing velocity. More precise measurements by Bucherer,[4] using a different technique, showed that for β-particle velocities between 0·32 and 0·7 times the velocity of light the variation of e/m was in excellent agreement with the supposition that the charge of the β-particles was fixed and that the mass varied with the velocity as predicted by the theory of relativity, that is,

$$m = m_0 / \sqrt{(1 - v^2 / c^2)} .$$

Further, the limiting value for the specific charge at zero velocity, e/m_0, as measured by Bucherer was $1·73 \times 10^{11}$ coulomb/kgm compared with the then accepted value of $1·77 \times 10^{11}$ coulomb/kgm for electrons. Thus the identity of the β-particle as a very fast-moving electron was regarded as established.

One other feature of the behaviour of β-particles may be mentioned at this point. This concerns their ranges in absorbing

[1] P. and Marie Curie, *Comptes Rendus*, **130**, p647 (1900).

[2] Becquerel, *Comptes Rendus*, **130**, p809 (1900).

[3] Kaufmann, *Physikalische Zeitschrift*, **4**, p54 (1902).

[4] Bucherer, *Annalen der Physik*, **28**, p513 (1909); **29**, p1063 (1909).

materials. In this respect, they are very different from the α-particles. Mono-energetic α-particles have a fairly well defined range in a given absorbing medium. This means that as the thickness of absorber is increased, practically all of the α-particles from the incident beam still emerge from the absorber, until a critical thickness is reached at which the number which emerge falls off rapidly for a small additional increase in absorber thickness. Very soon thereafter a thickness is reached through which none of the α-particles can penetrate. β-particles, on the other hand, do not have such a well defined range. Even for monoenergetic β-particles, the number which emerge after their passage through an absorbing layer falls gradually as the thickness of this layer increases. Figures 5·8 and 5·9 show this difference in behaviour. Furthermore, the energies of the β-particles emitted from a radioactive source are generally not confined to a few discrete values, like those of the α-particles, but may take any values within a certain range. This point will be discussed more fully later in the book. However, it is clear that this variation in energy will further complicate any description of the absorption of the β-particles emitted from a particular source.

5·6 The γ-Rays

The early supposition that these penetrating rays are identical in character with X-rays, and differ only in being of shorter wavelength has been completely verified. γ-rays cannot be deflected by electric or magnetic fields; they travel with the velocity of light; they can be diffracted like any other form of electromagnetic radiation; they eject photoelectrons from materials. In fact, the ranges of X-ray wavelengths and γ-ray wavelengths overlap considerably. Many γ-rays have wavelengths of 0·3 Å or more, corresponding to photon energies of less than 40 keV. 40 kV is not a particularly high operating potential for many types of X-ray tube.

It follows that the absorption of γ-rays takes place according to the exponential absorption law for X-rays which was discussed in Chapter 4. This is

$$I = I_0 \, e^{-\mu x},$$

where, if I_0 is the intensity of a parallel beam falling on a slab of absorber of thickness x, the intensity of the parallel emergent beam is I. μ is then the linear absorption coefficient of the material of the absorber.

The simplest way to measure μ is to measure I for various values of x. Then, if $\log I$ is plotted against x, the result should be a

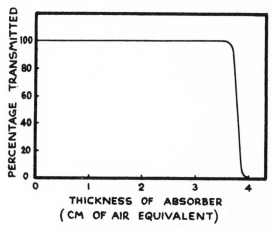

Fig. 5·8—*Transmission of polonium α-particles through various thicknesses of absorber*

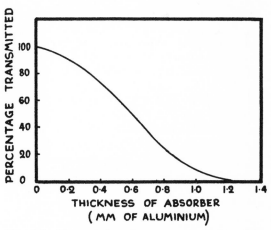

Fig. 5·9—*Transmission of mono-energetic β-particles through various thicknesses of aluminium*

straight line of slope $-\mu$. When this procedure is followed for most radioactive substances, however, the resultant log I versus x graph is not a simple straight line. The reason for this is that γ-rays of more than one energy are usually emitted, and each γ-ray energy has a different absorption coefficient. At the same time, these γ-ray energies do not form a continuous spectrum, like those of the β-rays, but are limited to a few discrete energy values, in just the same way as are the energies of α-particle groups.

5·7 Radioactive Transformations

While some workers were studying the properties of α-, β- and γ-rays, there were others who were concentrating on investigations of the properties of the radioactive substances themselves. For example, Crookes[1] and Becquerel[2] both showed that, *apparently*, all of the activity could be removed from uranium by simple chemical processes. This was not *really* what was happening, and the effect which they observed was due to their use of a photographic plate wrapped in paper to detect the activity of their samples. This meant that they did not detect the strong α-activity which remained with the uranium. However, it was certainly true that the β-activity was removable chemically, thus indicating that the α- and β-activities of the uranium were due to two separate chemical substances. The really startling discovery was made a year later, however, when the two separated fractions were re-examined. Then it was found that the uranium had completely recovered its β-activity, while the fraction which had initially contained all of the β-activity had become completely inactive!

Rutherford and Soddy[3] set out to measure the rates of growth and decay of the activities in cases of this kind. They found that they could easily separate an intense α-emitter,

[1] Crookes, *Proceedings of the Royal Society*, **A 66**, p409 (1900).
[2] Becquerel, *Comptes Rendus*, **131**, p137 (1900).
[3] Rutherford and Soddy, *Philosophical Magazine*, **4**, pp370, 569 (1902).

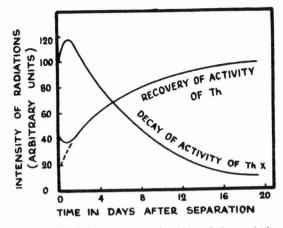

Fig. 5·10—*Behaviour, as a function of time, of the activities of separated Th and ThX samples. The dotted section is explained in the caption to Figure*

which they called Thorium X (ThX) from thorium (Th), which is itself an α-emitter. Using electrical detection, they found that the Th activity was reduced by about 60% at the time of separation but recovered to its original strength after about a month. In the same period of time, the activity of the ThX fell from its initial intensity to zero. Their measurements of the growth and decay of these separated fractions are shown in Figure 5·10. The initial 'bumps' in these curves were later shown to be due to another substance again, Thorium C. When its contribution is subtracted the curves of Figure 5·11 are obtained. These curves can be very well described by equations of the following kinds:

$$I_t = I_0 e^{-\lambda t}$$

for the decaying ThX, where I_0 is its initial activity and I_t its activity after time t; and

$$I_t = I'(1 - e^{-\lambda t})$$

for the recovery of the Th activity, where this time I_t is the Th activity at time t after the separation and I' is its final activity a very long time later.

The significant features of these equations are firstly, the exponential decay of the isolated radioactive substance, which is found to be characteristic of *every* single radioactive

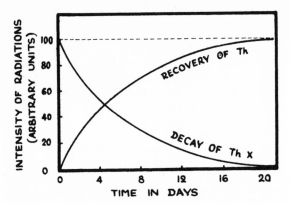

Fig. 5·11—*Decay and recovery curves for ThX and Th. The recovery curve is redrawn from that of Figure 5·10 after subtraction of the initial constant activity obtained by extrapolation to zero time as shown by the dotted curve in that Figure*

element, and secondly, the fact that the 'decay constant', λ, the value of which determines the rate of decay of the ThX, appears again in the equation describing the recovery of the Th activity. In fact the recovery, at any time, may be regarded as proceeding at the same rate as the decay of the separated fraction. Rutherford and Soddy proposed two hypotheses which gave a satisfactory explanation of these observations. Firstly, the ThX was being produced at a constant rate from the Th. Secondly, it was decaying according to the exponential decay law found above, with this decay process commencing right from the time of its production.

Let us now show that these hypotheses do in fact lead to the above recovery and decay laws. Suppose that we have, at time $t = 0$, a quantity of Th with the ThX completely removed from it, and that thereafter ThX is created at a constant rate Q per second. Let the decay constant for ThX be λ, and the total activity contributed by ThX at time t be I_t. Now consider what happens in a small time interval, dT, which occurred at a time T (earlier than t). In this time interval, the amount of ThX created was $Q\,dT$. The intensity of the radiations given off by this small quantity at that time was proportional to the quantity itself, so that we may write,

for this intensity, $(dI)_0 = kQ\,dT$. The activity due to this particular quantity at the later time, t, would then be, according to the second hypothesis,

$$dI = (dI)_0\,e^{-\lambda(t-T)}$$
$$= kQ\,e^{-\lambda(t-T)}\,dT\,.$$

Thus the total activity at time t due to all such small quantities created at earlier times would be,

$$I_t = \int_0^t kQ\,e^{-\lambda\,(t-T)}\,dT$$
$$= \frac{kQ}{\lambda}(1 - e^{-\lambda t})\,.$$

After a long time, I_t approaches the value $\dfrac{kQ}{\lambda}$; so that, writing $\dfrac{kQ}{\lambda} = I'$, we have

$$I_t = I'(1 - e^{-\lambda t})\,,$$

in agreement with the experimentally determined recovery law.

Clearly, after this long time the amount of ThX present is constant, the rate of production equalling the rate of decay. If the ThX is then separated off it will, as a whole, decay exponentially with the decay constant λ.

This decay and recovery process was found to occur with many other radioactive substances, whenever an equilibrium between one substance and its continually decaying product was upset by a chemical separation of the two. The value of the decay constant, λ, was found to vary from one pure radioactive substance to another, and it has become convenient to characterise a particular radioactive decay by a related constant, the *half-life*, defined in the following way.

Suppose that there is a quantity Q_0 of a radioactive substance at the initial time, $t = 0$, which decays to a quantity Q_1 at time t_1. Now we are interested in the time, τ, which elapses while Q_1 decreases by one half. Now

$$Q_1 = Q_0\,e^{-\lambda t_1}\,,$$

where λ is the decay constant of this particular

substance. Because of the way in which τ has been defined, it follows that

$$\tfrac{1}{2}Q_1 = Q_0\, e^{-\lambda\,(t_1 + \tau)}\,.$$

From these two relations we find that

$$\tfrac{1}{2} = e^{\lambda\tau}\,,$$

or

$$\tau = \frac{1}{\lambda}\log_e 2\,.$$

Thus it is seen that the time, τ, during which *any* quantity of this substance decays by half is a constant of the decay process, since the value deduced for τ is quite independent of the time, t_1, chosen as the starting point for this 'decay-by-half'. Therefore, no matter how much or how little of this substance is present initially, the amount left after time τ will always be just one half of the initial amount. Figure 5·12 illustrates this point. It is this characteristic time, τ, which is called the *half-life* of the radioactive substance. Of course the intensity of the radiations given off by the substance also decays with this half-life, since this intensity, at any time, is proportional to the amount of the substance present. The half-lives of radioactive substances vary over an enormous range. Among the naturally-occurring radioactive elements, half-lives as

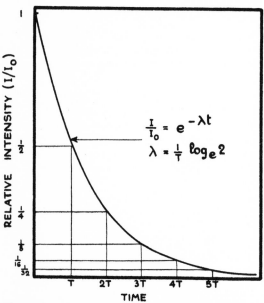

$$\frac{I}{I_0} = e^{-\lambda t}$$

$$\lambda = \frac{1}{T}\log_e 2$$

Fig. 5·12—*Curve showing the exponential decay law.*

small as 10^{-6} second and as large as 10^{10} year are found.

Although this exponential law describes very accurately the rate of decay of a radioactive substance, it gives no explanation of what is actually happening in radioactive decay. Two other facts provided important clues. Firstly, the energies of α-particles had been measured and they were nearly all of the order of magnitude of 10^{-12} joule per α-particle. Now while this is a tiny amount of energy, it is about a million times greater than the amount of energy released or absorbed by an atom in the average chemical reaction. For example, in the simple reaction

$$C + O_2 \rightarrow CO_2\,,$$

the amount of heat given out—the heat of combustion, as it is called—is $9\cdot7 \times 10^4$ calorie for each gram-atom of carbon burned. This amounts to about 7×10^{-19} joule per carbon atom. The heats of combustion and heats of reaction of other chemical processes are not vastly different. Thus it appears that the energy changes which take place when atoms rearrange themselves in chemical reactions are far smaller than those which occur when α-particle decay takes place. Hence it seemed most improbable that radioactive decay could be any sort of chemical process.

The other line of evidence leading to the same conclusion is best summarised by Rutherford himself.* He points out that no-one had been able to find any way in which the value of the decay constant, λ, for any single radioactive substance could be made to alter. He goes on to say

The rate of decay is unaltered by any chemical or physical agency, and in this respect the changes in radioactive matter are sharply distinguished from ordinary chemical changes. For example, the decay of activity of any product takes place at the same rate when the substance is exposed to light as when it is kept in the dark, and at the same rate in a vacuum as in air or any other gas at atmospheric pressure. . . . The activity of the matter is unaffected by ignition or chemical treatment. The material giving rise to the activity can be dissolved in acid and re-obtained by

* *Radioactive Substances and their Radiations* (Cambridge University Press, 1913 Edition).

evaporation of the solution without altering the activity. The rate of decay is the same whether the active matter is retained in the solid state or kept in solution . . . and is the same at red heat as at the temperature of liquid air. In fact, no variation of physical or chemical conditions has led to any observable difference in the decay of activity of any of the numerous types of active matter which have been examined.

No chemical change is known which proceeds at the same rate under such a wide variety of conditions.

In the light of this information, many theories of the nature of the radioactive process were put forward, mostly suggesting hypothetical mechanisms whereby radioactive substances might be able, in some way, to draw the large amounts of energy involved from their surroundings. All such theories were open to serious objections. The only one which provided a satisfactory explanation of all the available observations, and which has stood the test of time is the 'spontaneous disintegration theory' advanced by Rutherford and Soddy.*

They proposed that radioactive decay should be regarded as a process in which individual atoms of a substance undergo actual transformations as a result of which the atoms of one element break up and become new atoms of another element. In the case of α-decay, the new element has an atomic weight which is less than that of its parent by 4 units — the atomic weight of helium. When a β-particle is emitted, however, the new substance formed, while having quite different chemical properties from those of its parent, has the same atomic weight. In both cases, the product, or 'daughter' atoms may themselves be unstable and spontaneously disintegrate, with the process continuing until a stable atom is reached.

On this theory, the large energy changes associated with the decay process could be regarded as plausible, since the 'explosion' of an atom might well be expected to be a much more violent change than that of re-arrangement of molecules, as happens in a chemical reaction. At the same time, one may

* Rutherford and Soddy, *Philosophical Magazine*, **5**, p576 (1903).

suppose that this disintegration has a probability of occurrence which is in no way influenced by the presence of any neighbouring atoms. Then the decay would be unaffected by the physical or chemical condition of the radioactive substance, as is seen to be the case. Indeed, if the probability of any one atom disintegrating in a short time interval Δt at time t is proportional to Δt and independent of t, we may write this probability as $\lambda \Delta t$, λ being a constant. Further, if there are N such atoms present at this time, t, the number which decay in the subsequent time interval Δt, will be $\Delta N = N\lambda \Delta t$. It then follows, with the use of a little calculus, that $N = N_0 e^{-\lambda t}$, so that this hypothesis is entirely consistent with the observed law of radioactive decay.

While the spontaneous disintegration theory gave some explanation of the large number of radioactive substances which had been separately identified by physical and chemical means, the very existence of this large number raised the question of how they could all be fitted in to the periodic table of the chemical elements. Soon it became fairly certain that a few cases occurred in which radioactive substances had clearly different radioactive properties (half-lives, types of radiation etc.) but were chemically indistinguishable. For example, *ionium* (the parent of radium), *radiothorium* (the parent of the ThX) and thorium itself all show exactly the same optical spectra and are chemically inseparable. However, their half-lives are 10^5 year, $1\cdot9$ year and 10^{10} year respectively. In addition, their atomic weights are different.

The explanation of these anomalies became apparent with the discovery by Thomson of the existence of atoms of the same chemical element having different atomic weights (see Chapter 10). Such atoms were given the name *isotopes* by Soddy, and it was a logical step to suggest that isotopes of an element, while having the same chemical behaviour, could differ not only in weight, but in other physical properties as well. In particular, they might well have different modes of radioactive decay.

Thus by about 1912, a satisfactory and consistent picture of the effects of radioactive decay had emerged. However, no explanation of the causes and mechanisms of the decay process had been found. Many questions remained. Why are α-, β- and γ-rays the only types of radiation emitted? Why, for example, are ionised hydrogen atoms never emitted? What is the reason for the large range of half-lives observed? Why does radioactivity only appear to occur in the heaviest elements? Why do α-particles have single energy values while β-particles are emitted with a continuous range of energies? These and many other questions have since been answered and we shall discuss some of them in later chapters.

CHAPTER 6

Relativity

6·1 Observers and their Frameworks

Suppose we are going to perform a simple experiment in mechanics. It could be a measurement of g using a falling object, or a determination of the velocity of a horizontal water jet by measuring the horizontal distance it travels while falling a certain height. In this sort of work, some distances and (perhaps indirectly) some times have to be measured. In each case, the distance and time scales used (metre rules and clocks) are stationary with respect to the observer. In a more sophisticated way, we may say that an observer has to specify a set of co-ordinate axes which is fixed in his laboratory. He measures all distances in terms of co-ordinates along these axes in order to obtain measurements which he can compare with one another. In the same way he has to specify the time scale which he is using. This combination of a fixed set of axes and a time scale is called the *frame of reference* or *framework* of the observer in question. Obviously any number of observers who were in fixed positions relative to one another could use the same framework.

Now the subject of relativity is concerned with the differences between the ways in which one set of events is described by different observers whose frameworks are moving with respect to one another. Let us construct a simple example to illustrate this difference of description. Imagine a fairground in which the merry-go-round is close to a straight section of the miniature train track, as shown in Figure 6·1. Suppose we have observers O_1 who is on the merry-go-round, O_2 who is on the train and O_3 who is standing on the ground nearby. At the instant at which the velocities of O_1 and O_2 are 15 ft sec^{-1} and 10 ft sec^{-1} relative to O_3 in the directions shown in the Figure, O_1 throws a ball horizontally with a velocity of 15 ft sec^{-1} *relative to himself* in the direction opposite to that in which he is moving, that is, parallel to the direction of motion of O_2.

Now each of the three observers describes the subsequent motion of the ball quite differently. O_3, of course, says that the ball merely falls vertically downwards. O_2 says that it moves in a parabolic arc, while O_1 reports that it moves in a rather complicated fashion with the horizontal component of its motion being, as far as he is concerned, an arc of a circle. (Remember that the co-ordinate axes of O_1's framework are rotating with him.) Scientists must be very clear in their under-

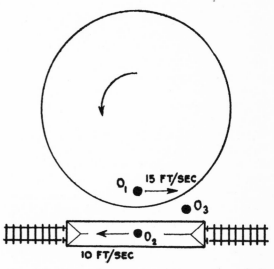

Fig. 6·1—*Three observers in relative motion. O_1 is on a merry-go-round, O_2 on a miniature train and O_3 on the ground*

61

standing of whatever relationships may exist between these differences of description, since all of Science is concerned with the description of phenomena by means of measurement and the deduction of the laws according to which these phenomena proceed. If the descriptions are different for different frameworks, the laws of nature might be expected to take different forms for different frameworks.

In fact, the laws of mechanics are not the same for all frameworks. In our simple example above, Newton's first law does not hold for the observer on the merry-go-round. His version of the corresponding law would read something like this: 'A body remains in a state of rest if, and only if, a force acts on it, this force being directed towards a fixed point and proportional to the distance of the body from this point.' Whatever law he was able to produce corresponding to Newton's second law would be a vastly more complicated affair.

It is this line of thought which leads to the question, 'for what framework or set of frameworks do Newton's laws hold *exactly*?' It is known that they are valid to a very good approximation for many situations which can be observed in a laboratory on the earth. For all practical purposes, the motion of a projectile over a short distance and the motion of a simple pendulum during a few minutes are both described, to a high degree of precision, by equations derived from Newton's laws. However, if a shell is fired over a long distance in a north-south direction, its trajectory, even after correction for such effects as air resistance, deviates measurably from a parabola. In terms of a co-ordinate system fixed at the point of firing, this trajectory does not even lie in one plane. Similarly, a carefully constructed simple pendulum, swinging in a laboratory, gradually changes its plane of oscillation over a period of hours. So Newton's laws do not hold exactly for an earth-bound laboratory, and the deviation is ascribed to the rotation of the earth. That is, the co-ordinate axes are rotating, just like those of the observer on the merry-go-round.

If, for convenience, an *inertial framework* is defined as one in which Newton's laws *do* hold exactly, a framework fixed with respect to the earth is *not* an inertial framework. However, we still have not found a framework which *is* an inertial framework. Newton suggested that an appropriate framework would be one which was fixed relative to the 'fixed stars'. This turns out to be a very useful idea in that it supplies a framework which is an excellent approximation to an inertial framework for all practical purposes — even for motions involving such large distances and long times as those of the planets of the solar system. But, in fact, there appear to be no such things as truly fixed stars. Over periods of hundreds of years the constellations move, almost imperceptibly it is true, but nevertheless they do move. So, no matter how good an approximation they may provide, they cannot really be regarded as defining an inertial framework.

It was this search for an inertial framework which led, ultimately, to Einstein's formulation of the theory of relativity.

6·2 The Propagation of Light and the Aether

The early part of the nineteenth century saw a marked revival of interest in the wave theory of light. Although this theory had been suggested earlier in various forms, it was greatly extended and improved by the work of Huyghens, published in 1690. Newton had shown a preference for a corpuscular theory of the transmission of light, and such was his prestige that, for the best part of a century, this theory was generally held to be superior to the wave theory.

However, the experiments of Young on the interference between beams of light, the work of Malus who discovered the phenomenon of polarisation, and of Fresnel who developed a theory which satisfactorily described many diffraction effects, gave a strong impetus to the wave theory. This was later brought to an apparent state of perfection by the electromagnetic theory of Maxwell. For our immediate purpose, no understanding of the details of this theory is needed. It is sufficient to realise that, towards the end of the nineteenth century, it was firmly believed that light was propagated from every light source in the form of a wave of very high velocity — 3×10^8 metre sec^{-1} — with a wavelength which varied from about 4×10^{-4} millimetre at the blue end of the visible region to about 7×10^{-4} millimetre at the red end. A very important feature of Maxwell's theory is that these waves must be transverse.

From the very earliest suggestions of the wave theory, it had been realised that such a theory carried with it the implication of the presence of some medium through which the waves were propagated. It became clear that this medium, which came to be called the *aether* had to have very curious properties. Not only did it have to be absolutely transparent, but it had to exert a completely negligible drag on solid objects — for example, planets — which moved through it. This latter requirement suggested something like a perfect fluid with no 'inter-molecular' forces which could give rise to a viscous drag. At the same time, the aether had to be able to transmit a transverse wave, and this presented a great difficulty, because all ordinary fluids are only able to transmit longitudinal waves. Only in solids, in which the forces of cohesion between atoms are so great that these atoms are held in fixed positions relative to one another, is the transmission of transverse waves observed. Thus, some very strange types of substances indeed — unlike any other known substance — were invented to provide plausible models of the aether.

However, despite the strangeness of its properties, the aether did have the attractive feature that it had to pervade all space and could probably be regarded as being completely at rest. Therefore, there was the strong possibility that the aether might provide an excellent 'foundation' for a true inertial framework. If this possibility is to be realised, however, it is clearly necessary for an earth-bound observer to be able to 'locate' such a framework, and to do this he has to determine how the earth moves relative to the aether.

So, over a period of many years, a great number of experiments were devised in an effort to detect the motion of the earth through the aether — the 'aether drift', as it came to be called.

Because the aether had no significance in connection with any branch of physics other than the propagation of light, it seemed likely that this aether drift could only be detected by some optical method. Furthermore, although no-one had any idea of how large the aether drift was likely to be, it was certain that it had to be at least as large as the orbital velocity of the earth around the sun, should the sun happen to be at rest in the aether. Now this orbital velocity is not so very small; it is about 3×10^4 metre sec^{-1} (or about 70,000 m.p.h.). But the velocity of light is 10,000 times greater. Thus, any change in the observed value of this velocity due to the motion of the observer through the aether might be as small as one part in 10^4.

It should be pointed out that this expected change in the observed velocity depended on the supposition that light behaved like other types of wave motion. This implies that once light has been emitted from a source, it travels through the medium at a speed characteristic of the medium itself and independent of any motion of the source. For example, there is very good evidence that the velocity of light emitted by stars is quite independent of their various velocities. This being so, the change in the measured velocity due to the motion of the observer may be seen from the following analogy.

Suppose a train, 360 ft long, is travelling at 100 ft sec^{-1} along a straight track, that there is no wind blowing, and that the velocity of sound in still air is 1100 ft sec^{-1}. At a given instant, the train whistle blows. Any stationary observer, who happened to be 360 ft away from the engine in any direction would hear the sound $360/1100 = 0.327$ second later. Because the guard of the train is moving towards the direction of approach of the sound waves, he hears the sound a little earlier. In fact the time interval which elapses in his case is 0.300 second, because in this time the sound wave has travelled 330 ft and the train has moved 30 ft, so that then the guard is also 330 ft from the point in the air at which the sound wave was emitted. Hence, according to the observers on the train, the sound has travelled 360 ft in 0·3 second, so that their measurement of its velocity relative to them is 1200 ft sec^{-1}. In general then, if the velocity of a wave in a medium is c and the velocity of an observer through the medium is v, the observer's estimate of the velocity of the wave in the case of sound or water waves is either $c + v$ or $c - v$, depending on whether he moves towards, or away from the advancing wave. The same result was expected to hold for light waves.

We shall not concern ourselves here with the details of any of the aether drift experiments except the most refined and decisive of them all, the famous Michelson-Morley experiment, performed in 1887. Michelson and Morley used a device known as an interferometer, of a type originally devised by Michelson. This instrument, in effect, compared the observed velocities of light along two long paths which were always at right angles to each other. Now although the direction of the aether drift is quite unknown, by rotation of the interferometer in the laboratory and by taking measurements at different times of the year, it must be possible to arrange that, at some time, one of these light paths is parallel to the aether drift and the other at right angles to it. Under these conditions the observed light velocities along these paths were expected to be different.

The apparently extraordinary result of this experiment was that no difference between the velocities in the two directions could be detected, despite the fact that the sensitivity of the apparatus was sufficient to detect an aether drift about 40 times smaller than the orbital velocity of the earth. Repetition of the measurement under different circumstances and at different times of the year always gave the same null effect. Because this null result is equivalent to the aether drift being effectively zero at all times it became apparent that, for some reason, the

motion of the earth through the aether can never be detected. Therefore, no matter what *his* velocity at the time may be, an observer always gets the same value for the velocity of light.

6·3   Einstein's Postulates and Their Consequences

Let us restate the paradox arising from the result of the Michelson-Morley experiment in terms of the concept of the observers' frameworks which were discussed in Section 6·1. Suppose there are two observers whose coordinate axes are parallel to one another and moving relative to one another in the direction of their x-axes. Imagine, for instance, that the observers are on two trains travelling along parallel tracks and that each observer sets up his x-axis in the direction along the train. Let us refer to these two frameworks as S and S', and let S' be moving with a velocity v with respect to S in the positive x-direction, as in Figure 6·2. For convenience, the zero of the time scale for each framework may be taken as the instant when the two origins, O and O' pass each other.

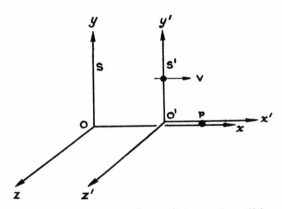

Fig. 6·2—*Two frameworks in relative motion. S' has a velocity* v *with respect to S*

Now observers who are accustomed to thinking in terms of Newtonian mechanics will readily arrive at the following conclusions; in fact, they would regard them as obvious. If a particular event is recorded by the observer in the framework S as occurring at time t at the point P (co-ordinate x), the observer in S′ will find that it occurs at a distance $x - vt$ from O′ (since the distance OO′ is just vt). Furthermore, he will agree about the time t, at which it occurs. Put more formally, the relationship between the co-ordinates of the same event as observed from the two frameworks is

$$\left.\begin{array}{l} x' = x - vt \\ t' = t \,. \end{array}\right\} \qquad (6\cdot1)$$

and

The second of these equations is a formal way of saying that the time-scale for the two frameworks is the same; or, as Newton put it, 'Absolute, true and mathematical time, of itself, and by its own nature, flows uniformly on without regard to anything external'. Note that for simplicity, only events happening at points along the x-axes are going to be considered. Even if this were not so we would feel justified in assuming that the y- and z-co-ordinates of an event were unchanged by any relative motion of the observers in the x-direction.

The equations (6·1) are called the 'Newtonian transformation' between the co-ordinate systems of the two frameworks and it is from them that the relationship between the velocities of the same moving object as measured by the two observers is deduced. If the observer in S′ finds that an object is at points x'_1 and x'_2 at times t'_1 and t'_2 respectively, he will say that its velocity — if it is constant — is

$$u' = \frac{x'_2 - x'_1}{t'_2 - t'_1}\,.$$

At the same time, the observer in S who records the same two positions of the object as occurring at points whose co-ordinates are x_1 and x_2 at times t_1 and t_2 obtains, for its velocity,

$$u = \frac{x_2 - x_1}{t_2 - t_1}\,.$$

From equations (6·1), we can substitute for the dashed co-ordinates in terms of the undashed ones and get

$$u' = \frac{(x_2 - vt_2) - (x_1 - vt_1)}{t_2 - t_1}$$
$$= \frac{x_2 - x_1}{t_2 - t_1} - v$$
$$= u - v.$$

Now this is precisely the relationship between relative velocities which was used in the example in the previous section of the measurement of the velocity of a sound wave. In that case, the ground would be framework S′ of Figure 6·2, the train would be framework S, moving with velocity v to the left relative to S′, and the sound wave would be the 'object', moving to the right with velocity u' relative to S′. Then u, the velocity relative to S, is equal to $u' + v$, as before.

Now the dilemma resulting from the Michelson-Morley experiment may be summarised thus:

(a) If the Newtonian transformation holds, the velocity of a given motion *must* have different values if measured by observers moving relative to one another.

(b) The Michelson-Morley result suggests that the velocity of light as measured by a particular observer is quite independent of any constant velocity which he may have.

Despite the fact that the conclusions expressed in these two statements appear to contradict one another flatly, many attempts were made to reconcile them, but none of these was really successful. Finally, Einstein, in a paper entitled 'On the Electrodynamics of Moving Bodies'[*] suggested that we should accept the experimental fact of statement (b) and find an alternative to statement (a), since this statement is, after all, something of an assumption. While this may now seem to be a perfectly reasonable line of approach, it should not be forgotten that Newtonian mechanics had provided the basis for all successful developments in the physical sciences for over two centuries. The abandonment of such a basic concept as the Newtonian transformation represented a real revolution in physical thought.

[*] Einstein, *Annalen der Physik*, **17**, p891 (1905).

Einstein's theory was developed from the two following postulates:

1. The laws of physics take exactly the same form for all inertial frameworks — that is, all co-ordinate systems which have a constant translational velocity relative to one another.
2. The speed of light in a vacuum as measured relative to any inertial framework is constant. That is, it is independent of both the velocity of the source and the velocity of the framework.

The first of these postulates was, of course, a restatement of an already firmly established principle. If there is one inertial framework, then it is a consequence of the Newtonian transformation that, in any other framework moving with a constant velocity relative to the first, the laws of mechanics take exactly the same form. Thus the second framework is also an inertial framework. In fact, it is because of this feature that it is most convenient for the formulation of the laws of physics to select frameworks of this type, rather than rotating frameworks or those accelerating in some other way. In addition, of course, the laws are most simply expressed in terms of such frameworks.

However, the second postulate, which is based on the result of the Michelson-Morley experiment, implies the rejection of the Newtonian transformation, and this is the starting point for the radically new ideas introduced by Einstein's theory. If the Newtonian transformation is to be rejected, it must be replaced with some other transformation between the co-ordinates of inertial frameworks. The existence of *some* such transformation is essential. Otherwise it would not be possible to predict the way in which a series of events will be described in terms of one inertial framework, if its description from the point of view of another inertial framework travelling with a constant velocity relative to the first, is known. Einstein was able to show that it is possible to find such a transformation only if there is a radical revision of ideas about the measurement of time. It is necessary to accept the fact that if an observer makes successive observations of

a clock which is moving relative to him, he will find that it does not keep the same time as an identical clock which is stationary with respect to him. In other words, the Newtonian concept of 'universal time' must be abandoned. This allows the possibility that the measures of time elapsed during a given process may not be the same for different frameworks which are in motion relative to one another. Not only is this a possibility — it is found that this state of affairs *must* exist as a consequence of the Einstein postulates, so that there is no longer equality between the time-co-ordinates t and t' as in the Newtonian transformation.

Einstein found that the appropriate transformation was one which had already been derived by the Dutch physicist Lorentz from other considerations. For the simple case of the two frameworks S and S' which were discussed earlier, this transformation takes the form

$$x' = \frac{x - vt}{\sqrt{1 - v^2/c^2}} \, ,$$

$$t' = \frac{t - vx/c^2}{\sqrt{1 - v^2/c^2}} \, ,$$

where c is the velocity of light.

Let us now consider a few of the consequences of this 'Lorentz transformation', as it has become known. Firstly, it should be observed that if v is very small compared to c, this transformation approximates to the Newtonian transformation. It is rather to be hoped that this would happen, since the Newtonian transformation is found to hold to such a high degree of precision between the inertial frameworks in which it is possible, in practice, to perform measurements. The relative velocities of such frameworks are, in fact, small compared to the velocity of light.

Next, there is this phenomenon of clocks running at different rates. Suppose that there is a set of observers situated at various points along the x'-axis of S', each of whom has an identical clock, all of these clocks being synchronised to show the same time, t'. Now an observer in framework S, also carrying an identical clock, moves past this other set of observers. As he passes each one, he compares the times t_1, t_2, t_3, ... etc., shown by his clock with the corresponding times t'_1, t'_2, t'_3, ... shown by the S'-clocks. As he goes from the first to the second of these he will find that the time which has elapsed as shown by those clocks is $t'_2 - t'_1$, and from the Lorentz transformation

$$t'_2 - t'_1 = \frac{(t_2 - t_1)}{\sqrt{1 - v^2/c^2}} - \frac{(x_2 - x_1)v/c^2}{\sqrt{1 - v^2/c^2}}.$$

However, the clock in S does not move in its framework, that is $x_2 = x_1$; and $(t_2 - t_1)$ is just the time elapsed according to it. So, since

$$(t_2 - t_1) = (t'_2 - t'_1)\sqrt{1 - v^2/c^2},$$

and $\sqrt{1 - v^2/c^2}$ is less than 1, the observers in S' find that the clock in S shows a smaller elapsed time than their own clocks. That is, the S-clock, although identical with their own, appears to them to be running at a slower rate when it is moving with respect to them. This phenomenon is clearly going to be very difficult to observe unless the moving clock has a speed relative to the observers which is an appreciable fraction of the velocity of light. However, it has been found that certain subatomic particles called mesons have decay times which depend on their velocities with respect to the observer. To an earth-bound observer, they appear to decay at a much slower rate when they are travelling at high speed through the atmosphere than they do after having been effectively brought to rest in the laboratory.

Another interesting effect is that of length contraction. Suppose that an object which is stationary in framework S' has a length l' according to an observer in S'. He notes the co-ordinates of its two ends, x'_2 and x'_1 and finds its length by subtraction, that is

$$l' = x'_2 - x'_1.$$

Now observers in S will find the length of this object by noting simultaneously — according to them — the co-ordinates of its ends in their framework. They will say that its length is

$$l = x_2 - x_1.$$

However, from the Lorentz transformation,

$$x'_2 - x'_1 = \frac{(x_2 - x_1) - (t_2 - t_1)}{\sqrt{1 - v^2/c^2}},$$

and since the observers in S make their measurements simultaneously, $t_2 = t_1$, and so

$$l' = l/\sqrt{1 - v^2/c^2}.$$

Thus, l is less than l', so that an observer finds that his measure of the length of an object as it moves past him is less than its length when stationary with respect to him.

Since distances and time intervals are no longer the same as judged from two different frameworks, the simple relationship between relative velocities used in Newtonian mechanics will also require modification. Earlier in this section it was shown how the equation relating the velocities u and u' of a moving object as seen from the frameworks S and S', namely $u' = u - v$, was derived from the Newtonian transformation. Now if we follow exactly the same method of derivation, but use the Lorentz transformation, it is quite easy to arrive at the result

$$u' = \frac{u - v}{1 - uv/c^2}.$$

Thus, the simple rule that 'velocity relative to S' equals velocity relative to S minus velocity of S' relative to S ' no longer holds. This new relation between relative velocities has one rather important feature. Suppose that, instead of a moving object, we are concerned with a light wave. The velocity with which it travels relative to S is, of course, c. Now if $u = c$ is put in the above expression, it follows that

$$u' = \frac{c - v}{1 - v/c} = c.$$

Thus the velocity of the wave, as viewed from S' is also c. This result, of course, is exactly what is expected, since it is just Einstein's second postulate, which was used to produce the Lorentz transformation. From this in turn, we arrived at the equation relating relative velocities. Nevertheless there is always some satisfaction in demonstrating that a result is entirely consistent with the assumptions from which it was derived!

Finally, one of the most important results of this theory is the inter-relationship between the energy, mass and velocity of a body. It may be shown, from consideration of some elementary situations in mechanics such as the bouncing of elastic balls that, if the laws governing such phenomena are to be the same for two frameworks moving relative to one another, it is impossible to have conservation of momentum under all circumstances unless the mass of a body is no longer regarded as a fixed quantity. Now the conservation laws governing energy and momentum are regarded as among the most important and fundamental in physics. Therefore they are retained and it then becomes necessary to define the mass of a body as measured by an observer to be

$$m = m_0 \,/\, \sqrt{1 - v^2 / c^2}\,,$$

where v is the speed of the body with respect to the observer at the time of the measurement. m_0 is then the mass of the body when it is at rest in the framework of the observer — its 'rest mass'. The validity of this concept that the mass of an object increases with its velocity was first established by the measurements of Bucherer* who was able to measure the ratio e/m for β-rays with velocities between 0·32 and 0·7 times the velocity of light. He found close agreement with the relation given above.

It is interesting to notice that, as the speed of the object increases, and v approaches c, the value of m approaches infinity. The velocity of light is thus regarded as an upper limit which cannot be equalled or exceeded by the speed of any material object. Note that the speed of light which is concerned here is its speed in a vacuum; its speed in a refracting

* Bucherer, *Annalen der Physik*, **28**, p513 (1909).

medium can be much smaller. In fact useful measurements can be made using particles whose speed in, say, a block of glass does exceed the speed of light in the same block. Such particles, however, always have speeds lower than that of light in a vacuum.

With the variation of mass with velocity known, the work done on a body in increasing its speed from zero to a value v can be calculated. This work is, of course, the kinetic energy of the body and the result obtained is

$$\text{Kinetic Energy} = \frac{m_0 c^2}{\sqrt{1 - v^2/c^2}} - m_0 c^2.$$

Once again, it is not difficult to show that, as the velocity of the body becomes small compared to c, this expression for the kinetic energy approaches the Newtonian value, $\frac{1}{2}m_0 v^2$. However, this expression can be interpreted in a rather more general way. Re-writing it as

$$\text{Kinetic Energy} = mc^2 - m_0 c^2\,,$$

the first term, mc^2, can be taken as a measure of the *total energy* of a body in motion, while $m_0 c^2$ represents the *rest energy* of the body. The sum of the rest energy and the kinetic energy then gives the total energy. Because of the association of the rest energy with the rest mass of the body we can generalise even further, and predict that when any system gains an amount of energy E from any source its mass will increase by an amount Δm given by

$$E = \Delta m\, c^2\,.$$

Conversely, if, in some way, the mass of a closed system can be made to decrease by an amount Δm, this will result in a release of energy given by this same relation. This mass-energy relationship has been amply verified in nuclear physics, the most dramatic demonstration of its application being in the release of nuclear energy in fission and fusion.

The Structure of the Atom Emerges

In the last five chapters we have seen how several discoveries made at the turn of the century gave a tremendous new impetus to the subject of physics. Attention became focused, in particular, on the problem of the structure of atoms.

In the next three chapters we shall see how Rutherford was led to the conclusion that atoms have a central core or nucleus and how Bohr proposed the 'sun and planet' picture of an atom, according to which electrons revolve in orbits around a central positively charged nucleus. As is the case so often in physics, the simple picture which emerged would not have been thought of in the absence of knowledge gained in other parts of the subject. Thus Bohr's thinking was profoundly influenced by the quantum theory, which had its first major triumph in the explanation of the photoelectric effect, and by the discovery of the empirical relations between the wavelengths of spectral lines.

The Rutherford-Bohr picture of the atom was refined and extended until by the middle twenties atomic theory was able to explain adequately optical spectra, the absorption of X-rays and their spectra, the position of elements in the periodic table and, in general terms, the chemistry of the elements. Once again, however, some awkward unexplained facts remained. We shall see, in Chapter 10, that careful measurements of the masses of atoms confirmed the suspicion, aroused by the study of radioactivity, that each element could exist in more than one form. The existence of these 'isotopes' suggested that the nucleus must itself have some form of structure.

CHAPTER 7

The Radiations Given Off By Atoms

7·1 The Early Days of Spectroscopy

Systematic study of the nature of light began with the experiments of Newton. He showed that, when a narrow beam of sunlight entering a darkened room through a small circular aperture was allowed to fall on one face of a triangular glass prism, the light which emerged was no longer white, but was spread out into a spectrum of colours. From various different observations of this phenomenon, Newton concluded that the prism did not change the nature of the light passing through it, but that white light was really composed of a superposition of many beams of different colours and that all the prism did was to separate out these beams.

It was not until about 150 years later that any notable advance was made in the study of spectra. At that stage three outstanding contributions came from Joseph Fraunhofer, a German lens manufacturer. His first step was the design of a spectrometer. Instead of using just a narrow beam of sunlight from a

pinhole he used a slit placed at the focus of a convex lens so that a parallel beam of light fell on the prism. The refracted beam was then examined with a small telescope. The principle of this instrument is shown in Figure 7·1, and exactly the same arrangement is still used for many purposes. Then Fraunhofer used this spectrometer to make a systematic study of the spectrum of sunlight. He found that the spectrum contained a number of well-defined black lines and was able to show that these lines had fixed positions in the spectrum. These 'Fraunhofer lines', as they are still called, he recognised as corresponding to radiations in which the solar spectrum is deficient and used them as standards for the measurement of the refractive indices of the glasses he used in lens making.

The third major achievement was the construction of the first diffraction grating which he made by stretching silver wires between fine-threaded screws held in a frame. Later he produced gratings by ruling equally spaced parallel straight lines with a diamond point

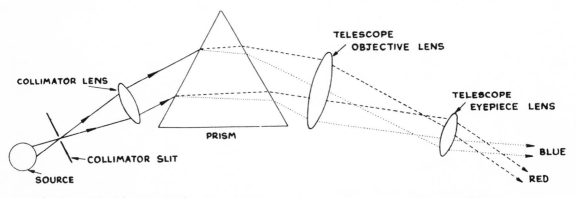

Fig. 7·1—*Principle of a simple prism spectrometer, showing separation of light of two different colours*

on a glass surface. With these gratings it was possible to make the first measurements of the actual wavelengths of light and in particular he was able to make accurate determinations of the wavelengths of yellow sodium light and of the Fraunhofer lines.

It now became possible to make quantitative investigations of the light emitted by sources of all types. Before long it was realised that all such 'emission' spectra could be classified into three distinct types. *Continuous spectra* are emitted, for example, by heated solids, and the form of the spectrum depends on the temperature of the source and the nature of its surface. Thus a piece of hot steel, the filament of an electric light globe and a globule of molten glass all emit radiations of every possible wavelength, although the extent to which the various wavelengths are present varies from one source to another. One example of a continuous spectrum is the thermal radiation spectrum which has already been discussed in Section 3·3.

The principal feature of any continuous spectrum is that, although all wavelengths are present, there is a fairly well-defined range of wavelengths within which most of the radiant energy is emitted. There is always a particular wave length at which maximum emission occurs and this maximum occurs at progressively shorter wavelengths as the temperature of the source is increased.

In the other two types of emission spectrum only certain discrete wavelengths are present. A spectrometer produces a series of images of the illuminated slit, the image for each wavelength present being located at a different position in the field of view of the telescope. Hence, a source which emits only particular wavelengths will produce a spectrum consisting of a number of separated images of the narrow slit. These are the so-called *spectral lines*. In some cases a part of the source structure may get rather hot during operation in which case the lines may be superimposed on a faint continuous spectrum rather than on a completely black background.

Band spectra consist of a number of groups of closely spaced lines, each group being itself well-defined. Within each group or band, the lines become closer and closer together on one side, so that this side has a rather sharp, bright edge. Any chemical compound which can be made to emit light—for example, by introducing it as a gas or vapour into a discharge tube—will produce a band spectrum.

Line spectra are those in which separate lines appear, and usually there is little, if any, obvious grouping of the lines. The different lines have different intensities and, if they can be examined closely, it is found that they do not all have the same appearance. Some are quite sharp, but others are somewhat diffuse on one or both sides.

The great importance of line spectra was first realised in 1860 by Kirchhoff and Bunsen. They pointed out that each *element* gave rise to a unique line spectrum and that no two of these were the same. Thus spectroscopy became a powerful tool in chemical analysis, for the line spectrum of any substance was then just the sum of the line spectra of its components. In this way, Kirchhoff and Bunsen discovered the elements rubidium and caesium.* Moreover the sensitivity of this method is far greater than that attainable in ordinary chemical analysis. For example, the dominant feature of the spectrum of sodium is an intense pair of yellow lines—hence the yellow light from a sodium vapour street lamp. As little as 10^{-7} milligramme of sodium introduced into a bunsen flame can be detected by the subsequent appearance of these yellow lines in the spectrum of the flame.

7·2 The Search for Regularities in Line Spectra

In the twenty years following the work of Bunsen and Kirchhoff an overwhelming mass of information about the wavelengths of spectral lines was accumulated. During this period several attempts were made to bring about some order in this chaotic state of affairs by finding numerical relationships between the wavelengths of the lines of some elements. The discovery of such relationships

* Another example of this technique has already been mentioned in connection with the identification of the α-particle (Section 5·4).

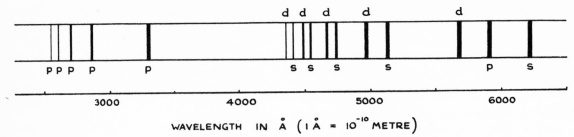

Fig. 7·2—*Most prominent lines of the ultraviolet and visible spectrum of sodium, showing 'sharp' (s), 'principal' (p) and 'diffuse' (d) series*

would, it was expected, give a lead towards the understanding of the underlying mechanism of spectral emission.

Most of these early attempts were strongly influenced by the supposition that light resulted from the vibration of atoms. It was then thought that such vibrations might have related frequencies in much the same way as do the familiar harmonics which occur in sound vibrations. Some of the investigations in this direction seemed promising, but it was soon found that the few relationships of this type which were 'discovered' were disproved when more accurate wavelength measurements became available. Nevertheless some progress was made in that the presence of recognisable *series* of lines in spectra was discovered, even though the laws governing such series were not found. Figure 7·2 shows part of the spectrum of sodium. In this simplified diagram the series are fairly obvious, but in an actual spectrum, in which many other lines are visible, the assignment of lines to the various series may not be at all easy.

The major discovery which provided the key to the analysis of spectra was made by a Swiss school teacher, Johann Balmer.* He attacked the problem of the simplest spectrum, that of hydrogen, which has just four lines in the visible region. Balmer treated this situation as a straight-out problem in numerology. Given a set of numbers, the problem is to discover whether or not a single formula involving an integer, n, can reproduce the given set of numbers. In simple

* Balmer, *Annalen der Physik und Chemie*, **25**, p80, (1885).

cases, this problem presents no great difficulty. It is fairly easy to discover, for example, that the numbers, 12, 20, 30, 42 and 56 are values of the expression $n(n-1)$. Balmer found that the four lines concerned, with wavelengths of 6562·10, 4860·74, 4340·10 and 4101·20 A, could be fitted by the expression

$$\lambda = b\,\frac{n^2}{n^2-4}, \ (n = 3, 4, 5 \text{ and } 6) \quad (7\cdot1)$$

where b is an empirically determined constant whose value, to give λ in Angström units, is 3645·6 A. Then, when his attention was drawn to measurements of more hydrogen lines in the ultra-violet spectra of stars, Balmer applied his formula with higher values of n and still found excellent agreement between the calculated and observed wavelengths. Table 7·1 is taken from Balmer's paper.

Table 7·1 — *Data on the spectrum of hydrogen, as presented by Balmer (1885)*

Name of Line	n	Wavelength (λ) in A	
		Calculated using eq. (7·1)	Observed
Hα	3	6,562·08	6,562·10 *
Hβ	4	4,860·80	4,860·74 *
Hγ	5	4,340·0	4,340·10 *
Hδ	6	4,101·3	4,101·2 *
Hϵ	7	3,969·7	3,968·1 †
Hζ	8	3,888·6	3,887·5 †
Hη	9	3,835·0	3,834·0 †
Hθ	10	3,797·5	3,795·0 †
Hι	11	3,770·2	3,767·5 †

* Lab. source. † Stars.

It will be noticed that there is a slight, and apparently increasing discrepancy between the observed and calculated wavelengths of the higher order spectral lines. This discrepancy has since been removed, principally due to more precise experimental determinations of the wavelengths.

A striking feature of the Balmer formula is its prediction that, as the value of the integer n increases, the change in wavelength from one line to the next becomes smaller and the wavelengths of the lines approach the 'series limit' $\lambda_\infty = b$. This behaviour is clearly seen in Figure 7·3.

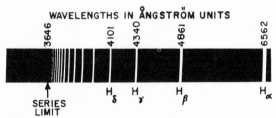

WAVELENGTHS IN ÅNGSTRÖM UNITS

3646   4101   4340   4861   6562

SERIES LIMIT H_δ H_γ H_β H_α

Fig. 7·3—*The Balmer series of the hydrogen spectrum. The wavelength scale is not uniform in this diagram*

The success of Balmer's formula led many workers to search for similar expressions which would describe series of lines in the spectra of other elements. One of the most successful was the Swedish spectroscopist, Rydberg.* Concentrating, in the first instance, on extensive tables of the spectra of the alkali metals which had been published by Liveing and Dewar in 1883, Rydberg was able to show that three chief species of series were recognisable. Those containing the strongest and most persistent lines he called the *principal* series. Others in which the lines, although somewhat weaker, were sharply defined, he called the *sharp* series, while he applied the name *diffuse* series to those in which the lines were comparatively broad. All these series tended to converge to limits, usually in the ultra-violet region. Figure 7·2

* A brief summary of this work appears in the *Philosophical Magazine*, **29**, p331 (1890).

shows the principal, sharp and diffuse series in the sodium spectrum.

Rydberg found it convenient to work in terms of the 'wave number' f of a spectral line, which is just the reciprocal of its wavelength. He found that many series could be described with good accuracy by an expression of the form

$$f = f_\infty - \frac{R}{(n + \mu)^2}, \qquad (7·2)$$

with n an integer increasing by unity from one line of the series to the next. In this *Rydberg formula*, as equation (7·2) is called, f_∞, the wave number corresponding to the limit of the series, and the constant μ (which is always less than 1) have different values for different series. On the other hand, the constant R has the same value for all the series of a given element and varies very little from one element to another. This constant, R, is known as the *Rydberg constant* for the particular atom under consideration.

The Balmer formula, equation (7·1), can be rewritten as

$$f = \frac{1}{b}\left(1 - \frac{4}{n^2}\right)$$
$$= \frac{1}{b} - \frac{4/b}{n^2}. \qquad (7·3)$$

Thus this expression is a special case of the Rydberg formula with $\mu = 0$, $f_\infty = 1/b$ and $4/b = R_H$, the Rydberg constant for hydrogen.

The values of the Rydberg constants are of particular theoretical interest. It will be shown in Chapter 9 that one of the triumphs of the Bohr theory of the atom was its prediction that the Rydberg constant for the hydrogen atom should be expressible in terms of a number of other fundamental physical constants.

Rydberg found that further relationships existed between the formulae of the type (7·2) describing the principal, sharp and diffuse series for a single element. Firstly he was able to show that the three wave numbers corresponding to the series limits all had values which could be expressed as

$$f_\infty = \frac{R}{(1 + \eta)^2}$$

with η being a constant which, like μ, was less than 1. Thus each of the three series could be described by a formula of the type

$$f = \frac{R}{(1 + \eta)^2} - \frac{R}{(n + \mu)^2}.$$

Secondly the values of η and μ in these three formulae were not all independent. For example, the value of μ for the principal series was identical with the value of η in the sharp series, and other equalities between some of these six constants were found.

It then occurred to Rydberg that these formulae might be special cases of a more general formula of the type

$$f = \frac{R}{(n_2 + \mu_2)^2} - \frac{R}{(n_1 + \mu_1)^2}, \quad (7\cdot4)$$

in which the value of n_2 happened to be unity. If this were so, other spectral lines might be found corresponding to different values of n_2.

Rydberg was unable to find any evidence of such series, but the matter was taken up again by Ritz,* who found lines of this type. The fact that lines can be described by the difference of two terms, as in the general expression (7·4), has come to be known as the *Ritz combination principle*.

7·3 The Main Features of Atomic Spectra

It is now possible to summarise the main features of atomic spectra in the following way.

1. The wave number of each spectral line may be expressed as the difference of two *spectral terms*, each of the form

$$\frac{R}{(n + \mu)^2}$$

in which R is a constant for the atom under consideration. Only a few values

* Ritz, *Physikalische Zeitschrift*, **9**, p521 (1908).

of the constant μ occur for each atom and each of these values of μ then determines an infinite *series of terms* in each of which n is equal to a different positive integer. Thus the terms in each of these series converge towards zero.

2. The differences between a fixed term of one such series and all smaller terms of another series give the wave numbers of a *series of spectral lines*, all of which have a similar character. Such a series of spectral lines converges to a *series limit*, this limit always corresponding to a *shorter* wavelength than any line in the series. The wavelength of this series limit is then given by the reciprocal of the fixed term in the formula describing the series of lines.

It must be realised that this description of atomic spectra is only a first approximation to the actual state of affairs. In the first place many of the spectral lines described in this way are not single lines at all. Close inspection, using a spectrometer of high resolving power, shows that many 'lines' really consist of a pair of lines very close to one another. Such a pair is called a *doublet*. Many others are really *triplets* or groups having even more components. Many of the series consist of series of doublets or triplets rather than series of single lines. Indeed all of the three series of lines in the sodium spectrum of Figure 7·2 are actually series of doublets. In cases such as this, separate Rydberg formulae must be used for the components of these 'multiple' lines. In addition, the simple general expression quoted above for a spectral term is not exact. More accurate term formulae have been devised.

Despite these minor reservations, it is obvious that this picture of the relationships between spectral lines produces a high degree of orderliness in what was an apparently unrelated mass of information. Without this insight into the regularities which do occur in spectral series, the emergence of a satisfactory theory of the origin of spectral lines might well have been delayed for a considerable period.

7·4 Additional Series in the Hydrogen Spectrum

The re-arranged form of the Balmer formula, equation (7·3), can be written as

$$f = R_\mathrm{H} \left(\frac{1}{2^2} - \frac{1}{n^2} \right), \qquad (7·5)$$

in which case it has the same form as the general Rydberg formula (7·4) with both the constants μ_1 and μ_2 equal to zero. Balmer himself suggested that additional series of lines might be found, corresponding to the replacement of the number 2^2 in this expression with numbers such as 1^2, 3^2, 4^2 and so on.

The occurrence of spectral series of this nature would be quite consistent with the general picture of combination of spectral terms outlined in the previous Section. For, if all the constants μ in the terms for a particular atom happen to be equal, the various *series of terms* all reduce to a single series. In such a case, differences between a fixed term of one series and the variable terms of another become, instead, differences between a fixed term of this single term series and the other variable terms of the same series.

Balmer's speculation thus led to a search for additional lines in the hydrogen spectrum. The Balmer series has its limit in the ultra-violet, the wave number of this limit being $R_\mathrm{H}/2^2$. If the number 2^2 in (7·5) is replaced by 1^2, this should lead to a series with a limit whose wave number is $R_\mathrm{H}/1^2$, so that the wavelength of this limit will be one quarter of that of the Balmer series. This limit will thus be in the far ultraviolet. By a similar argument, the series obtained by replacing 2^2 with 3^2 should have its limit at a wavelength of $9/4$ times that of the Balmer limit, and this falls in the infrared region. All other possible series would be even further into the infrared.

The first discovery of additional lines was made by Paschen. He found two infrared lines corresponding to $n = 4$ and 5 in the series whose limit is $f_\infty = R_\mathrm{H}/3^2$. Other lines were soon found and the known hydrogen series, named after their discoverers, are set out in Table 7·2. In Section 9·3, it will be seen that not only the occurrence but also the actual wavelengths of the lines in all of these series are very satisfactorily predicted by the Bohr theory of the atom.

Table 7·2 — *Series of lines in the emission spectrum of hydrogen. The wave numbers of the lines in each series are given by the expression*

$$f = R_\mathrm{H} \left(\frac{1}{a^2} - \frac{1}{n^2} \right).$$

Name of Series	a	Values of n	Region of Spectrum
Lyman	1	2, 3, 4, . . .	Ultraviolet
Balmer	2	3, 4, 5, . . .	Ultraviolet and visible
Paschen	3	4, 5, 6, . . .	Infrared
Brackett	4	5, 6, 7, . . .	Infrared
Pfund	5	6, 7, 8, . . .	Infrared

CHAPTER 8

The Electric Charges in Atoms

8·1 Early Ideas about the Structure of the Atom

Even before the discovery of cathode rays, it had been suggested that the atom was composed of negatively and positively charged particles held in equilibrium by electrical forces. The discovery of the electron, and especially the demonstration that it is a constituent of the atoms of all elements, gave a great impetus to the formation of more concrete ideas on atomic structure. There was one fundamental difficulty, however. While negative electricity had been shown to exist in independent units (electrons) whose mass was very small, the corresponding unit of positive electricity was not found associated with a mass less than that of the atom of hydrogen. Scientists, including Rutherford, felt that there should exist a unit of positive electricity associated with a mass which was approximately the same as that of the electron. Thus the role of the positive electricity in the atom was the subject of much conjecture. The following are typical of the questions asked:

(a) How are the electrons distributed with respect to the positive charge, which must be present in sufficient quantity to make the atom electrically neutral?

(b) What role does the positive charge play, and how is it distributed?

(c) How many electrons are there in an atom?

(d) Can this number be related to any other property of the element?

These questions were answered in a series of classic investigations, both experimental and theoretical, which will be described in the next two chapters.

Since electrons are negatively charged, and atoms are electrically neutral, there must be some positively charged part of the atom. The presence of positive and negative electric charges in an atom poses a problem concerning the stability of such a system. If only electrostatic forces are considered, then it is clear that the positively and negatively charged parts of an atom cannot be separated in space and at rest, since they would immediately tend to coalesce. On the other hand, suppose that a stable arrangement could be devised in which these separated charges were in motion. Then any acceleration which the particles underwent would, according to the electromagnetic theory, lead to the emission of radiation with a consequent loss of energy. From these considerations, it was concluded that permanent unchanging atoms could not be formed with the positive and negative charges separated in space.

Faced with this situation, Kelvin[1] and J. J. Thomson[2] independently suggested that the positive charge was uniformly distributed over a sphere in which the electrons were embedded. This model combined simplicity with relative ease of mathematical manipulation. Since the electrons were put in the sphere of positive charge like plums in a pudding, this model has come to be known as 'Thomson's plum pudding atom'.

Thomson showed how such a model could lead to a stable atom. With the electrons in

[1] Kelvin, *Philosophical Magazine*, **3**, p257 (1902).
[2] J. J. Thomson, *The Corpuscular Theory of Matter* (Constable, 1907).

the positively charged sphere it is possible to balance the attraction of each negatively charged particle to the centre of the sphere with the mutual repulsion between the electrons. For example, if we have a one-electron atom, the electron will go to the centre of the sphere. In a two-electron atom, the two electrons will, in equilibrium, be situated on the surface of the sphere, and at opposite ends of a diameter.

For the more complex atoms, Thomson was led to the hypothesis of rings of electrons within the positive charge. Thus, in a striking way, he foreshadowed the idea of discrete electron orbits, or 'shells', which was to emerge later. One other important feature was pointed out by Thomson, as follows:

Since the mass of a corpuscle (electron) is only about one-seventeen-hundredth part of that of an atom of hydrogen the mass of the atom must in the main be due to its other constituent – the positive electricity.

Thus he introduced a further idea which has persisted, even though the plum-pudding model was later shown to be incorrect.

8·2 The Nuclear Atom: Preliminary Experiments

The discovery of α- and β-particles, combined with the genius of Rutherford, led to a new attack on the problem of atomic structure. The method used was to study the deflection of swiftly moving α- and β-particles in their passage through matter. It was found that these rays are always scattered, that is, a narrow pencil of rays opens out into a diffuse beam. The α- and β-particles from naturally radioactive substances are high velocity particles, and are able actually to pass through the structure of the atom and be deflected by intense forces within the atom itself.

Geiger and Marsden[1] first studied an unexpected effect with α-particles. They found that, when a pencil of α-particles fell on a thin metal foil, the great majority of the particles passed through with little deflection. Some,

however, were scattered through quite appreciable angles, while a few were found to be so scattered that they were turned back through an angle of greater than 90°. That is, a small fraction of the α-particles emerged from the foil on the same side as that on which the α-particle source was placed.

Geiger continued to experiment further on the scattering of α-particles and made measurements of the most probable angle of scattering and its dependence on the thickness and atomic weight of the scatterer. Geiger[2] refers to his previous work as follows:

It was found that some of the α-particles falling on a metal plate appear to be reflected, i.e. they are scattered to such an extent that they emerge on the side of incidence. It was shown that from gold, one in about 8000 of the incident α-particles suffers reflection, and that this reflection takes place within a relatively thin surface layer equivalent to about 5 mm of air.

Now the 'plum-pudding' model of the atom had earlier been used by J. J. Thomson as a basis for a calculation of the most probable angle of scattering of the α-particles. He assumed that the scattering of a particle passing through even a thin foil was the result of compounding a relatively large number of deflections, each of which was due to a single atom. He predicted on this basis that the most probable angle of scattering should vary as the square root of the thickness of the foil. Geiger's experiments showed that this relationship holds, at least for thin scatterers.

However, the calculation of J. J. Thomson also predicted the probability of scattering of a particle through any given angle. Geiger compared this prediction with his experimental results, and stated his conclusion as follows:

. . . the probable angle through which the α-particles are turned in passing through this equivalent thickness of gold is only about 1°, and a simple calculation . . . shows that the probability of an α-particle being scattered through an angle exceeding 90° is extremely small, and of a different order from that which the reflection experiment suggests.

This last conclusion is stated in very moderate terms, considering that the discrepancy

[1] Geiger and Marsden, *Proceedings of the Royal Society*, **A 82,** p495 (1909).

[2] Geiger, *Proceedings of the Royal Society*, **A 83,** p492 (1910).

between the calculation referred to and experiment is a factor of 10^{30}.

Therefore, while the data on the scattering of α-particles through *small* angles were in agreement with Thomson's calculations and the 'plum-pudding' model, the 'reflection' data of Geiger and Marsden were in gross disagreement with it. Remember that the proportion of 'reflected' α-particles, that is the proportion which did not behave in accordance with the Thomson model, was only one in eight thousand.

It is a good measure of the genius of Rutherford that he saw in this one part in 8000 — this small detail — the evidence that was necessary to postulate a new atom model that was consistent with all Geiger's data.

8·3 The Nuclear Atom: Rutherford's Theory

Photographs of tracks of α-particles in the Wilson cloud chamber, taken later by C. T. R. Wilson, showed that α-particles often travel for a considerable distance in a straight line, and then suddenly, are deflected through a large angle. The cloud chamber photographs provided evidence that large-angle deflections can be produced by a single scattering event. In Rutherford's first assumption[*] he distinguished between small-angle scattering due to multiple interactions with atoms of a foil and large-angle scattering which, he suggested, could be due to interaction with a single atom.

Rutherford noted further that if the forces causing a single large deflection were electrostatic, it was at once evident that the electric field within the atom was very intense. In fact, the distribution of positive electricity assumed in the Thomson 'plum-pudding' atom was much too diffuse to produce the intense field required.

Therefore, Rutherford assumed that the positive charge of the atom, instead of being distributed throughout its entire volume, was concentrated in a very minute volume or nucleus. The radius of the atom was known to be about 10^{-10} metre, and Rutherford

* Rutherford, *Philosophical Magazine*, **21**, p669 (1911).

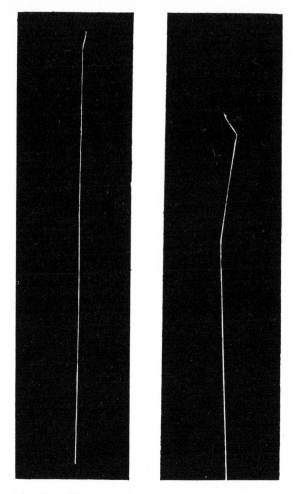

Fig. 8·1—*Photograph of α-particle tracks showing sharp deviations*

showed that, according to this model, the nuclear radius of gold would have to be in the vicinity of 10^{-14} metre. He assumed that the nucleus was surrounded by a distribution of negative electrons which extended over a distance comparable with the diameter of the atom. Further, Rutherford retained in the model the finding of Thomson that the mass of the atom was almost entirely associated with its positive charge. In this type of atom, the large deviation (Geiger's 'reflection') of the α-particle takes place when it passes through the intense electric field close to the nucleus. The nearer it passes to the nucleus, the greater

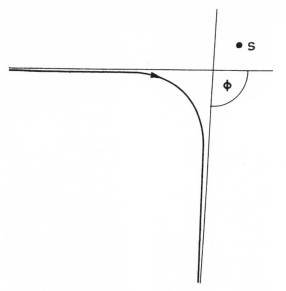

Fig. 8·2—*Orbit of a scattered α-particle near a nucleus*

is the angle through which the particle is deflected.

Rutherford assumed that the force between the α-particle and the nucleus was entirely electrostatic, and therefore that the force between the particles varied as the inverse square of their distance apart, even for the small separations involved. Such a force law

would require the α-particle to describe a hyperbola, with the nucleus, S, of the atom at one focus as shown in Figure 8·2.

Then, assuming a narrow pencil of α-particles directed at a thin sheet of matter containing atoms distributed throughout its volume, Rutherford calculated the number of α-particles which would pass through a detector at some distance r from the point of incidence of the α-particles. The detector was positioned such that the path traversed by a scattered α-particle makes an angle ϕ with its initial direction, as shown in Figure 8·3. ϕ is known as the angle of scattering. The number of such α-particles incident per second on unit area of the detector was calculated to be

$$\frac{A\,n\,t\,b^2}{16\,r^2\sin^4(\phi/2)}.$$

A is the number of α-particles impinging on the foil per second, n is the number of atoms per unit volume of the foil, and t is the foil thickness. Also

$$b = \frac{Q\,q}{2\pi\epsilon_0\,m\,u^2},$$

where Q is the central charge of the atom, m, q and u are respectively the mass, charge and velocity of the α-particle and ϵ_0 is the permittivity of free space.

Thus the number of deflected α-particles

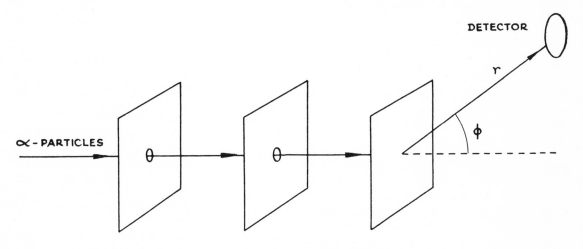

Fig. 8·3—*The geometry of an α-particle scattering experiment*

depends on the significant parameters of the experiment in the following way:

(i) It is inversely proportional to $\sin^4(\phi/2)$.

(ii) It is proportional to t, the thickness of the scatterer, provided this is sufficiently small to ensure single rather than multiple scattering.

(iii) It is inversely proportional to the fourth power of the velocity or to the square of the kinetic energy of the incident α-particles.

(iv) It is proportional to Q^2, the square of the charge on the central nucleus.

In the derivation of the scattering law given above, it is assumed that the distribution of the electrons around the central positive charge has negligible effect. Rutherford calculated the quantity b, which, it transpires, is equal to the distance of closest approach of an α-particle to the nucleus in a 'head-on collision. He assumed a central nuclear charge of 100 times the electronic charge and an α-particle velocity of 2×10^7 m sec^{-1} and obtained a value of $3 \cdot 4 \times 10^{-14}$ metre for b. This is to be compared with 10^{-10} metre for the value of the atomic radius. Rutherford inferred that, on the basis of this nuclear model of the atom, the α-particles should penetrate very close to the centre of the electron distribution.

He was able to show, in addition, that even for collisions in which the α-particle was deflected through only a small angle, it passed by the nucleus at a distance which was still very much less than the radius of the atom. Therefore it was clear that in an atom having this nuclear structure, the electrons around the nucleus would play virtually no part in the scattering of an α-particle.

8·4 The Nuclear Atom: Test of Rutherford's Theory

The scattering theory was tested by Geiger and Marsden* in 1913 on each of the four points listed above. It is to be noted, however, that they had no means of obtaining a value for the nuclear charge from other data.

*Geiger and Marsden, *Philosophical Magazine*, **25**, p604 (1913).

They had to use the assumption that the atomic weight was proportional to the nuclear charge. In consequence, they investigated the relation between the number of scattered α-particles and the square of the atomic weight of the scatterer.

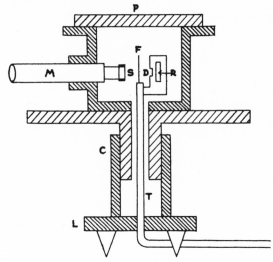

Fig. 8·4—*Geiger and Marsden's apparatus for testing the angular dependence of α-particle scattering*

The apparatus used by Geiger and Marsden is shown in Figure 8·4. The source of α-particles R, the scattering foil F and the detector of the scattered α-particles were contained in a robust metal box. The detector consisted of a screen S of zinc sulphide which was known to produce a minute scintillation when struck by an α-particle. A small well-defined area of the screen was viewed by the microscope M to which it was rigidly attached. The source R and the foil F were fixed to the central tube T through which the whole apparatus was evacuated. The platform supporting the box could be rotated in the air-tight joint C, and its position (and therefore the position of the microscope and ZnS screen) determined by reference to a graduated scale.

The source of α-particles was radium emanation contained within a thin-walled vessel. By means of the diaphragm at D, a narrow pencil of α-particles was directed normally on to the foil F. The positions of the source and foil relative to each other were fixed, while the screen S could be rotated with respect to them.

It is worthwhile to pause and consider the extremely difficult task which confronted Geiger and Marsden. Their method, that of visual observation of scintillations in a zinc sulphide screen, was severely limited in the accuracy obtainable by the rates at which scintillations could be counted. They themselves stated that '. . . it was not possible to count with certainty more than 90 scintillations per minute or less than 5 per minute'. The investigation sought to establish a proportionality between the number of scattered particles and the quantity $1/\sin^4(\phi/2)$, which varies by a factor of 250,000 over the range of angles 5° to 150°. In view of this, Geiger and Marsden were compelled to investigate the small angle scattering separately from the scattering through angles greater than, say, 45°.

The number of scintillations N at each angle was observed, and a correction had to be made to allow for the decay of α-particle intensity during the measurements. Since the proportionality of N to $\dfrac{1}{\sin^4(\phi/2)}$ was being tested, the product $N\sin^4(\phi/2)$ was formed, and should be independent of angle if the proportionality holds. Figure 8·5 shows a typical set of Geiger and Marsden's results, plotting $N\sin^4(\phi/2)$ versus ϕ. These results were obtained using a silver foil as scatterer. Note that the source was strong enough to

make the errors in counting large for angles less than 30°. The measurements at these angles were performed separately using a much weaker source, in order to reduce the number of scintillations observed per minute at the small angles.

Geiger and Marsden* concluded that their experiments, which showed $N\sin^4(\phi/2)$ to be constant to about 20% accuracy for a range of angles from 5° to 150° were sufficiently accurate to demonstrate the required proportionality.

The dependence on foil thickness was investigated by fixing the scattering angle and measuring the number of α-particles scattered through that angle for a number of thicknesses of the scattering foil. The result confirmed the proportionality between the number of scattered particles and the foil thickness. Rutherford's formula predicted that the number of α-particles scattered through an angle ϕ should be inversely proportional to the square of the kinetic energy of the α-particles, that is inversely proportional to the fourth power of the velocity. There were few radioactive sources available to Geiger and Marsden which gave monoenergetic α-particles and so they varied the energy of the α-particles leaving the source R (Figure 8·4) by inserting stopping foils of mica. Mica was used because it produced little scattering of the α-particles.

* Geiger and Marsden, *Philosophical Magazine*, **25**, p604 (1913).

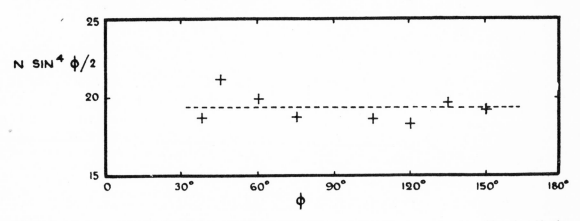

Fig. 8·5—*Plot of a typical set of Geiger and Marsden's results showing (for ϕ greater than 30°) that N, the scattering probability, is proportional to $1/\sin^4 \phi/2$)*

However, they did lose in the mica a proportion of their kinetic energy, the energy loss being dependent on the thickness of the mica.

To estimate the velocity of the α-particles as they emerged from these stopping foils, Geiger and Marsden observed their range in air at standard temperature and pressure. They then used an empirical rule established by Geiger[1] to relate the α-particle range R to its initial velocity u. This rule stated that

$$R = a\,u^3,$$

where a is a constant whose value depends on the units used for u and R.

Geiger and Marsden found that, within experimental errors, the quantity Nu^4 was constant for a given scatterer and a given angle of scattering.

To investigate the variation of scattering as a function of the central nuclear charge, Geiger and Marsden assumed that it was proportional to the atomic weight, since they had no better information to refer to. The experiment then consisted of observing the number of α-particles scattered at a fixed angle, for scattering foils of different atomic weight, and making the required allowance for variation in foil thickness and the number of atoms per unit volume. The results obtained indicated that the number of scattered particles was proportional to the square of the atomic weight, within an accuracy of about 15%. The relation was tested for foils of atomic weight from that of carbon to that of gold.

Geiger and Marsden[2] then attempted to determine the actual fraction of α-particles of a given energy scattered through an angle of $45°$ by a particular foil. This measurement presented considerable difficulty since it required an estimate of the number of α-particles incident on the scatterer. As has previously been pointed out, this number is enormously greater than the number scattered through any appreciable angle. Knowing the thickness and atomic weight of the scattering foil, they then had sufficient information to make a

calculation of Q, the nuclear charge given in the Rutherford scattering formula. Q can be expressed as a multiple of e, an elementary charge numerically equal to that of the electron, by writing $Q = Ke$. Geiger and Marsden found that K for gold was a number equal to about half its atomic weight (197), and quoted $K = 98 \pm 20$ for that element. This result agreed well with an estimate of this quantity made by Rutherford[3] on the basis of an earlier experiment performed by Geiger.[4]

In 1920, Chadwick[5] improved greatly on the technique of Geiger and Marsden for this type of experiment, and succeeded in measuring the value of K with much better precision. The principle of this measurement was exactly the same as that of Geiger and Marsden, namely, to measure the absolute scattering probability at some given angle, and from it and the Rutherford formula to compute the value of K. For copper, silver and gold foils he obtained

$$\text{copper} : K = 29 \cdot 3 \pm 0 \cdot 5,$$
$$\text{silver} \ : K = 46 \cdot 3 \pm 0 \cdot 7,$$
$$\text{gold} \ \ : K = 77 \cdot 4 \pm 1 \cdot 0.$$

These results were sufficiently precise to establish the fact that K was *not* equal to half the atomic weight of the element concerned. In fact it seemed highly probable that K could be identified with the atomic number, Z, of the element in question. This latter number, representing the position of the element in the periodic classification, had already been shown by Moseley in 1913 (see Section 9·13) to be strongly associated with the physical properties of atoms concerned with the production of X-rays. For the three elements used by Chadwick, the values of Z are 29, 46 and 77, respectively.

8·5   The Number of Electrons in an Atom

The measurement which first gave a means of calculating the number of electrons per atom was that of the scattering of X-rays performed

[1] Geiger, *Proceedings of the Royal Society*, **A 83**, p505 (1910).
[2] Geiger and Marsden, *Philosophical Magazine*, **25**, p604 (1913).
[3] Rutherford, *Philosophical Magazine*, **21**, p669 (1911).
[4] Geiger, *Proceedings of the Royal Society*, **A 83**, p492 (1910).
[5] Chadwick, *Philosophical Magazine*, **40**, p734 (1920).

by Barkla.[1] When a beam of X-rays passes through a material medium, not only is some of the energy of the beam absorbed by the medium but a part of the beam is found to be scattered in much the same way as are the α-particles of the Geiger and Marsden experiments.

J. J. Thomson[2] pointed out that a mechanism could be found on the basis of the electromagnetic theory which seemed to provide a satisfactory explanation of this phenomenon. If X-rays are electromagnetic waves, they should cause electrons in their path to execute forced oscillations. These oscillating electrons should then emit radiation of the same frequency as that of the incident wave. This 're-emitted' radiation would not then proceed solely in the direction of the incident beam but because it has the same frequency it should be indisinguishable in character from it. Thus this radiation would have the appearance of having been scattered from the original beam.

Thomson showed that, according to this theory, the fraction of the energy of the incident beam which is removed per unit thickness of scatterer could be calculated. This quantity, σ_0, the *scattering coefficient*, he found to be equal to the product of a number of fundamental physical constants and n, the number of electrons in unit volume of the scatterer. Thus a measurement of σ_0 and a knowledge of the density ρ of the scatterer would give a value of the ratio σ_0/ρ and hence of n/ρ, the number of electrons per unit mass of the scatterer. However, if Avogadro's number N_0 and the atomic weight M of the scatterer are also known, the number of atoms of the scatterer per unit mass is just N_0/M. Hence the number of electrons per atom can be estimated from these two ratios.

Barkla's experiment thus consisted essentially of a measurement of the scattering coefficient. Using a number of scatterers from among the light elements, he found that in all cases the number of electrons in each atom was approximately equal to one-half of its atomic weight. More extensive measurements were made by Hewlett[3] using a carbon scatterer for which he found the number of electrons per atom to be six.

Unfortunately, this evidence which leads to a perfectly correct conclusion is much less convincing when examined in the light of later knowledge. The measured scattering coefficient σ for X-rays is not independent of the material of the scatterer and of the wavelength of the X-radiation, as is the coefficient σ_0 which emerges from Thomson's theory. σ can be many times greater or many times less than σ_0 depending on the conditions of the experiment. In fact, had Barkla used, for example, an iron scatterer and X-rays of rather longer wavelength he might well have deduced a value for the number of electrons per atom which was too large by a factor of five. Thus it was fortunate that Barkla and Hewlett used just the X-ray wavelength that they did and scattered those X-rays from carbon.

The measurements of Barkla complemented the results of the α-particle scattering experiments in that both investigations suggested that the number of electrons contained in an atom was equal to about half its atomic weight. At about the same time, it was also realised[4] that if the elements in the periodic classification are arranged in order of increasing atomic weight, the number which indicates the position of each element in this table is also equal to about half its atomic weight. Whether this 'atomic number' or the atomic weight of an element was the parameter which determined the electron structure of an atom could not be decided from the evidence available at the time. A clear-cut indication in favour of the atomic number being the significant quantity in this connection was provided by the experiment of Moseley which will be discussed in the next chapter.

[1] Barkla, *Philosophical Magazine*, **21**, p648 (1911).

[2] J. J. Thomson, *Conduction of Electricity through Gases*, 2nd edition, p326 (Cambridge University Press, 1906).

[3] Hewlett, *Physical Review*, **20**, p688 (1922).

[4] Van der Broek, *Physikalische Zeitschrift*, **14**, p32 (1913).

CHAPTER 9

The Development of the Nuclear Atom

9·1 Objections to Rutherford's Model of the Atom

As has been seen in the previous chapter, the α-particle scattering results led Rutherford to the conclusion that the positive charge in an atom must be concentrated at its centre and that the negative charges must move around outside this nucleus. In some ways, however, this concept seemed to be a backward step in the theory of atomic structure, for it suggested a model that had previously been rejected on the grounds that such an atom would be unstable. In fact, the Thomson 'plum-pudding model' of the atom had been postulated with just this difficulty in mind.

Thus we find the critics of Rutherford's nuclear atom pointing out that an electron moving about a nucleus would undergo acceleration because the direction of its velocity is constantly changing, and that an accelerated electron, according to electromagnetic theory, would radiate energy continuously. As the electron loses energy by radiation, the radius of its orbit would decrease. This would increase its acceleration and further increase the rate at which it radiated energy. The net result of this process would be that the electron would fall into the nucleus of the atom so that such an atom would not be a stable structure. In fact, Jeans estimated that, on the arguments just stated, a hydrogen atom would vanish in less than 10^{-10} second.

This argument can be carried further. Since the acceleration of the electron would be a continuously changing quantity, such an atom would emit a continuous spectrum of radiation. On the other hand, if some mechanism could be found which prevented the electron from spiralling in towards the nucleus, its *constant* acceleration should then result in a hydrogen spectrum consisting of one line only.

Neither of these predictions is borne out by experiment, and the critics of the Rutherford atom felt confident that his model could not be right. We saw in Chapter 7 that hydrogen produces a *line spectrum* rather than a *continuous spectrum*. Further, the analysis of this spectrum by Balmer indicated that the lines in the visible region had wave numbers given by

$$f = \frac{1}{\lambda} = R_H\left(\frac{1}{2^2} - \frac{1}{n^2}\right), \; n = 3, 4, 5 \ldots \; (9·1)$$

where R_H is Rydberg's constant for hydrogen.

Thus we see that the Rutherford model brought with it real difficulties. The Geiger-Marsden experiments interpreted by Rutherford required a nuclear atom, but current knowledge of electrodynamics said firstly, that such an atom could not exist, and secondly, that it could not emit a line spectrum. Some revolutionary ideas were needed to overcome this impasse, and these were provided by Niels Bohr* who was at that time a relatively unknown physicist working in Rutherford's laboratory at Manchester.

9.2 Bohr's Radical Postulates

The theory put forward by Bohr accounted for the Balmer analysis of the hydrogen spectrum, in terms of the Rutherford model. In producing his theory, Bohr made use of the ideas put forward earlier by Planck con-

* N. Bohr, *Philosophical Magazine*, **26**, pp1, 476, 857 (1913).

cerning the quantum nature of electromagnetic radiation. These had already been used by Einstein in his treatment of the photoelectric effect (see Chapter 3).

In adopting Rutherford's picture of a nuclear atom, Bohr had to overcome the problems posed by classical electrodynamics, which have been discussed above. This he did by making the simple but bold assumption that not all of the classical laws of electrodynamics are valid within an atomic system. In particular, he assumed that, *under normal conditions, atoms do not radiate energy at all.* The assumptions were strongly supported by the striking successes of Bohr's theory, and were later justified when the more elaborate theory of wave mechanisms was applied to the solution of problems in atomic physics. We shall now discuss Bohr's theory of the atom, in terms of the radical postulates that he introduced.

POSTULATE I

The electrons in atoms can exist only in certain discrete orbits, and while in these orbits they do not radiate energy.

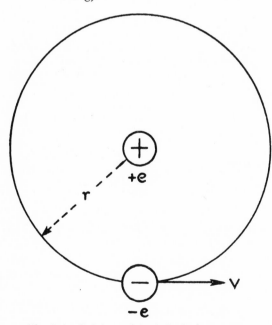

Fig. 9·1—*Bohr's model of the hydrogen atom*

As we shall see later, the total energy of an electron in an orbit around a nucleus is uniquely determined once the geometry of the orbit is specified. As a result of this, Bohr's first postulate requires the atomic electrons to possess only certain discrete values of energy. Bohr was able to devise a method, based on classical dynamics, for calculating the energies of these allowed orbits. He wished, however, also to allow for the possibility of an electron moving from one orbit to another and it was at this point that he found it necessary to depart from classical theory. Indeed he gave no mechanical explanation of *how* such transitions could take place but found it sufficient to describe the *result* of such a transition in the following way.

POSTULATE II

The process in which an electron 'jumps' from one stable orbit to another of lower energy is followed by the emission of a single quantum of radiation. The frequency ν of this radiation is the one given by Planck's quantum theory, namely

$$h\nu = W_1 - W_2,$$

where W_1 and W_2 are the energies of the electron in the initial and final orbits respectively.

These two postulates taken together describe a type of atom which is normally stable and emits no radiation. If, on the other hand, some disturbance of the atom causes an electron to jump from one orbit to another, the emitted radiation will have a discrete wavelength. Transitions of this type between different orbits will result in the emission of a number of discrete wavelengths, that is, a *line spectrum.* Thus a model of this type is capable of explaining, at least qualitatively, the fact that the emission spectra of the elements are all line spectra.

9·3 Application of Bohr's Postulates to the Hydrogen Atom

In order that the theory should also provide a quantitative description of line spectra it was necessary for Bohr to provide an appropriate method for determining the energies of electrons in their allowed orbits. Obviously, the simplest case to consider was that of the hydrogen atom, consisting of a single electron revolving about the positively charged nucleus. Furthermore, the simplest possible orbit is a circular one (see Figure 9·1).

Firstly, the energy of the electron in *any* orbit of radius r may be calculated. Bohr assumed that the force between the nucleus and the electron is purely electrostatic. In this case, the centripetal force necessary to hold the electron in the circular orbit is provided by the electrostatic attraction between the positively charged hydrogen nucleus, or *proton* as it is now called, and the negatively charged electron. Since both charges have magnitude e, the force between them is

$$F = \frac{e^2}{4\pi\epsilon_0 \, r^2}, \qquad (9\cdot2)$$

where r is the distance between the proton and electron and ϵ_0 is the permittivity of free space. If the electron has a tangential velocity v, and m is its mass, equation of this force to the centripetal force gives

$$\frac{mv^2}{r} = \frac{e^2}{4\pi\,\epsilon_0 \, r^2}. \qquad (9\cdot3)$$

Thus the kinetic energy of the electron in its orbit is

$$T = \tfrac{1}{2}mv^2 = \frac{e^2}{8\pi\epsilon_0 \, r}. \qquad (9\cdot4)$$

The electron also possesses potential energy by virtue of its position. Suppose for the moment that the electron is at rest at a distance r_1 from the proton. In order to move it to a new position at a radial distance r_2, work must be done because of the electrostatic force between the two particles. When the electron is moved in this way, the work done against the electrostatic force is defined to be the *change* in the potential energy of the electron. This definition is quite analogous to the more familiar situation in which we speak of an object lifted above the earth's

surface as having had its potential energy increased. It is not difficult to show* that the change in potential energy when the electron moves from radius r_1 to radius r_2 is

$$\Delta U = \frac{e^2}{4\pi\epsilon_0}\left(\frac{1}{r_1} - \frac{1}{r_2}\right). \qquad (9\cdot5)$$

We now define the *potential energy* of the electron at any radius r to be equal to the *change* in its potential energy as it is moved from infinity to that radius. Thus, the potential energy U is obtained from (9·5) by putting $r_1 = \infty$ and $r_2 = r$, so that

$$U = -\frac{e^2}{4\pi\epsilon_0 r}. \qquad (9\cdot6)$$

Two points about this potential energy should be noted. Firstly, the situation in which the electron has been completely removed from the proton is arbitrarily taken to be the position of zero potential energy. Secondly, the potential energy of the electron at any finite distance from the proton is *negative* which is consistent with its having lost potential energy in 'falling in' from infinity to the point concerned.

From equations (9·4) and (9·6) the *total*

---

* Consider the case in which the distance between the electron and the proton is r and the electron is then moved a small distance dr away from the proton along the line joining the two particles. This motion is opposed by the electrostatic force of attraction, and the small amount of work done against this force is

$$dU = \frac{e^2}{4\pi\epsilon_0 \, r^2} \, dr.$$

Then the total amount of work done in moving the electron in this way, from a point distant r_1 from the proton to another at a distance r_2 is

$$\Delta U = \int_{r=r_1}^{r=r_2} dU = \frac{e^2}{4\pi\epsilon_0} \int_{r_1}^{r_2} \frac{dr}{r^2}$$

$$= \frac{e^2}{4\pi\epsilon_0}\cdot\left(\frac{1}{r_1} - \frac{1}{r_2}\right).$$

The same result holds for any two points at these same distances from the proton, even though these two points need not, in general, lie on the same radial line drawn through the point at which the proton is located.

energy of the electron in an orbit of radius r is found to be

$$W = T + U$$

$$= \frac{c^2}{8\pi\epsilon_0 r} - \frac{e^2}{4\pi\epsilon_0 r}$$

$$= -\frac{e^2}{8\pi\epsilon_0 r}. \qquad (9\cdot7)$$

Thus this relation confirms the statement that the total energy of the electron is uniquely determined by the radius of the orbit.

It should be remembered that Bohr's first postulate was that only certain discrete orbits should be stable. In consequence, r in equaiton (9·7) must in some way be limited to certain prescribed values. At the same time the allowed values of W which then come from this equation must be such that differences between them result, in accordance with the second postulate, in the emission of radiation of wavelengths corresponding to those actually observed. The problem of obtaining quantitative agreement between theory and experiment thus becomes one of choosing the correct way of specifying the allowed orbits.

Bohr found that the appropriate condition to meet this requirement is that the angular momentum of the electron in its orbit should be 'quantised', according to the relation

$$\text{angular momentum} = n\frac{h}{2\pi},$$

where n is any integer and h is Planck's constant. This results in the radii of these orbits being determined by the equation

$$mvr = n\frac{h}{2\pi}. \qquad (9\cdot8)$$

Eliminating v between this equation and equation (9·3) leads immediately to

$$r = n^2\frac{h^2\epsilon_0}{\pi me^2}, \quad n = 1, 2, 3 \ldots. \qquad (9\cdot9)$$

Thus the radii of the allowed orbits increase as the squares of integers. It is interesting to note that it is possible to estimate the size of a hydrogen atom from equation (9·9). If one assumes that, in its most stable state, the electron resides in the innermost of the avail-

able orbits, that is the orbit with $n = 1$, then the radius of the orbit can be computed in terms of known physical constants. The value obtained is $0\cdot53 \times 10^{-10}$ metre which is of the same order of magnitude as estimates made on the basis of the Kinetic Theory of gases.

The energies of the allowed Bohr orbits are simply obtained by substituting the allowed values of r from equation (9·9) into equation (9·7). Thus the energy of the electron in the nth orbit is

$$W = -\frac{me^4}{8\epsilon_0^2 h^2}\frac{1}{n^2}. \qquad (9\cdot10)$$

Often orbits of this kind are referred to as the *allowed* or *stationary states* of the system and one often speaks of 'the energy of a state' rather than 'the energy of the electron in a given orbit'. It should be noted that the term *stationary* does *not* imply that the electron has zero velocity. It simply means that in the allowed orbit the electron does not radiate energy.

According to Bohr's second postulate, emission of light takes place whenever an electron jumps from an orbit of higher energy to one of lower energy, that is, from an orbit of larger radius to one of smaller radius. Absorption of light demands a transition by the electron in the opposite direction.

If W_1 and W_2 are the total energies of the electron in the two states (or orbits), then the energy of the radiation emitted is equal to the difference in energies of the two states, and this radiation is emitted as one quantum. Thus, the energy of the radiation emitted is

$$h\nu = W_1 - W_2$$

$$= -\frac{me^4}{8\epsilon_0^2 h^2}\left(\frac{1}{n_1^2} - \frac{1}{n_2^2}\right)$$

$$= \frac{me^4}{8\epsilon_0^2 h^2}\left(\frac{1}{n_2^2} - \frac{1}{n_1^2}\right). \qquad (9\cdot11)$$

Thus the wave number of this radiation is given by

$$f = \frac{1}{\lambda} = \frac{1}{hc}\frac{me^4}{8\epsilon_0^2 h^2}\left(\frac{1}{n_2^2} - \frac{1}{n_1^2}\right). \qquad (9\cdot12)$$

In this expression the integer n_1 specifies the initial state and n_2 the final state. For the emission of radiation, W_1 must be greater than W_2, that is, n_1 greater than n_2.

Thus Bohr had obtained a formula of the form required by the Ritz Combination principle (see Section 7·3), and of the same form as the Balmer series relation (9·1). If n_2 is put equal to 2 in equation (9·12), and n_1 is allowed to take all integral values greater than 2, the Balmer series formula, equation (9·1), is given exactly, provided the constant term outside the brackets can be identified with the Rydberg constant R_H. The experimental value of this constant is $1·0968 \times 10^7$ metre^{-1} for the lines of the hydrogen spectrum. Putting in the values for the constants, m, e, ϵ_0 and h, the value of $\dfrac{me^4}{8\epsilon_0{}^2 h^3 c}$ is computed to be $1·0974 \times 10^7$ metre^{-1}.

Thus Bohr had produced a theory which could not only account for the form of the Balmer formula, but could also give a value for the Rydberg constant which was very close to the measured value. This was a major triumph and a vital piece of evidence in justifying the postulates upon which the theory was based.

9.4 First Refinement of Bohr's Theory

As has just been mentioned, the calculated value of the Rydberg constant was not *quite* equal to the measured value. It was soon shown that this discrepancy was due to the assumption, implicit in our treatment of the Bohr theory, that the nucleus remained

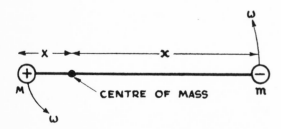

Fig. 9·2—*Illustration of the motion of an electron and a nucleus about their common centre of mass*

stationary at the centre of the circular orbits. However, this can be strictly true only if the central nucleus is infinitely heavy.

If the nucleus has mass M and the electron mass m, then both electron and nucleus will rotate about the centre of mass of the system with some common angular velocity ω as shown in Figure 9·2. The distances of the two particles from their centre of mass are related by

$$\frac{X}{x} = \frac{m}{M},$$

where their distance apart is

$$r = x + X.$$

Thus

$$X = \frac{m}{m + M} r, \text{ and } x = \frac{M}{m + M} r.$$

Now the basic equations from which the Bohr theory is developed are somewhat modified. Instead of equation (9·3) it is necessary to use the relation

$$\frac{mv^2}{x} = \frac{e^2}{4\pi\epsilon_0 r^2}$$

and equation (9·8) must be replaced by one in which the total angular momentum of the system is quantised, so that

$$(mvx + MVX) = n\frac{h}{2\pi},$$

where v is the tangential velocity of the electron and V is that of the proton. Instead of dealing with the energy of the electron alone, it is necessary to take account of the energy of the whole system. Its kinetic energy is

$$T' = \tfrac{1}{2}mv^2 + \tfrac{1}{2}MV^2,$$

while the potential energy is still

$$U = - \frac{e^2}{4\pi\epsilon_0 r}.$$

In dealing with these equations it is convenient to express the velocities v and V in terms of the angular velocity ω of the system, that is

$$v = \omega x \quad \text{and} \quad V = \omega X .$$

When this is done, it transpires that the total energy of the system is still given by the expression

$$W = - \frac{e^2}{8\pi\epsilon_0 \, r} ,$$

while the radii of the allowed orbits are given by

$$r = \frac{h^2 \epsilon_0}{\pi\mu \, e^2} n^2 ,$$

where

$$\mu = \frac{mM}{m + M} = m \cdot \frac{1}{1 + m/M} \quad (9\cdot13)$$

is called the *reduced mass* of the electron. Thus the final result differs from that obtained previously only in the replacement of the mass of the electron by its reduced mass.

Equation $(9\cdot12)$ now becomes

$$f = R_{\text{H}}\left(\frac{1}{n_2{}^2} - \frac{1}{n_1{}^2} \right) \quad (9\cdot14)$$

with

$$R_{\text{H}} = \frac{e^4}{8\epsilon_0{}^2 ch^3} \cdot \frac{m}{1 + m/M} \quad (9\cdot15)$$

This refinement to the theory has two desirable effects. The first is to reduce the Rydberg constant for hydrogen by about one part in 2000, thus bringing it into excellent agreement with the experimental value. The second desirable effect is that it gives different values of the Rydberg constant for central nuclei of different masses. This is observed experimentally, and has important consequences. It is truly remarkable that the theory should produce such a combination of unrelated constants which gives a value of R_{H} in complete agreement, within the limits of error, with that obtained directly from spectroscopic observations. Presently accepted values of some of the Rydberg constants are as follows:

For hydrogen,
$$R_{\text{H}} = (1\cdot096,775,76 \pm 0\cdot000,000,12) \times 10^7 \, \text{m}^{-1}$$
For helium,
$$R_{\text{He}} = (1\cdot097,222,67 \pm 0\cdot000,000,12) \times 10^7 \, \text{m}^{-1}$$
For an 'infinitely heavy' atom,
$$R_\infty = (1\cdot097,373,09 \pm 0\cdot000,000,12) \times 10^7 \, \text{m}^{-1}.$$

This slight variation of the Rydberg constant led to an important discovery in 1932 by Urey, Brickwedde and Murphy.[1] They observed a faint 'satellite' to each Balmer series line on photographs of narrow regions of the hydrogen spectrum. After a series of tests, they were led to the conclusion that these satellite lines were due to hydrogen atoms having approximately twice the mass of the vast majority of hydrogen atoms. The Rydberg constant for these atoms is thus slightly larger than that for normal hydrogen atoms. In this way they discovered *deuterium*, the isotope of hydrogen which has atomic mass of about two. For this work Urey received the Nobel Prize for Chemistry in 1934. Note that this work required spectroscopy of high precision. The Balmer series line at a wavelength of 6562 Angström units is separated from its deuterium satellite by less than two A.

9·5   Further Predictions of the Bohr Theory

Bohr obtained the formula for the Balmer series by putting $n_2 = 2$ in the expression $(9\cdot14)$ for the wave number of any spectral line. This equation then gives the wave numbers of the spectral lines emitted as the result of transitions in which the electron moves from an outer orbit $(n_1 \geqslant 3)$ in to the orbit specified by $n_2 = 2$.

It also follows from the Bohr theory that other spectral series should exist, and should correspond to transitions in which the electron moves from an outer orbit to one defined by $n_2 = 1$ or 3 or 4 and so on. If we put $n_2 = 3$, we obtain an expression for the wave numbers of a series in the infra-red region of the electromagnetic spectrum, which had been discovered by Paschen in 1908. For other values of n_2 we may quote Bohr[2] as follows:

If we put $n_2 = 1$, and $n_2 = 4$, 5, . . . , we get series respectively in the extreme ultraviolet and the extreme infra-red, which are not observed, but the existence of which may be expected.

[1] Urey, Brickwedde and Murphy, *Physical Review*, **40**, p1 (1932).
[2] N. Bohr, *Philosophical Magazine*, **26**, p1 (1913).

Thus, this prediction of the theory was exactly in agreement with the prediction of the existence of such series which had been arrived at purely from consideration of empirical regularities in optical spectra. This has already been discussed in Section 7·4.

It was therefore a triumph for the theory when, in 1914, Lyman announced the discovery of the first two members of the series given by $n_2 = 1$. Furthermore, they had the wave numbers which were predicted by the Bohr theory, within the limits of experimental error. The series with $n_2 = 4$ was found by Brackett in 1922, that with $n_2 = 5$ by Pfund in 1924, and that with $n_2 = 6$ by Humphreys in 1953. Each of these discoveries adds to the quantity of irrefutable evidence indicating the essential correctness of Bohr's assumptions.

A further important quantity predicted by the Bohr theory is the energy necessary to ionise a hydrogen atom, that is the energy required to take the electron from the most stable orbit (that with $n = 1$) to infinity. Thus from equation (9·10), replacing m by the reduced mass μ we obtain

$$W_I = \frac{\mu e^4}{8\epsilon_0{}^2 h^2}, \qquad (9·16)$$

since the total energy of the atom is zero when the electron is removed to infinity. W_I is the *ionisation energy*. If the values of the constants are substituted in (9·16), the value computed for W_I is $2·177 \times 10^{-18}$ joule, or $13·60$ electron volt. The measured value of this quantity is $13·60$ electron volt, in exact agreement.

So far, we have considered only the particular case of a single electron in orbit around a proton. In the more general case, the motion of a single electron around a nucleus of charge Ze is studied. In this case, equation (9·3) becomes

$$mv^2/r = Ze^2/4\pi\epsilon_0 r^2. \qquad (9·3a)$$

This means that everywhere through the theory given, e^2 should be replaced by Ze^2 if a nucleus of charge Ze is being considered. Thus the only change in the theoretical result

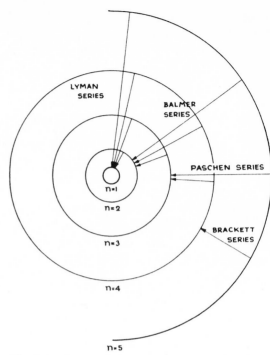

Fig. 9·3—*Geometrical representation of the several spectral series. The representation is in terms of the radii of the circular orbits of the hydrogen atom*

is that the expression for the wave number becomes

$$f = Z^2R \left(\frac{1}{n_2{}^2} - \frac{1}{n_1{}^2} \right),$$

where the Rydberg constant R has the same form as the expression (9·15) for the case of hydrogen but with M representing the actual mass of the nucleus concerned.

One such series was discovered early by Pickering in the spectrum of ionised helium. It is represented by $n_2 = 4$ and $n_1 = 5, 6 \ldots\ldots$ It was, in fact, first thought to be a series belonging to hydrogen because of its similarity to the Balmer series. Similar hydrogen-like atoms are those of doubly-ionised lithium, triply-ionised beryllium, and so on.

The alkali metals also show spectra which have similar characteristics, as has been discussed in Section 7·2. The hydrogen-like nature of these spectra is accounted for by the observation that the atoms of these elements contain 'closed shells' of electrons with one lone electron outside. This closed shell structure will be discussed in Section 9·12. It is this one electron which determines the chemical behaviour of the element, and which also allows us to treat these atoms as hydrogen-like. In this case the central charge must be written in terms of an effective nuclear charge because it is difficult to estimate exactly the 'shielding effect' that the inner electrons have on the nucleus as it is seen by the lone outer electron.

9·6 Energy Levels of the Hydrogen Atom: Quantum Numbers

Bohr's first postulate said in effect that the *total* energy of the hydrogen atom can only have one of a certain number of specified values. These allowed energies are called *energy levels*. The energy level concept enables the several spectral series of the hydrogen atom to be displayed pictorially in two alternative ways. Remembering that the frequencies of spectral lines correspond to differences between the energies of allowed states divided by Planck's constant, the two alternative pictures shown in Figures 9·3 and 9·4 are obtained.

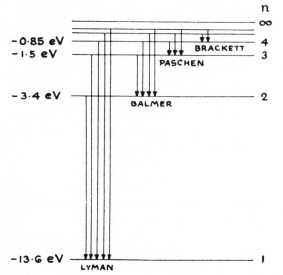

Fig. 9·4—*Energy level representation of the spectral series in hydrogen. The total energies of the four lowest states are shown on the left of the diagram.*

In Figure 9·3 the allowed states are shown in terms of the radii of the circular orbits to which they correspond. The transitions which give rise to the various spectral lines are shown in the diagram. In Figure 9·4 the energy levels are plotted by showing the total energy of the atom in the various states. Again, the transitions in the various series are shown. Also shown on these diagrams is the constant n which characterises each state, and which is used in the computations. To recapitulate, the total energy of the atomic state given by equation (9·10) depends on $1/n^2$. It is therefore said that the total energy of the atom is *quantised*, that is, it is determined only by integral values of n. n is called the *total* or *principal quantum number*.

9·7 Sommerfeld's Extension of Bohr's Theory: Elliptic Orbits

The circular orbits discussed in detail by Bohr are not the only ones which satisfy the condition which he placed on the angular momentum of the electron in the orbit. In fact, Bohr himself recognised this and he commenced his classic paper with a discussion of elliptic orbits. If the Bohr assumption that the angular momentum should be $nh/2\pi$ (with n an integer) is applied to elliptic orbits, it is found that the energy of any state is again dependent only on n. Thus equation (9·10) holds for all elliptic or circular orbits which satisfy Bohr's angular momentum assumption. There is no limit to the eccentricity of the orbits which may be described. Thus the theory outlined appears to be satisfactory in that *initial* consideration of elliptic orbits gives rise to no new energy levels.

In the case of circular motion, any one orbit is completely specified in terms of one variable, its radius. Thus if orbits are to be selected by some quantisation process, only one quantisation condition need be applied as is done in the simple Bohr theory. Sommerfeld pointed out that a particle describing an ellipse about a nucleus alternately approaches it and recedes from it. This motion may therefore be resolved into a circular motion about the nucleus combined with a radial oscillation. Sommerfeld suggested that both of these motions should be subject to *separate* quantisation conditions.

In consequence, the state of an electron in an elliptic orbit should be specified by two quantum numbers rather than the one demanded by the Bohr theory. Quantisation of the azimuthal motion produces one quantum number k, the value of which determines the angular momentum of the electron in its orbit. While the angular momentum and energy are related in a circular orbit, so that specification of one of these quantities fixes the other, this is not the case for elliptic orbits. Given the angular momentum, an additional quantity must be fixed to specify the orbit completely and this is the role of the quantisation of the radial motion. This quantisation determines a radial quantum number n_r whose value determines the eccentricity of the ellipse.

Given k and n_r, the orbit is now completely determined and the energy of the system may be calculated. It transpires that the simple theory shows this energy to depend not on k and n_r separately but on their sum

$$n = k + n_r. \qquad (9 \cdot 17)$$

Furthermore, this energy turns out to be identical with that of an electron in a circular orbit defined by the same value of n in terms of the simple Bohr theory. Because of its importance in this regard n is called the principal quantum number. Because of the relation (9·17) between them, specification of any two of these three quantum numbers fully determines the orbit. Thus these orbits are invariably specified by giving the values of the two quantum numbers n and k.

To illustrate, let us consider the possible orbits for $n = 2$. These may be represented by the symbols 2_2, 2_1, 2_0, where the subscript is the azimuthal quantum number. The 2_2 orbit has zero radial quantum number, and thus zero radial motion. That is, it corresponds to a circular orbit. The 2_0 orbit is one for which all the energy is associated with radial motion; there is no angular motion. Therefore in this case the electron

would have to pass through the nucleus, and thus the 2_0 orbit is regarded as physically impossible. The 2_1 orbit is an ellipse, the total quantum number n being divided equally between angular and radial motion.

The energy associated with all elliptic orbits having the same principal quantum number n has been stated to be independent of the value of n_r, which determines the eccentricity of each ellipse. This is not in fact true. It would be true if the mass of the electron were constant. In an elliptic orbit, the speed of the electron varies, being greatest when it is closest to the nucleus. Hence, relativity predicts that the mass of the electron varies round the orbit. Sommerfeld showed that if this is taken into account, the total energy of the electron, and therefore of the atom, increases slightly with increasing ellipticity of the orbit.

This been verified experimentally. The energy level characterised by $n = 2$, for example, has been shown to consist of a *doublet*, that is, two levels very close together. These correspond to the levels we have designated as 2_2 and 2_1, namely the levels associated with a circular orbit and an elliptic one.

9·8 Electron Spin

Under extremely close investigation, many of the closely spaced spectral lines which were accounted for by the Sommerfeld theory were shown to be resolvable into further doublets. Such Sommerfeld orbits must therefore represent not single energy levels, but pairs of levels which differ slightly in energy. An explanation of this fine structure was given in 1926 by Uhlenbeck and Goudsmit.[*] They suggested that the electron is spinning as well as moving around the nucleus. (Compare this with the earth spinning on its axis as it circles the sun, and remember the solar system analogy of atomic structure which the Rutherford atom model conjured up.)

Now Sommerfeld had postulated that every orbit must be characterised by the property that the electron possesses an integral number of $h/2\pi$ units of angular momentum. If then

[*] Uhlenbeck and Goudsmit, *Nature*, **117**, p264 (1926).

the electron is considered as an extended body (in contrast to a point charge) which is spinning about an axis, it must be considered to have additional angular momentum. Since many Sommerfeld levels turn out to be doublets, the immediate suggestion is that the combination of a non-zero 'orbital' angular momentum with the 'spin' angular momentum can take place in only two ways. That is, the electron spin angular momentum vector must be either parallel or anti-parallel to the orbital angular momentum vector, and the two vectors can combine in no other way. If the orbital angular momentum is zero, there is then no reference direction along which the spin angular momentum can align, and in this case the existence of electron spin produces no level splitting.

It transpires that the spin angular momentum can be either plus or minus $\frac{1}{2}h/2\pi$ units. The possibility of two spin states for the electron necessitates the introduction of a spin quantum number s which can have values of $+\frac{1}{2}$ or $-\frac{1}{2}$. Since an electron can have two different spin states, those Sommerfeld energy levels which are split are then required to be doublets.

9·9 Wave Mechanics

It must be emphasised that the account given above of the structure of the hydrogen atom is only a picture, in spite of its being a very detailed one. It constitutes the best picture that can be given in terms of phenomena with which we are all familiar.

In the first decade of this century, Einstein had shown that the photoelectric effect can be accounted for only if the incident radiant energy is assumed to have particle-like properties. Furthermore, the picture of radiation consisting of 'quanta' or 'photons' is fundamental to the Bohr theory of the atom. At the same time, phenomena such as interference and diffraction are best treated by assuming that light is a wave motion. Thus, the dual picture of light, as discussed in Section 3·7, became generally accepted.

In 1923, de Broglie[1] postulated that the same duality might be attributed to the atoms, molecules, protons and electrons which we tend to call the 'particles' of modern physics. De Broglie suggested that a particle with a momentum p should have a wavelength $\lambda = h/p$ associated with it, h being Planck's constant.

In 1927, Davisson and Germer[2] confirmed de Broglie's hypothesis by observing that electrons exhibited diffraction effects when reflected from single nickel crystals. As noted above, the best way to treat diffraction phenomena is to assume that the incident beam consists of waves. The wavelength which had to be assigned to the electron to explain Davisson and Germer's results was just that predicted by de Broglie. To show that this wave property was not limited to electrons alone, T. H. Johnson later carried out similar experiments with hydrogen atoms and showed that the same relationship between wavelength and momentum applied. Further experiments showed that helium atoms and hydrogen molecules also exhibited wave properties. In other words, it was shown that for all particles, it is possible to associate a *de Broglie wavelength* with their momentum through the relation $\lambda = h/p$.

In 1925-6 two new mathematical methods of treating atomic problems were developed by Heisenberg and Schrödinger. As soon as it is possible to assign a wavelength to a particle, it becomes reasonable to set up an equation to describe the wave motion, that is, a *wave equation*. Using de Broglie's hypothesis, this is exactly what Schrödinger did. He then applied his wave equation to the problem of the allowed energies in the hydrogen atom and immediately obtained the same results as Bohr.

This new *wave-mechanical* treatment has two great advantages. Firstly, it shows that what were *postulates* in the Bohr theory become direct *consequences* in the wave-mechanical theory. Secondly, the Schrödinger theory enables the computation of the relative intensities of spectral lines. The computed

[1] De Broglie, *Philosophical Magazine*, **47**, p446 (1924).

[2] Davisson and Germer, *Physical Review*, **30**, p705 (1927).

and observed values are in good agreement. Bohr's theory was unable to give any value for the expected intensities of the spectral lines.

The introduction of wave mechanics necessitates some revision of our 'picture' of an atom. Wave mechanics does not permit one to speak of definite discrete orbits in which the electrons move, but only of the probability of finding an electron at some given distance from the nucleus. In consequence, Bohr's allowed states cannot properly be thought of as orbits. Rather one speaks simply of the *stationary state*, or *eigenstate*, or sometimes the *orbital* associated with a particular set of quantum numbers and the 'sun and planet' model is considered to be a rather crude and inadequate picture of an atom. In an atom, each orbital has a definite prescribed energy and spectral lines result from the transitions of electrons between orbitals.

9·10 The Experiments of Franck and Hertz

Bohr's theory and its extension indicated the existence of discrete energy levels and we have seen how these predictions were verified by spectroscopic measurements. Bohr's results also suggested to Franck and Hertz* an alternative method of observing the energy levels. If atoms are supplied with energy in any way, the Bohr theory indicates that they can only absorb it in amounts exactly corresponding to the difference in energy between two stationary states.

In the Franck and Hertz experiments, the energy was supplied by a beam of electrons passing through a gas or vapour. Figure 9·5 shows their apparatus in schematic form. The electrons are produced at a filament F by thermionic emission and their effective initial velocity is approximately zero. The gas pressure and the distance between the filament and the grid are chosen so that, on the average, the electrons suffer at most one collision in the gas between filament and grid G. The grid is at a potential V_1, positive with respect to the filament.

* Franck and G. Hertz, *Physikalische Zeitschrift*, **17**, p409 (1916).

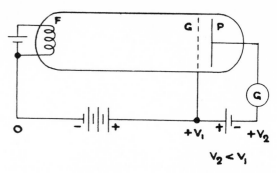

Fig. 9·5—*Schematic diagram of the apparatus of Franck and Hertz*

If the electron has suffered no collision between filament and grid, and therefore has lost no energy, its velocity will be given by

$$\tfrac{1}{2}mv^2 = V_1 e . \qquad (9·18)$$

Let us now suppose that V_1 is slowly increased from zero. For small values of this accelerating voltage, any collisions of the electrons with the gas or vapour are elastic, that is no energy is lost because of these collisions. The plate P is at a small negative potential with respect to the grid and as soon as the value of V_1 exceeds this retarding potential, the electrons are able to reach the plate and will thus give rise to a current through the galvanometer. When the value of V_1 has increased to some value $(V_1)_L$, two features are observed. Firstly, there is a drop in the galvanometer current, and secondly, there is radiation emitted. At this critical value of the accelerating voltage, electrons which have not previously suffered a collision have an energy, when they reach the vicinity of the grid, which is just sufficient to raise an electron of one of the gas atoms from its lowest energy state, or *ground state* to the next state above it in energy. Thus these electrons, if they collide with a gas atom in the region near the grid, lose all their energy and are then unable to reach the plate. Hence the current detected at the plate falls abruptly. The absorbing atom is now in an unstable state, and its electron will return to the ground state with the emission of electromagnetic radiation whose frequency is given by

$$\nu = (V_1)_L \, e/h \,. \qquad (9 \cdot 19)$$

If the accelerating voltage, V_1, is increased above $(V_1)_L$, there will be no other spectral lines emitted until the electrons have sufficient energy to excite the second energy state of the atom in an inelastic collision, say when $V_1 = (V_1)_M$.

The voltages $(V_1)_L$ and $(V_1)_M$ at which the new lines appear and which correspond to the stationary states of the atomic system are called *critical potentials*. Measurements such as those of Franck and Hertz serve to confirm the validity of Bohr's view that the electrons in an atom can exist only in certain discrete energy states.

In these experiments, it is also possible to give the incident electron sufficient energy to completely remove an electron from a gas atom. The smallest value of the accelerating potential at which this effect occurs is known as the first ionisation potential of the gas atom. The electron removed in this case is the one which is most loosely bound to the atom.

There followed on the measurements of Franck and Hertz many such experiments using a variety of gases. All of these tended to confirm the correctness of Bohr's ideas and assisted in the more complete understanding of the structure of even complex atoms.

9·11   The Periodic Table: Pauli's Exclusion Principle

So far, we have seen how the quantum numbers n and k fit into the picture of atomic structure. First, the spectrum of the hydrogen atom was computed in terms of the total quantum number n, alone. Then it was seen how the theory of Sommerfeld necessitated a **second quantum number** k, which determined the angular momentum of an electron in an elliptic orbit. In the more rigorous wave-mechanical treatment, the angular momentum is specified in terms of a different quantum number l, which is such that it can take any integral value from 0 to $n - 1$.

If one observes the spectrum of a sample of hydrogen which is placed in a strong magnetic field, it is found that each energy level is split into $(2l + 1)$ levels, where l is the orbital quantum number. This effect is known as the Zeeman Effect, and its interpretation requires the introduction of a third quantum number m, which may take any integral value between $-l$ and $+l$, that is, any one of $(2l + 1)$ values. m is known as the magnetic quantum number. Finally, the splitting of levels due to the electron spin necessitates the use of a fourth quantum number, the spin quantum number s, whose values may be $+\frac{1}{2}$ or $-\frac{1}{2}$, corresponding to a spin angular momentum of plus or minus $\frac{1}{2} h/2\pi$. The possible values of these four quantum numbers are shown in Table 9·1. This group of quantum numbers is found to be sufficient to designate any atomic state or orbital.

Table 9·1 — *Values of the quantum numbers*

$$
\begin{aligned}
n &= 1, \, 2, \, 3, \, 4, \, \ldots\ldots\ldots \\
l &= 0, \, 1, \, 2, \, 3, \, \ldots\ldots, \, (n - 1) \\
m &= -l, \, -(l - 1), \ldots\ldots, \, (l - 1), \, l \\
s &= -\tfrac{1}{2}, \, +\tfrac{1}{2} \,.
\end{aligned}
$$

In 1925, Pauli made, on empirical grounds, a generalisation which is of the utmost importance in understanding atomic structure. Its statement is simple, namely that *in any one atom no two electrons can have identical sets of quantum numbers.*

Let us now look at the simpler atoms in the light of this principle. Hydrogen has but one electron, and in its lowest energy state this is specified by $n = 1$, and therefore $l = 0$, and $m = 0$. s can take the values $-\frac{1}{2}$ or $+\frac{1}{2}$. Let us suppose that it is $+\frac{1}{2}$. Helium has two electrons and since the first one has the quantum numbers assigned to the electron of hydrogen $(1, 0, 0, +\frac{1}{2})$, the only other place in this first orbit must be occupied by an electron having quantum numbers $(1, 0, 0, -\frac{1}{2})$. Since we have now used up all variations of s, and since l must remain less than n, the third electron in lithium must go into a state which has $n = 2$. In this second state,

l may take on the values 0 or 1, m may have values 0 or -1, 0, $+1$, and s the values $-\frac{1}{2}$ or $+\frac{1}{2}$. The building up of the electronic structure of the atoms of the elements up to potassium is shown in Table 9·2.

Table 9·2 — *Electronic structure of atoms having n = 1, 2, 3*

Element	Z	Quantum Numbers of *last-added* electron			
		n	l	m	s
H	1	1	0	0	$+\frac{1}{2}$
He	2	1	0	0	$-\frac{1}{2}$
Li	3	2	0	0	$+\frac{1}{2}$
Be	4	2	0	0	$-\frac{1}{2}$
B	5	2	1	-1	$+\frac{1}{2}$
C	6	2	1	0	$+\frac{1}{2}$
N	7	2	1	$+1$	$+\frac{1}{2}$
O	8	2	1	$+1$	$-\frac{1}{2}$
F	9	2	1	0	$-\frac{1}{2}$
Ne	10	2	1	-1	$-\frac{1}{2}$
Na	11	3	0	0	$+\frac{1}{2}$
Mg	12	3	0	0	$-\frac{1}{2}$
Al	13	3	1	-1	$+\frac{1}{2}$
Si	14	3	1	0	$+\frac{1}{2}$
P	15	3	1	$+1$	$+\frac{1}{2}$
S	16	3	1	$+1$	$-\frac{1}{2}$
Cl	17	3	1	0	$-\frac{1}{2}$
A	18	3	1	-1	$-\frac{1}{2}$
K	19	4	0	0	$+\frac{1}{2}$

The electrons of any atom may be conveniently classified according to the values of the principal quantum numbers n, of the states which they occupy. Whenever all possible states corresponding to a given value of n are occupied, an *electron shell* is said to have been completed or closed. The usual terminology for describing these shells is as follows:

states with $n = 1$ constitute the *K-shell*,

states with $n = 2$ constitute the *L-shell*,

states with $n = 3$ constitute the *M-shell*,

and so on. Each filled shell contains $2n^2$ electrons. It should be pointed out that, as the electron structure of successive elements is built up, it does *not* always happen that each shell is filled before any electrons are added to the next shell. An example of this behaviour is shown in Table 9·2 for the case of potassium which has one electron in the *N*-shell while its *M*-shell still has room for ten more electrons.

The chemical properties of the elements are closely related to the disposition of the electrons in their atoms. For example, arrangements in which all $l = 1$ states of a particular shell have just been filled are exceptionally stable. These atoms are those of the inert gases.

9·12 Characteristic X-Rays: Moseley's Law

In hydrogen, the transitions which left the electron in the innermost orbit ($n = 1$) were found to give radiation in the ultra-violet region (the Lyman Series). When heavier atoms are considered, these innermost electrons are bound by electrostatic forces to a central charge of Ze rather than to just a charge e. As has been pointed out in Section 9·5, a single electron in an orbit around such a nucleus will be described in the simple Bohr theory by the replacement of e^2 by Ze^2 in all of the equations governing its motion. In particular, the energy of an electron in any orbit will be Z^2 times the value given in equation (9·10). Thus the energy required to remove one of the innermost electrons of a heavy element may be several thousand times that required to ionise a hydrogen atom. For instance, as the energy of the $n = 1$ state in hydrogen is $-13\cdot6$ eV, the energy of the $n = 1$ state in lead will be $-(82)^2 \times 13\cdot6$ eV, at least in the first approximation. Further, if in some way it can be made to take place, a transition from the $n = 2$ state to the $n = 1$ state in lead will correspond to an energy change of about 68,000 electron volt, since calculation on the simple Bohr theory shows that such a transition would take place between states having energies of about $-23,000$ eV and of about $-91,000$ eV. For such transition energies, the wavelengths of the radiation emitted are well into the X-ray region. It was the observation of such spectra that led Moseley to propound the law which bears his name, and which finally and unequivocally identified the central nuclear charge and the number of electrons per atom with the number which specified the position of the element in Mendeleev's periodic table.

The production of X-rays, as described in Chapter 4, gives rise to two types of radiation, a *characteristic line spectrum* superimposed on a *continuous spectrum*. The continuous X-ray spectrum does not concern us here, and we shall confine our attention to the measurements made by Moseley of the characteristic radiation. He used a Bragg crystal spectrograph[1] to make a systematic study of the X-ray lines produced by thirty-eight elements distributed throughout the periodic table. Moseley[2] found more characteristic lines than did Bragg, and furthermore classified them into two general groups. First, there was a short wavelength group which was called the *K-series* radiation and then a longer wavelength group called the *L-series* radiation. The *K*-series radiation consisted of two lines (K_α and K_β), the former having the longer wavelength and being the most intense of all the characteristic lines. The *L*-series radiation consisted of three lines, L_α, L_β and L_γ in order of decreasing wavelength.

Moseley observed that if the spectra of the *K*-series were arranged in order of increasing atomic weight, there was a progressive shift towards shorter wavelengths in moving from one element to the ones of higher atomic weight. A similar behaviour is exhibited by the *L*-series radiation. However, in this progression there were some irregularities, some wavelengths appearing out of order. He expressed this orderliness by saying that a certain quantity '. . . increases by a constant amount as we pass from one element to the next'. To get over the difficulty posed by the irregularities, he gave each element a number which specified its position in the periodic table. He found that the wavelengths of

the radiations formed a more consistent set when plotted against this number than they did when plotted against atomic weight. The relationship between these quantities becomes apparent when the square roots of the *frequencies* of the X-ray lines are plotted against the atomic number as shown in Figure 9·6. The same figure also shows the more irregular plot of the square root of the frequency against the atomic weight. Comparison of these two graphs shows beyond all doubt that atomic number and not atomic weight is the significant quantity which distinguishes one element from another. Empirically, the relation between the frequency of the K_α-lines and the atomic number Z, is given by

$$\nu = 0{\cdot}248 \times 10^{16} (Z - 1)^2.$$

This relation is known as *Moseley's law*.

Moseley's work made a very important contribution to the data which were finally used by Kossel[3] in 1914 to form a consistent picture of atomic structure, and also to account for the characteristic radiations which were observed by Moseley. The explanation of this characteristic radiation is just the same as that for the optical spectra which have been under consideration in the previous Sections of this Chapter. Whenever an electron 'jumps' from a higher to a lower energy state, energy equal to the difference in energy between the two states is emitted as a quantum of radiation. However, when this energy difference becomes large, as it can do in the case of the heavier elements, the resulting radiation may have a wavelength in the X-ray region.

The only material difference between these X-ray transitions and those occurring in optical spectra lies in the manner in which the transition is brought about. Optical spectra result from the addition of energy to atoms, as may occur, for example, in the gas of a discharge tube. This energy results in one of the outermost electrons of the atom being raised to a state of higher energy, from which it soon falls back to its original state with the emission of a photon. The energies of

---

[1] A device in which the ionisation chamber of the Bragg spectrometer (Figure 4·10) is replaced by a photographic plate.

[2] Moseley, *Philosophical Magazine*, **26,** p1024 (1913); **27,** p703 (1914).

[3] Kossel's work is reviewed in *Zeitschrift für Physik,* **1,** p119 (1920).

such photons are thus determined by the differences in energy between the higher energy levels of atoms. These differences are usually of the order of a few electron volts. On the other hand, X-rays are produced by transitions between relatively widely spaced energy levels. In consequence X-ray wavelengths are far shorter than optical wavelengths.

The atoms of the target of an X-ray tube are bombarded by electrons which may have energies of tens of thousands of electron volts. If an incident electron in the X-ray tube has sufficient energy to remove an electron from the innermost orbit of a target atom (that is, one of the most tightly bound electrons) it will in general prefer to do so, and to leave the outer, less tightly-bound electrons alone. This process is called K-shell ionisation. Let us now consider what will happen. An electron has been removed from the K-shell and there is now a vacancy in that shell. It will be filled by one of the electrons from an outer shell making a transition, and thereby giving rise to the emission of radiation. The radiation emitted in this process is characteristic of the

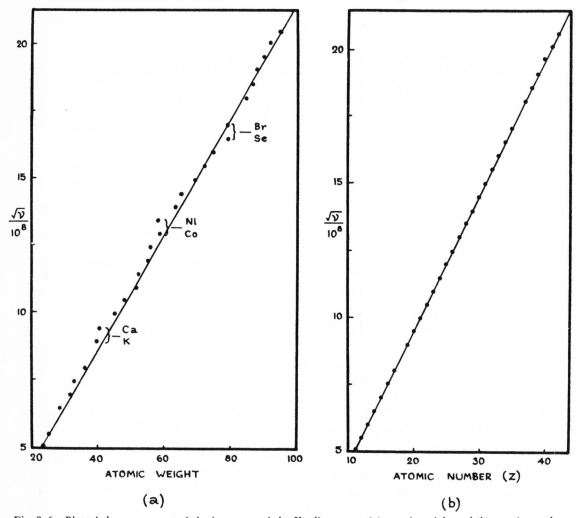

Fig. 9·6—*Plot of the square root of the frequency of the K_{α_1} line versus (a) atomic weight and (b) atomic number, number, showing the far smoother dependence on the latter quantity*

target atom concerned, since its energy depends on the energy of the electrons in the 'shells' of that atom. Thus we obtain the so-called characteristic radiation.

K-series X-rays come from radiative transitions initiated by a vacancy in the *K*-shell. Thus we have K_α-rays produced by *L*-shell to *K*-shell transitions, and K_β-rays produced by *M*-shell to *K*-shell transitions. If the bombarding electrons in the X-ray tube have insufficient energy to produce *K*-shell ionisation, they may remove an electron from the *L*-shell. By a similar process the *L*-series of X-rays is formed. This mechanism is shown schematically in Figure 9·7. It should be noted that if *K*-shell ionisation occurs, the *K*-series radiation will be accompanied by all other series. Vacancies in the higher shells are left by electrons falling into the *K*-shell and these vacancies in turn are filled by electrons from higher shells.

In the previous Sections, it has been shown that the energy level corresponding to any one value of the principal quantum number *n*, is in fact split into several levels due to the effect of the varying velocity of an electron in an elliptic orbit and to the effect of its spin. This level splitting gives rise to a fine structure in the X-ray emission spectra so that each line indicated on Figure 9·7 may in fact consist of several closely spaced lines. In the

discussion which follows, fine structure will be ignored and the energy levels will be assumed to be specified by the principal quantum number *n* alone.

The regularity in the behaviour of the frequencies of the characteristic radiation can be well understood in terms of the Bohr theory. Let us consider a hypothetical atom which has just one electron but which has a central charge *Ze*. This results in the substitution of Ze^2 for e^2 in the simple Bohr theory and the frequency of the radiation emitted in a transition of this electron from one state to another would then be, according to equation (9·11),

$$\nu = \frac{me^4}{8\epsilon_0^2 h^3} Z^2 \left(\frac{1}{n_2^2} - \frac{1}{n_1^2} \right). \qquad (9\cdot20)$$

Thus it would be expected that plotting the square root of the frequency against *Z* for hypothetical atoms of this type should indeed give a linear graph like that obtained by Moseley. This strongly suggests that the electrons concerned in the emission of *K*-series lines must, for some reason, be very little affected by the presence of other electrons, so that they behave in a similar manner to the single electrons in our hypothetical atoms.

However, graphs of the type shown in Figure 9·6 do not pass quite through the origin, as equation (9·20) suggests that they

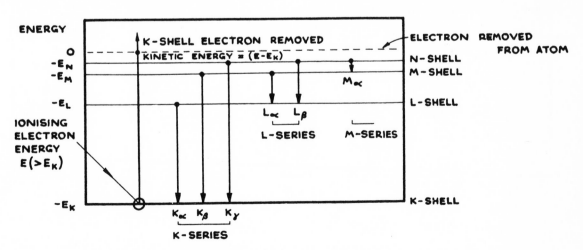

Fig. 9·7—*Diagrammatic representation of the electron transitions leading to the characteristic X-ray spectrum*

should. In fact for K-series lines they pass through the point ($\sqrt{\nu} = 0$, $Z = 1$). This difficulty is removed by recalling that there is still one electron in the K-shell of an atom after K-shell ionization takes place. That is, the electrons in the L-shell and the other outer electron shells move in the electrostatic field of a charge whose magnitude is not Ze, but rather $(Z - 1)e$. The remaining K-electron may, for this purpose, be treated as if it belonged to the central charge, and thus the effective value of this charge is reduced by one electronic charge. By replacing Z with $(Z - 1)$ in equation (9·20) good agreement is obtained between Moseley's experiment and the Bohr theory.

For L-series X-rays the constant which has to be subtracted from Z to give the magnitude of the effective central charge is no longer one, since there are more electrons shielding the nucleus from the outer electrons. Thus Moseley's law can be written for the more general case as

$$\sqrt{\nu} = a(Z - b), \qquad (9·21)$$

where a and b are constants whose values depend on the particular characteristic X-ray line under consideration.

One striking success of this work was that apparent discrepancies in the periodic table were removed and made understandable. For instance, Moseley's work showed that cobalt ($Z = 27$) should come before nickel ($Z = 28$) in the periodic table. This conclusion is not in agreement with the order suggested by their atomic weights, which are 58·94 and 58·69 respectively. Similarly, argon was shown to have $Z = 18$, and potassium $Z = 19$, even though their atomic weights are 39·94 and 39·10 respectively.

Moseley's conclusion was that the atomic number of an element was a measure of its nuclear charge, and that this quantity had a more fundamental effect on the electron orbits than did the atomic weight, just as was predicted by Bohr's theory. This is of fundamental importance because it not only fixes the number of electrons in all atomic species, but it shows conclusively that the properties of an atom are determined not by its atomic

weight but by its nuclear charge. Further, Moseley identified the nuclear charge with the position number of the element in the chemical periodic table with greater precision than was (or is) possible by any other means.

9·13 The Structure of the Atom

Due mainly to the efforts of Rutherford, Bohr and Moseley, a complete picture of atomic structure emerged. On the basis of the α-particle scattering experiments of Geiger and Marsden, Rutherford deduced that a nuclear atom was the only one that could account satisfactorily for their results. However, the existing electromagnetic theory insisted that such an atom could not live for any length of time.

Bohr overcame these objections with two radical postulates and abundantly justified these by the success of his theory in accounting for the spectra of atomic hydrogen and hydrogen-like atoms, and also in explaining Moseley's results on characteristic X-rays. Moseley's work also led to extensions of Bohr's theory being used to provide an understanding of the periodic table of the elements.

We have, therefore, the picture of the atom as consisting of a central nucleus whose mass is very nearly that of the whole atom and whose charge is exactly the atomic number Z, times the electronic charge. Around the nucleus there are distributed Z electrons so that the complete atom is electrically neutral. On the picture which has been given here these are arranged in orbitals according to the Pauli exclusion principle. These orbitals group themselves into shells such that the K-shell is filled with two electrons, the L-shell with eight electrons, and so on.

Once an insight into the arrangement of electrons around the atomic nucleus had been obtained, the next step in the search for knowledge about the atom was to ask questions concerning the structure of the nucleus itself. It is appropriate here to mention briefly the manner in which speculation regarding the structure of the nucleus was proceeding. The year 1920 is of some significance because in that year Rutherford delivered the Bakerian Lecture of the Royal Society,* and in it made many observations regarding the problem of the nucleus.

At this stage, Rutherford had reported the first nuclear disintegration (see Chapter 12) and had shown that one atomic species may be transformed into another by means of a nuclear reaction. However, this experimental fact did nothing to remove a very significant difficulty. How can a nucleus whose charge is Ze have a mass approximately $2Z$ atomic mass units?

In the Bakerian Lecture, Rutherford stated quite definitely that the nucleus was considered at that time to consist of a close combination of A protons and $(A - Z)$ electrons. This would then give a net charge of Ze as required, and an atomic weight of approximately A since the electron has an extremely small mass compared with that of a single proton.

* Rutherford, *Proceedings of the Royal Society*, **A 97**, p374 (1920).

Rutherford extended this idea, and in the extensions of it reside two remarkable pieces of foresight. Firstly, he considered that

. . . it seems very likely that one electron can also bind two H-nuclei and possibly also one H-nucleus. In the first case, this entails the possible existence of an atom of mass nearly two carrying one charge, which is to be regarded as an isotope of hydrogen.

Thus we have a prediction of the existence of deuterium, which was not discovered until twelve years later by Urey (see earlier in this Chapter). Secondly, Rutherford goes on to say

Under some conditions it may be possible for an electron to combine much more closely with the H-nucleus, forming a kind of neutral doublet.

In his lecture, Rutherford went further and predicted some properties of this 'neutral doublet'. Here, although the dominant idea at the time was that the nucleus consisted of protons and electrons, was a speculation on the existence of the *neutron*. This uncharged particle was also discovered twelve years later (see Chapter 12).

CHAPTER 10

The Masses of Atoms

10·1 The Discovery of Positive Rays

During the latter part of the 19th century many investigators were studying the production and properties of cathode rays. In 1886, Goldstein conducted some experiments with cathode rays during the course of which he employed a discharge tube with a perforated cathode of the kind illustrated in Figure 10·1. Goldstein observed streamers of light in the region to the left of the cathode. He assumed that these were due to some kind of rays travelling in the opposite direction to cathode rays and passing through the cathode. He called these rays *canal rays* since they passed through holes or canals in the cathode.

In 1898 Wien deflected the canal rays in a magnetic field and showed that they were positively charged. J. J. Thomson made a thorough study of these rays and called them *positive rays*. It was soon established that positive rays were produced when gases at low pressures were ionised in the presence of an electric field. In the ionisation process, one or more electrons are removed from the atom leaving the rest of the atom positively charged. The positive ions so produced are called positive rays if they are given appreciable velocities by acceleration in an electric field.

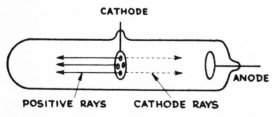

Fig. 10·1—*A discharge tube illustrating the production of positive rays*

10·2 Thomson's Experiments

J. J. Thomson[*] measured the charge to mass ratio of positive rays by observing the deflections they received as they passed through parallel electric and magnetic fields. Thomson's apparatus is illustrated in Figure 10·2. B is a large discharge tube with a cathode K sealed in at one side and an anode A located in a branch tube at the other side. The gas to be studied is admitted through a fine capillary at D while a low pressure is maintained in the discharge vessel by continuous pumping through E. The cathode K presents a hemispherical face to the discharge tube B, a funnel-shaped depression in the face connecting to a long thin canal passing through the cathode. If a high potential difference is applied between A and K with A positive with respect to K, a discharge takes place and positive rays are accelerated towards the cathode. Some of these pass through the canal and emerge from it in a thin stream. The positive ions are produced in a discharge as a result of ionisation of gas atoms throughout the region between cathode and anode. The energy of each ion as it reaches the cathode depends on the difference of potential between the point of its formation and the cathode. Thus, the positive ions leave the discharge tube with a range of velocities. Since the majority of the positive ions produced in B strike the cathode, it is necessary to cool it by means of the water jacket JJ.

The positive rays which emerge from the cathode then pass between the soft iron poles P_1 and P_2 of an electromagnet M_1, M_2. The

[*] J. J. Thomson, *Rays of Positive Electricity*, 2nd ed. (Longmans Green, 1921).

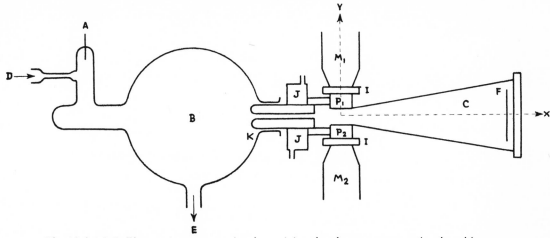

Fig. 10·2—*J. J. Thomson's apparatus for determining the charge-to-mass ratio of positive rays*

poles are insulated from the main iron core of the magnet by thin mica sheets I. An electrical potential difference can be applied between P_1 and P_2 so that in passing along the tube the particles are acted on by parallel electric and magnetic fields. These cause deflections of the particles. After emerging from the fields, they travel in straight lines through the evacuated camera C to a photographic plate F. If there are no fields between P_1 and P_2, the beam of rays will strike the photographic plate at a point in line with the

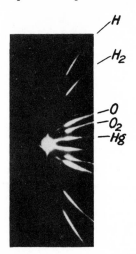

Fig. 10·3—*A photograph of typical positive ray parabolas obtained with apparatus of the Thomson type*

canal through the cathode. Thomson found, however, that when electric and magnetic fields existed in the region between P_1 and P_2, a series of parabolas, as shown in Figure 10·3, was produced on the photographic plate.

As a particle enters the region between P_1 and P_2, it has a velocity v_x parallel to and coincident with the X-axis of a rectangular system of coordinates with origin at the centre of the space between the magnet poles. It will be assumed that the electric field E, and the magnetic field B, are both in the Y-direction, that they have sharply defined boundaries and exist over a length l in the X-direction. Further, if the deflections produced by these fields are small, the deflecting force due to the magnetic field will, to a good approximation, always act in a fixed direction. In this case, this direction will be that of the Z-axis. The magnetic deflection will, as a result of this approximation, be independent of the motion of the particle in the X-direction. The particle will then take a time l/v_x to traverse the fields. The electric field exerts a force in the Y-direction

$$F_y = q E, \qquad (10·1)$$

which causes an acceleration

$$a_y = \frac{q}{m} E. \qquad (10·2)$$

103

The displacement y of the particle from the X-axis as it leaves the field is

$$y = \tfrac{1}{2} a_y t^2 , \qquad (10 \cdot 3)$$

where $t = l/v_x$ is the transit time through the field. Substituting for t and a_y yields

$$y = \tfrac{1}{2} \frac{q}{m} E \left(\frac{l}{v_x} \right)^2 . \qquad (10 \cdot 4)$$

In the magnetic field, the force in the direction of the Z-axis experienced by the particle is given by

$$F_z = q \, v_x B. \qquad (10 \cdot 5)$$

At the exit from the field there is therefore a displacement in the Z-direction,

$$y = \tfrac{1}{2} \frac{q}{m} B v_x \left(\frac{l}{v_x} \right)^2 . \qquad (10 \cdot 6)$$

After leaving the fields the particle travels in a straight line at some angle to the X-axis. If the distance from the fields to the photographic plate is large compared with l, the displacement at the plates will have co-ordinates Y and Z which are proportional to y and z. From (10·4) and (10·6),

$$Y = C \frac{q}{m} \frac{E}{v_x^2} \qquad (10 \cdot 7)$$

and

$$Z = C \frac{q}{m} \frac{B}{v_x} , \qquad (10 \cdot 8)$$

where C is a constant depending on the dimensions of the apparatus. Eliminating v_x from the last two equations gives

$$Z^2 = C \frac{q}{m} \frac{B^2}{E} Y, \qquad (10 \cdot 9)$$

which is the equation of a parabola. Accordingly, particles having various velocities v_x as they enter the fields between P_1 and P_2, but having the same charge to mass ratio $\dfrac{q}{m}$, strike the photographic plate at a series of points along the arc of a parabola. Provided the values of the fields B and E are kept constant, particles with different q/m ratios should produce different parabolas.

Thomson found well-defined parabolas as illustrated in Figure 10·3. The sharpness of the traces indicates that any one kind of atom has a definite mass, not a distribution of masses over a wide range. Thomson was able to identify traces due to single hydrogen atoms and due to molecular hydrogen. No other hydrogen parabolas were observed. From this data, it was possible to infer that the hydrogen atom has only one electron, since if it had more than one, parabolas corresponding to doubly ionised hydrogen atoms should have occurred. Helium was found to give two parabolas corresponding to singly and doubly charged ions. Since parabolas corresponding to trebly ionised atoms did not appear, it was concluded that the helium atom possesses two electrons.

By a systematic study of the relative positions of the parabolas appearing on a series of plates, Thomson was able to determine the masses of a number of atoms. Since his apparatus in fact measures q/m, it is necessary to assume a value for q before m can be determined. If for any one substance, measurements of the parabola with the lowest value of q/m are made, it can be assumed that the charge is numerically equal to the charge on an electron. This is implied by the simplest ionisation process in which one electron is removed from a neutral atom.

10:3   The Discovery of Isotopes

At the turn of the century it was known that the atomic weights of the elements were close to whole numbers when expressed on a mass scale with oxygen as 16·00. However, in the values of chemical atomic weights, significant departures from whole numbers were known. With the discovery of radioactivity, and the subsequent study of the naturally occurring radioactive series, some curious facts emerged.

In 1906 Boltwood* discovered what appeared to be a new element which he called ionium. This was produced in the radioactive decay series from uranium and was the parent substance from which radium was produced. Boltwood found that ionium was

* Boltwood, *American Journal of Science*, **22**, p537 (1906); **24**, p370 (1907).

chemically indistinguishable from thorium, although the radioactive behaviour of the two substances differed considerably. Subsequent careful chemical work failed to disclose any differences between the chemistry of the two materials. Similar chemical identities were found in other radioactive substances.

In 1910, Soddy[1] suggested that chemical homogeneity of a substance did not preclude the possibility that any one element was composed of atoms with several atomic weights. In 1912, Russell and Rossi[2] made a further study of the properties of ionium and thorium and in discussing possible explanations for their similarity, they also suggested that these might be substances having different atomic weights but identical chemical properties. This idea was taken up once again by Soddy in 1913[3] although it received a good deal of criticism at the time on the basis that there was insufficient evidence to support the suggestion. It was Soddy who proposed the name *isotopes*[4] for substances with different physical properties but identical chemistry.

By 1912, an improved version of Thomson's positive ray apparatus had been built in the Cavendish Laboratory, and the parabolas corresponding to masses differing by 10% could be clearly resolved. In November of that year neon was admitted to the system and photographs were obtained which showed parabolas corresponding to atomic masses of 20 and 22. Thomson reported his findings in an address to the Royal Institution on January 17, 1913.[5] The mass 22 parabola was found to be much fainter than that corresponding to mass 20, suggesting a smaller proportion of mass 22 neon. Since the chemical atomic weight of neon was known to be 20·2, the discovery gave strong support to the idea that there were two chemically identical neon isotopes with atomic masses 20 and 22 present in

the correct proportion to give an average atomic weight slightly greater than 20. The possibility existed, however, that the parabola corresponding to mass 22 was due to an impurity.

Aston attempted to separate the two neon isotopes by tedious fractionation and diffusion techniques but only indifferent success was achieved, and at the outbreak of war in 1914, the presence of two neon isotopes, while generally believed, could not be said to be proven. The war interrupted this work and it was not until 1919, when a new method of positive ray analysis had been developed, that it was finally shown beyond all doubt that isotopes did actually exist.

10·4   The Work of Aston

In Thomson's apparatus for the determination of the charge to mass ratio of positive rays, particles of different velocity struck the photographic plate at different points along the parabola. Aston[6] produced a rather different type of apparatus which brought all particles of a given charge to mass ratio to a focus at one point irrespective of their velocities. This had the advantage of greatly increasing the intensity of the photographic image so that it was possible to detect isotopes which were present in small concentrations. Aston's apparatus also gave a greater dispersion of the masses and consequently allowed the separation of isotopes with relatively small mass differences. A third advantage of Aston's equipment was the almost linear mass scale across the photographic plate which made the estimation of masses simpler. Because the photographic plate in his apparatus displayed the masses of positive rays as a series of lines similar to those obtained with optical spectrographs, Aston called his equipment a *mass spectrograph* and the record he obtained he called a *mass spectrum*.

The principles employed in Aston's mass spectrograph are illustrated in Figure 10·4. Positive rays from a discharge tube (not shown

[1] Soddy, *Chemical Society Annual Report*, **7**, p285 (1910).
[2] Russell and Rossi, *Proceedings of the Royal Society*, **A 87**, p478 (1912).
[3] Soddy, *Chemical News*, **107**, p97 (1913).
[4] *isos* — equal, *topos* — place. Isotopes occupy the same place in the periodic table of elements.
[5] Aston, *Mass Spectra and Isotopes*, p30 (Edward Arnold, London, 1933).

[6] Aston, *Philosophical Magazine*, **38**, p707 (1919); *Mass Spectra and Isotopes*, pp38-54 (Edward Arnold, 1933).

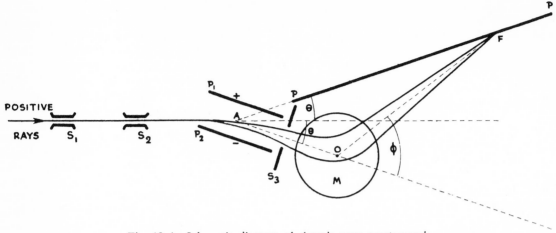

Fig. 10·4—*Schematic diagram of Aston's mass spectrograph*

in the diagram) pass through two fine collimating slits S_1 and S_2 so that a ribbon beam of particles, of small extent in the plane of the diagram but of relatively large extent normal to the plane, passes into the region between the electrostatic deflecting plates P_1 and P_2. A potential difference maintained between these plates causes a deflection of the particles towards the plate P_2. Since the positive ions have a range of velocities they will experience a range of deflections, the fastest particles being the least deflected.

A part of the velocity spectrum so produced is selected by slit S_3 and ions within the selected velocity range enter a magnetic field, normal to the plane of Figure 10·4, produced between the poles M, of an electromagnet. The magnetic field is arranged so as to deflect the positive rays in the opposite direction. This angle of deflection, ϕ, for the central ray is shown in the figure. Since particles of higher velocity, and with the one charge to mass ratio, are once again less deflected than those of lower velocity, the extreme rays which have passed through slit S_3 must now intersect beyond the magnetic field at a point F. If the instrument is correctly adjusted, all of the rays passing through S_3 meet at F, so that this point is now a focus for particles with a range of initial velocities. A photographic plate PP is located in such a way that F is a point on its surface. Since the slits S_1 and

S_2 have an appreciable length in the direction normal to the diagram, the focus at F is a line focus along the photographic plate in a direction into the paper. A different focus line will be obtained for particles with different charge to mass ratios, and the photographic plate can be placed so that all these focal lines are located at different points along its surface. The equations for the behaviour of the ions in the spectrograph are complicated, but it has been shown* that the desired velocity focusing is obtained if the photographic plate PP lies along a line which passes through the point A at the centre of the deflecting plates at an angle θ to the incoming beam of particles. θ is also the angle between the incoming beam and the line from A through the centre of S_3 to the centre of the magnetic field at O.

Aston's spectrograph was capable of separating masses differing by one part in 130 and it was possible to determine the masses of resolved 'lines' to an accuracy of 1 in 1000. The instrument was calibrated by examining the lines resulting from the introduction of oxygen, carbon monoxide and carbon dioxide into the discharge tube. The singly-charged oxygen molecule, and singly- and doubly-charged oxygen atoms produce reference lines corresponding to *singly-charged masses* of 32,

* Aston and Fowler, *Philosophical Magazine*, **43**, p514 (1922).

106

16 and 8 units respectively. CO and CO_2 produce further lines at mass numbers 28 (CO), 44 (CO_2), 12 (C singly-charged) and 6 (C doubly-charged). Other lines due to hydrocarbons were also identified.

As soon as the instrument was deemed to be functioning correctly, neon was introduced and two distinct lines at mass 20 and mass 22 were observed.[1] Aston reported the two masses to be exact integers to an accuracy of one-tenth per cent, and their intensities to be consistent with the accepted atomic weight of 20·20 for neon. He also detected a trace corresponding to mass 21 which he incorrectly attributed to an abnormal hydride. Later work[2] showed that there is a third neon isotope of mass 21 which is present in very small quantities.

Aston's experiment was probably the first definite proof of the existence of isotopes amongst the elements. Aston, realising that a new nomenclature would be required to describe isotopes of the same chemical element, suggested that the chemical symbol for the element should be used with a superscript giving the mass of the isotope. It was convenient to use a mass scale in which the mass of the oxygen atom was taken to be 16. The details of the choice of mass scale are further discussed in Section 10·7. Thus the three neon isotopes are written Ne^{20}, Ne^{21} and Ne^{22}. Sometimes it is desirable to add the atomic number, that is, the position of the element in the periodic table. This is written as a subscript on the left, so that the isotope of neon with mass 20 is written $_{10}Ne^{20}$. (Some physicists prefer to write the mass on the left also, for example $_{10}^{20}Ne$.)

Aston made a careful study of the masses of a number of elements and discovered many other isotopes such as those of chlorine (Cl^{35}, Cl^{37}), argon (A^{36}, A^{40}) and krypton (Kr^{78}, Kr^{80}, Kr^{82}, Kr^{83}, Kr^{84}, Kr^{86}). To the accuracy obtainable all these isotopes appeared to have masses which were exact integers. To find out whether this was really true, Aston re-designed and refined his spectrograph[3] to obtain a resolution of one part in 600 and an accuracy in mass determination of about 1 in 10,000. He then found that there were small, but as it turned out very significant, departures from the whole number rule. For example, Aston found the masses of the chlorine isotopes to be 34·983 and 36·980. In fact, taking oxygen at mass 16·000, isotopes of elements with masses less than 20 or greater than about 180 have masses which are slightly above an integral value. Elements between these limits have masses which are slightly less than an integer. With the exception of a few elements very high in the periodic table, the departure of the mass from an integral value never exceeds 0·1 mass units.

Aston's work showed firstly that isotopes, that is, chemically identical atoms with different masses, did exist; secondly, that the masses of all isotopes follow very closely a whole number rule if they are expressed on a scale with oxygen as 16·000, and thirdly, that there were small but significant departures from the exact integral values. The significance of these departures will be discussed later in this book.

10·5 Dempster's Mass Spectrometer

At about the same time as Aston was producing his spectrograph at the Cavendish Laboratory in Cambridge, Dempster[4] was building a quite different piece of equipment in Chicago. In Dempster's apparatus, the positive rays are accelerated to a definite velocity. If the velocity spread of the resulting beam is small, a magnetic field is sufficient to produce an analysis into different charge to mass ratio groups.

The principles of Dempster's equipment are illustrated in Figure 10·5. Ions are produced from heated salts deposited on the platinum strip P, the heating being produced by an electric current from the battery C. These ions are accelerated in the glass tube A, by a potential difference V, maintained

[1] Aston, *Philosophical Magazine*, **39**, p449 (1920).
[2] Hogness and Kvalnes, *Physical Review*, **32**, p942 (1928).
[3] Aston, *Proceedings of the Royal Society*, **A115**, p487 (1927).
[4] Dempster, *Physical Review*, **11**, p316 (1918).

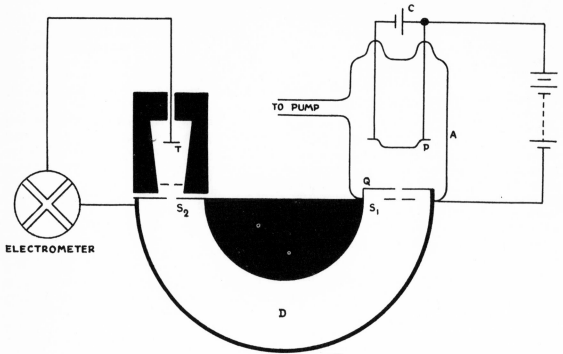

Fig. 10·5—*Dempster's first mass spectrometer*

between the platinum strip and an electrode Q. Provided an ion is produced with very low velocity at the platinum strip, its energy when it reaches the slit S_1 is given by

$$\tfrac{1}{2}mv^2 = Vq, \qquad (10\cdot10)$$

where q is the charge on the ion, m its mass, and v its velocity. In practice the ions have some velocity at production but provided the potential difference V is large enough, the resulting spread of velocities at S_1 will be small. In Dempster's apparatus the potential difference varied from 500 to 1750 volt.

After emerging from the slit S_1 into the brass deflecting chamber D, the positive ions enter a magnetic field B directed through D in a direction normal to and out from the plane of Figure 10·5. The magnetic field causes the particles to move in a circular path. The magnetic force on the ions is qvB normal to the path and this must equal the centripetal force mv^2/R where R is the radius of the path. Hence

$$mv = qBR. \qquad (10\cdot11)$$

Eliminating v from equations (10·10) and (10·11) yields

$$\frac{q}{m} = \frac{2V}{B^2R^2}. \qquad (10\cdot12)$$

Ions with the correct value of q/m to satisfy this relation will travel in a path of radius R through the slits S_1 and S_2 and strike the insulated plate T. The electrometer measures the current falling on the plate T.

In using this apparatus, Dempster maintained a constant magnetic field and plotted the ion current reaching the electrometer as V was varied. The peaks on the curves obtained in this way correspond to definite values of q/m determined by the voltage setting at each peak. The heights of the peaks indicate the relative quantities of the various ions present. The apparatus was capable of a resolution of about one per cent. Dempster's apparatus is called a *spectrometer* because the output is measured on some instrument, in this case an electrometer. Aston's apparatus on the other hand is a *spectrograph*, because the record is displayed in graphical form. The Dempster spectrometer has the advantage of permitting accurate estimates of relative abundances to be made. It suffers, however, from the limitation that any source of ions must yield particles whose velocity is very much less than that produced by acceleration through the potential difference V.

In 1920, Dempster used his spectrometer to investigate magnesium[1] and found that it had three isotopes Mg^{24}, Mg^{25} and Mg^{26} in proportions which accounted satisfactorily for the chemical atomic weight. He also confirmed the presence of the two lithium isotopes Li^6 and Li^7, found independently by Aston and G. P. Thomson.

10·6 Bainbridge's Mass Spectrograph

In 1933, Bainbridge[2] devised a mass spectrograph which had high resolving power and precision and the advantage of a linear mass scale. The essential details of the instrument are shown in Figure 10·6.

Positive ions are produced in a high voltage discharge tube (not shown in the diagram) and emerge with a range of velocities through the slit S_1 which is located in its cathode. This slit, together with S_2, then defines a narrow beam of ions. These ions, which have, in addition to their spread in velocity, a variety of charges and masses, then enter the region between slits S_2 and S_3.

A uniform magnetic field is applied normal to and out from the plane of the diagram everywhere below slit S_2. In the region between S_2 and S_3 an electric field is maintained between the insulated plates P_1 and P_2. Thus in this region, called the 'velocity selector', there are crossed electric and magnetic fields both perpendicular to the line through S_2 and S_3. Positive ions travelling from S_2 to S_3 experience forces to the right

[1] Dempster, *Proceedings of the National Academy of Science*, **7**, p45 (1921).

[2] Bainbridge, *Physical Review*, **42**, p3 (1932); *Journal of the Franklin Institute*, **215**, p509 (1933).

in Figure 10·6 due to the electric field and to the left due to the magnetic field. They will be undeflected and so pass through S_3 provided these two forces are equal. The electric force is qE where q is the charge of the ion and E the value of the electric field. The magnetic force is qvB where v is the velocity of the particle and B is the value of the magnetic field. The particles will be undeflected if

$$qE = qvB,$$

$$\text{or if} \qquad v = E/B. \qquad (10·13)$$

Thus, only particles whose velocity is equal to the ratio of the electric to magnetic field strength can pass through the selector system and out through S_3.

On emerging from S_3, the particles enter a region where only the magnetic field is effective. Here they travel in a circular arc of radius R and strike the photographic plate at a distance $2R$ from the centre of S_3. The

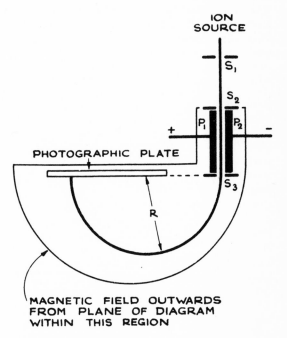

Fig. 10-6—*Bainbridge type of mass spectrograph with velocity selector. The magnetic field is directed outwards from the paper*

radius of the path in the magnetic field is given from equation (10·11) as

$$R = \frac{mv}{qB} \cdot \qquad (10\cdot14)$$

Inserting the value of v determined by (10·13) gives

$$R = \frac{m}{q}\frac{E}{B^2} \cdot \qquad (10\cdot15)$$

If E and B are kept constant, the radius of curvature R and therefore the position of impact on the photographic plate are linear functions of the mass to charge ratio. If the ions passing through S_1 have a variety of masses, a number of lines will be produced on the photographic plate and from their positions the particle masses may be determined.

10·7 Isotopic and Atomic Weights

Down through the years the techniques of mass spectroscopy have been refined, a very large number of isotopes have been identified, and their masses have been measured. It has been found that the masses of the isotopes are all very nearly whole numbers based on a scale with carbon as 12, but that there are small departures. It is usual to identify isotopes by their *mass number A*, the integer nearest to their exact isotopic mass and by their chemical symbol or alternatively, their atomic number Z.

Exact *isotopic masses* are now determined on the *atomic mass scale* with the mass of the isotope C^{12} defined to be exactly 12 *atomic mass units*. The atomic mass unit (a.m.u.) is equal to $1\cdot660 \times 10^{-27}$ kilogramme. This standard of atomic mass was accepted by the assembly of the International Union of Pure and Applied Physics, Ottawa 1960. This standard was chosen because mass spectroscopists almost universally measure masses of isotopes in terms of carbon and hydrocarbon compounds. This scale is adopted for all mass values used in the following pages of this book.

A previous commonly used scale had the mass of the isotope O^{16} defined to be exactly 16 atomic mass units and many tables of mass values will still be found to be based on this scale. Previously, chemists used a *chemical atomic weight* scale on which the average mass of an oxygen atom was taken to be $16\cdot000$. Since oxygen possesses several isotopes the proportions of which may vary slightly, this old scale was not very satisfactory. Chemists have now agreed to use the new C^{12} scale.

The Nucleus Comes Under Fire

In the concluding seven chapters of this book we shall see how attention became focused on the structure of the atomic nucleus. Rutherford's experiments with α-particles showed that nuclei could be changed into different species. Here at last, although only on a microscopic scale, was the transmutation of the elements so long sought after by the alchemists of old.

From Rutherford's early experiments grew the tradition of nuclear physics. In these chapters we shall discuss first the tools used by physicists in this quest for knowledge of the nucleus. One of the most fruitful avenues in this quest has been provided by the bombardment of nuclei with a wide variety of sub-atomic particles. Some of the highlights among the results of these researches were the discovery of the neutron, the production of artificial radioactivity, the finding of a whole host of new elementary particles, and the possibility of obtaining energy from nuclei. The dramatic demonstrations of this energy release in the form of bombs and nuclear reactors are now well known.

It would be satisfying to be able to conclude this book with a description of a theory which explained all the wealth of experimental facts concerning the nucleus which are now available. This no one can do at present, for the forces at work in the nucleus and the role of the many new particles are as yet not clearly understood. Indeed, one of the most eminent theoretical physicists of our time, the Russian L. D. Landau, is of the opinion that '. . . there is, at the present time, no rational theory of nuclear forces. . . .' Nuclear physics is a live subject and the problems remaining to be solved are both numerous and complex. Perhaps when the solutions finally appear the subject will no longer be 'Modern Physics'.

CHAPTER 11

Detectors of Nuclear Radiations

11·1 Introduction

In Chapter 5, it was shown that some atoms are radioactive, decaying by the emission of α-particles or β-particles, either of which may be accompanied by γ-rays. Many other types of nuclear reactions may be produced in the laboratory. In these, a wide range of 'nuclear radiations' may be emitted, the most common being protons, α-particles, neutrons and γ-rays. To study these nuclear processes adequately, suitable *detectors* must be employed to give information about the nuclear radiations which are emitted. There are three main groups of nuclear radiation, *charged particles* (protons, α-particles, β-particles etc.), *uncharged particles* (neutrons) and *electromagnetic radiation* (X-rays or γ-rays).

The fundamental requirement for the detection of any nuclear radiation is the dissipation of energy in the detector by that radiation. This energy dissipation may be caused by ionisation of atoms in the detector (as in the ionisation chamber, Geiger counter, cloud chamber and nuclear emulsion) or by excitation of the atoms without the actual removal of orbital electrons. This latter process occurs in the scintillation counter. Only charged particles are capable of producing either of these processes directly. Uncharged particles do not themselves produce ionisation or excitation and special techniques are required for their detection.

11·2 The Ionisation Chamber

In its passage through any substance, a charged particle will suffer many collisions with the atoms in the material. These collisions should not be thought of as being 'direct hits' in the way one speaks of collisions between large-scale objects. Rather, it should be remembered that these atomic particles are all charged and that electrostatic forces are acting btween them all the time as they approach one another. Thus on the atomic scale, there is no real distinction between a 'collision' and a 'near miss'. The consequences of a collision between a charged particle and a neutral atom depend principally on how closely they pass by one another.

As it approaches, the charged particle exerts an increasing force on each of the electrons of the atom. Unless this force becomes great enough to remove an electron the charged particle will lose none of its energy in such a collision. However, in a very close encounter, an electron may be dislodged from an atom leaving it in an *ionised* state. When this occurs, the energy necessary for ionisation is supplied at the expense of the kinetic energy of the charged particle. On the average, an energy of about 32 electron volt is required to produce an ion pair, that is, a positively charged atom and a free electron. This means that a charged particle with an energy of 1 MeV will produce about 30,000 ion pairs along its path before it comes to rest. The 30,000 ion pairs formed in this process carry a charge which is large enough to be detected with ease in a variety of ways.

In an ionisation chamber, the ions are produced in a gas between two electrodes as illustrated in Figure 11·1. If a potential difference is maintained between the positive electrode A and the negative electrode B, the electrons produced by ionisation are drawn towards A and the positive ions are accelerated towards B. If the potential difference

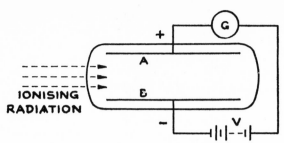

Fig. 11·1—*The ionisation chamber*

V is varied while a constant intensity of ionising radiation enters the chamber, the current indicated by the galvanometer G varies as shown in Figure 11·2.

When the value of *V* is low, the electric field between the electrodes is small. Thus under these conditions (the region OP of Figure 11·2) the ions produced in the chamber achieve only relatively low velocities. In consequence, many of the positive ions and electrons recombine to form neutral atoms before they reach the electrodes. As *V* is increased, the fraction of ions recombining becomes smaller and smaller until at a potential corresponding to Q, virtually all of the ions produced reach the electrodes and contribute to the current recorded by the galvanometer. Further increase in potential difference in the range between Q and R of Figure 11·2 results in no increase in current. The current in this region is equal to the total charge produced by ionisation every second and is called the *saturation current*.

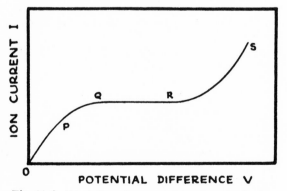

Fig. 11·2—*Variation of current through an ionisation chamber as a function of potential difference. The intensity of ionising radiation is kept constant*

It is a measure of the energy extracted from the ionising radiation every second.

Currents in ionisation chambers are very small. For example, a 1-MeV α-particle which stops in the chamber produces about 30,000 ion pairs corresponding to a charge equal to 60,000 times the electronic charge, that is about 10^{-14} coulomb. Thus one such α-particle stopping in the chamber every second would produce an ionisation current with an average value of 10^{-14} ampere. A good galvanometer might detect a current of about 10^{-10} ampere so that such instruments can only be used when some tens of thousands of particles per second pass through the ionisation chamber. More sensitive electronic devices have been developed and it is now possible to replace the galvanometer G in Figure 11·1 by an electronic amplifier which can even detect the pulse of current resulting from the passage of a single charged particle through the chamber.

If an ionisation chamber is operated in the saturation current region and if the path length of the ionising radiation through the chamber gas is sufficient to cause every ionising particle to lose all its energy, the pulse of current due to each charged particle has a magnitude proportional to the particle energy. In this way the ionisation chamber can be used to determine, at least approximately, the energies of particles detected by it. If the particles do not enter too frequently, the current pulses may be counted to record the number of charged particles entering the ionisation chamber. If large numbers of particles, all of the same energy, enter the chamber every second, the average current recorded is a measure of the number of particles arriving per second. To determine this number accurately it is necessary to know the ionisation charge produced by each particle.

Different types of particle of the same energy produce very different quantities of ionisation in traversing the same thickness of a gas at a particular pressure. For example, 5-MeV α-particles produce about ten times as much ionisation per unit path length as do 5-MeV protons. It follows that an ionisation chamber intended to stop protons must be larger than an α-particle chamber or alternatively, must contain gas at a higher pressure to provide more molecules per unit path length for collisions. An electron produces only about $0\cdot01$ times as many ion pairs per unit path length as are produced by an α-particle of the same energy. γ-rays can also be detected in an ionisation chamber, since they can eject high energy electrons from atoms, these electrons in turn ionising the gas. γ-rays produce about 10^{-4} times as many ion pairs per unit path length as do α-particles of the same energy. In consequence high gas pressures are commonly used for γ-ray detection.

11.3 The Geiger-Müller Counter

In Figure $11\cdot2$, showing the variation of ion current as a function of potential difference, the curve is seen to rise again for voltages greater than the value at R. In the region R to S, electrons produced by ionisation are accelerated to such a high velocity that they may themselves produce further ions by collision. This process, called *gas amplification*, results in a greater current for a given loss of energy by the original particle and consequently the detection device is more sensitive. This phenomenon of gas amplification provides the basis for the operation of the *Geiger-Müller counter*, which is illustrated in Figure $11\cdot3$.

The origins of this device can be traced back to 1908 when Rutherford and Geiger* arranged a cylinder and co-axial wire with a

* Rutherford and Geiger, *Proceedings of the Royal Society*, **A 81**, p141 (1908).

potential difference between them. When charged particles entered the volume enclosed by the cylinder, it was found that the pulse of current through the gas due to a single particle was magnified sufficiently to enable it to be detected by an electrometer of quite moderate sensitivity.

In a counting tube such as that shown in Figure $11\cdot3$, the central wire is maintained at a high positive potential with respect to the outer cylinder. If the central wire is very thin, the electric field in its vicinity becomes very high. Suppose an incident ionising particle produces one single ion pair in the volume enclosed by the outer cylinder. The resulting electron will be accelerated towards the positive central wire and will reach a relatively high velocity. It may itself produce a large number of additional ion pairs due to repeated collisions. These new electrons are also accelerated and may produce more ion pairs. As a result an *avalanche* occurs and a very large number of electrons reaches the anode. In this way, the initial formation of a single ion pair results in a very large pulse of current to the anode.

It might be expected that, if an ionising particle initially produces a trail of ion pairs in the gas, the resulting current pulse would be larger than that originating from a single ion pair. For moderate values of the potential difference between anode and cathode this is found to be the case. However, as this potential difference is increased, this variation in the size of the current pulse gradually disappears. Ultimately it is found that the size of the current pulse becomes effectively independent of the initial density of ionisation for quite a range of potential

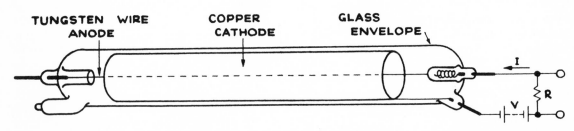

TUNGSTEN WIRE ANODE　　**COPPER CATHODE**　　**GLASS ENVELOPE**

Fig. $11\cdot3$—*A typical Geiger counter tube*

differences. The counter then gives a full avalanche of nearly constant size for any particle counted. In this region it is said to operate on the *plateau* or in the 'Geiger region'. This is the normal mode of operation since the counter sensitivity is highest and the counting efficiency is independent of tube voltage over a reasonable range, so that the supply voltage is not critical. A counter operated in this fashion can not give any information about the type of particle producing the count or its energy. The first counter of this type was constructed by Geiger and Müller* in 1928, and these devices are now most commonly known as *Geiger counters*.

If a resistor is connected in the Geiger counter circuit as shown in Figure 11·3, the current pulse I flowing through it produces a voltage pulse which can be amplified by an electronic amplifier and counted by an electronic counter.

The positive ions produced during an electron avalanche in a Geiger counter are subject to the same electrical forces as are the electrons. However, because of their much larger masses, they experience smaller accelerations and hence may be considered as being virtually stationary during the electron avalanche. After this avalanche, these positive ions, which are principally formed close to the central wire, move outwards towards the cathode. When they reach it, some time later, they have considerable energies and some of them will release electrons as they bombard the cathode surface. In this way a second avalanche is started, and thus a succession of discharges will follow. This process will continue for a relatively long time unless some method of *quenching* the discharge is provided.

One method of limiting the discharge is to use a very large series resistance R. When a large current pulse occurs, the momentary voltage drop across the resistance lowers the Geiger tube voltage sufficiently to extinguish the discharge. This technique is rarely employed nowadays since it results in a relatively long time interval after one pulse before the

* Geiger and Müller, *Physikalische Zeitschrift*, **29**, p839 (1928).

counter recovers sufficiently to detect a new particle. The period following one count during which the counter is insensitive is called the *dead time* of the counter.

A second and more satisfactory method for quenching the discharge is to use an electronic circuit to remove the counter voltage for a short period immediately following a count. With this technique dead times of about 400 microsecond are common. Either of these two quenching systems is referred to as *external quenching*. It is also possible to quench the discharge internally by introducing into the counter tube a small quantity (of the order of 10%) of a polyatomic gas such as ethyl alcohol. This *quenching agent*, in effect, prevents the release of electrons from the cathode surface by positive ion bombardment. Thus only one avalanche occurs for each ionising particle passing through the tube.

Geiger counters may be made in a variety of sizes but they customarily have anode wires a few thousandths of an inch in diameter. A common filling gas is argon at a pressure of about 10 cm of mercury. For internal quenching, a partial pressure of about 1 cm of ethyl alcohol is commonly used. Such internally quenched counters operate with potential differences of one to two thousand volt. More recently, counters whose quenching agent is a halogen gas have been produced. A typical filling for a counter of this type is 0·01 cm partial pressure of chlorine or bromine in 10 cm pressure of neon. Special precautions have to be taken in selecting the right electrode materials because of the extremely high chemical reactivity of the halogens. Counters of this type operate satisfactorily with potential differences of a few hundred volt.

It is instructive to consider the curve of count rate as a function of tube voltage. A typical curve of this type is shown in Figure 11·4. If the voltage is low, a single initial ion pair does not produce a full avalanche although some gas amplification still occurs. The size of the current pulse at the anode is then proportional to the number of ions initially formed. In consequence, a detector of finite sensitivity will record the large pulses

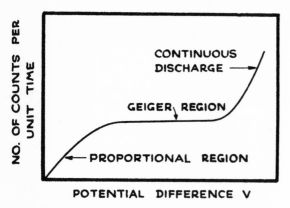

Fig. 11·4—*The variation of count rate with potential difference across a Geiger counter. The intensity of ionising radiation is constant*

but miss the small ones, resulting in a low count rate. Counters operating in this region can be used to differentiate between different types of particle. With higher tube voltages, the count rate increases and then becomes constant for a range of potential differences. This range is, in fact, the *plateau region* which was mentioned earlier.

When the voltage is raised above this plateau or Geiger region, the quenching action is incomplete and one initial particle may give rise to more than one count. The count rate increases due to these spurious output pulses and at slightly higher voltages the counter goes into continuous discharge. This region of voltage is of no practical use and damage to the tube may ensue.

For the detection of α-particles and slow β-particles, counters with thin windows are employed. More penetrating particles will pass through a glass wall of normal thickness. The counting efficiency of a Geiger counter is high. This means that extremely few ionising particles can pass through the counter without being recorded, provided they do not arrive during the dead time following a previous count. Geiger counters can be used to count γ-ray photons by detecting electrons ejected from the walls of the tube. However, the efficiency in this case is usually less than 1%.

11·4   The Scintillation Counter

In some early atomic physics experiments α-particles were detected by the light flashes, or *scintillations* produced when they struck certain materials such as zinc sulphide. The individual flashes were counted by an experimenter watching a small section of the scintillating screen through a low-power microscope. This technique was extremely laborious and is clearly impracticable for any but very low count rates. In consequence scintillation counting was abandoned with the advent of the Geiger counter.

In 1947, Marshall and Coltman[1] in the U.S.A. and Kallman[2] in Germany introduced a new technique in which the light flashes from a suitable scintillator were detected by a device known as a photo-multiplier tube. The resulting *electrical* impulses could then be amplified and recorded by means similar to those employed with Geiger counter tubes. This technique has proved to be very versatile and capable of handling count rates far in excess of those possible with Geiger counters. The scintillation counter is now one of the commonest devices for the detection of nuclear radiations.

The complete scintillation counter consists of three basic parts:

(a) The scintillating material or *phosphor* which produces a tiny light flash when a charged particle passes through it.

(b) The photomultiplier tube which detects the light flash and produces an electrical impulse.

(c) Amplifiers and electronic circuits which record and count the electrical impulses from the photomultiplier tube.

The passage of a charged particle through the scintillating material causes some of the scintillator atoms to become excited. As the electrons in these excited atoms return to their ground states, photons are emitted. The number of photons will depend on the energy lost by the charged particle traversing the phosphor, so that the total intensity of the

[1] Marshall and Cottman, *Physical Review*, **72**, p528, (1947).
[2] Kallman, *Natur und Technik*, **1**, (July, 1947).

light flash will depend on the energy given up by the charged particle. In many cases the light flashes are not sufficiently intense to be seen by the human eye but they can be detected by a sensitive photomultiplier tube.

Many materials have been investigated to find the most suitable scintillation phosphors for various applications. Caesium iodide in crystalline form is very popular as a phosphor for the detection of protons and α-particles. A small quantity of thallium is added to such a crystal to 'activate' it and produce the optimum scintillation effect. The action of activators, which replace a few of the usual crystal atoms, is somewhat complex. It suffices to say that minute quantities of impurities in a crystal can have a profound effect on its scintillating properties. If the light intensity produced in a scintillator is to be proportional to the energy of the incoming particle, the phosphor must be thick enough to stop the particle entirely. Particles with energies of the order of 10 MeV or less will be stopped by phosphors a few millimetre thick.

Sodium iodide, activated with thallium, is an extremely useful scintillator for the detection of γ-rays. Because of the relatively high atomic number of the iodine atoms in this crystal, there is a large probability of a γ-ray photon releasing an electron which can then produce a scintillation in the crystal. Since γ-rays are extremely penetrating, quite large crystals are often employed, linear dimensions of about 12 cm being common.

Figure 11·5 shows a schematic representation of a scintillator and photomultiplier. The photons from the scintillator strike the semi-transparent *photocathode* in the photomultiplier tube and cause photoelectric emission. Ideally each incident photon would produce one electron at the photocathode. In practice, the efficiency of electron production is about ten percent. Electrons produced at the photocathode can be accelerated from it towards the first *dynode* D_1 which is held positive with respect to the cathode. The number of electrons emitted at the photocathode will be proportional to the number of photons incident on it and therefore to the energy of the original incoming particle.

The dynode D_1 has a specially prepared surface favourable to *secondary emission*. In the process of secondary emission, an electron hitting a surface can result in the ejection from it of more than one electron. The secondary emission ratio, that is, the number of secondary electrons emitted per incident electron, depends on the surface treatment of the electrode and on the potential difference through which the incident electron has been accelerated. In practice, secondary emission ratios of the order of four are employed.

The electrons from D_1, which are emitted with near zero velocity, are accelerated towards the second dynode D_2 where secondary emission again occurs. In a practical photomultiplier tube ten or eleven dynodes are usually employed, resulting in a large 'multiplication'

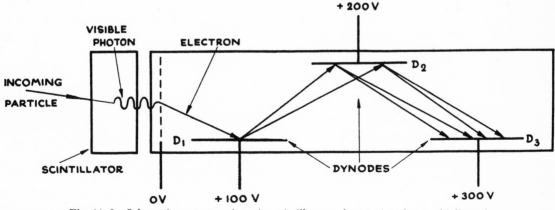

Fig. 11·5—*Schematic representation of a scintillator and part of a photomultiplier tube*

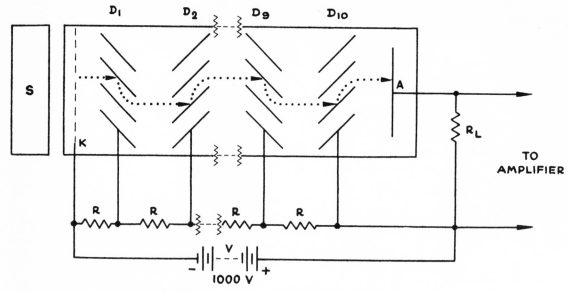

Fig. 11·6—*The 'venetian blind' photomultiplier tube*

of the electrons emitted at the photocathode. For example, if the secondary emission ratio is 4 and there are eleven dynodes, 4^{10} electrons reach the last dynode for each electron emitted from the photocathode. The tube is said to have a gain of 4^{10} or about 10^6. Thus a single electron emitted by the photo-cathode can result in a detectable current pulse at the last dynode, which is usually called the *collector* of the photomultiplier.

The design of commercially available photo-multiplier tubes varies considerably. The arrangement of the dynodes in one common type is illustrated schematically in Figure 11·6 together with the chain of resistors which maintains the correct dynode potentials. Light flashes from the scintillator S eject electrons from the photocathode K. Each dynode is shaped like a venetian blind and the electrons experience accelerations down the tube resulting in trajectories somewhat as illustrated. For simplicity, only one electron path is shown from each dynode. Electrons emitted from the last dynode D_{10} reach the collector A and the resulting pulse of current produces, across the resistance R_L, a voltage pulse which can be amplified by electronic amplifiers.

A second type of tube is illustrated in Figure 11·7. The dynodes are arranged to produce a focusing action for the electrons accelerating from one dynode to the next. The focusing electrode and grill have the effect of directing as many as possible of the photoelectrons on to the first dynode. Multiplication takes place at the dynodes 1 to 10 and the electron pulse is collected at electrode 11. In all types of photomultiplier tube a very high vacuum must be obtained and care must be taken to ensure that as many as possible of the photons produced in the scintillation process are able to reach the photo-cathode.

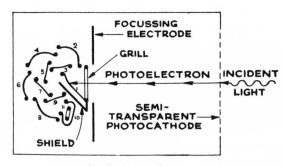

I–10 : DYNODES
II : COLLECTOR

Fig. 11·7—*A photomultiplier with focusing dynodes*

Scintillation counters are capable of detecting particles whose times of arrival are separated by considerably less than 10^{-6} second. They are therefore much 'faster' than Geiger counters. Furthermore, the voltage pulse produced by the photo-multiplier tube has an amplitude proportional to the energy dissipated in the phosphor by the incident particle, so that it is possible to determine the energies of individual incoming particles.

11·5 The Wilson Cloud Chamber

The techniques for the detection of nuclear radiations which have been discussed so far allow individual particles or photons to be detected and counted. The *expansion chamber*, or *cloud chamber*, developed at Cambridge by C. T. R. Wilson,* allows the tracks of charged particles to be made visible. The method depends upon the fact that when dust-free air, saturated with water vapour, is suddenly expanded and thereby cooled, condensation can take place on any ion present in the air.

When a gas containing a vapour at saturation pressure is expanded rapidly and cooled, the gas becomes supersaturated. There is then an excess of vapour over the quantity required to saturate the gas at this lower temperature under equilibrium conditions. If dust particles are present, condensation of the vapour takes place and droplets form around the dust particles. However, if the gas is free of dust, it is possible to produce a quite large expansion, and consequently a high degree of supersaturation, without condensation occurring. Wilson found that dust-free air saturated with water vapour could be expanded, without condensation, to 1·25 times its initial volume.

With expansion ratios in excess of 1·25, the vapour condenses in droplets, with any negative ions present in the gas acting as condensation nuclei. An expansion ratio in excess of 1·31 results in condensation on positive ions as well, while expansion ratios greater than 1·40

* C. T. R. Wilson, *Proceedings of the Royal Society*, **A 85**, p285 (1911); **A 87**, p277 (1912); **A 104**, p1 (192²).

result in condensation on neutral molecules. Wilson showed that if expansion ratios between 1·31 and 1·40 are used, condensation takes place on the ions left by the passage of a charged particle. It is necessary for the particle to traverse the sensitive volume of the chamber just before the time at which the expansion occurs.

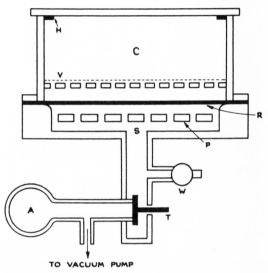

Fig. 11·8—*Schematic diagram of the Wilson cloud chamber*

Figure 11·8 shows the principal features of a Wilson cloud chamber. The rubber diaphragm R forms a gas-tight seal between the chamber C and the space S below it. The chamber C consists of a cylindrical glass wall with a plate-glass cover and in its base is a perforated metal plate covered by a black velvet cloth V. This cloth provides a dark background against which observations of the illuminated tracks are more easily made. A sprinkling of water or alcohol on this cloth provides sufficient vapour to saturate the air in the chamber.

In order to expand the air in C, the piston T is withdrawn so that the space S is connected to the evacuated container A. The sudden reduction in pressure below the diaphragm pulls it down rapidly against a second perforated plate P. The vertical position of this plate is adjustable and in this way the expansion ratio of the air in the total volume above the diaphragm may be varied. After each expansion, the piston T is used to seal off the container A and air is slowly re-admitted to the space S via the small valve W. In this way the diaphragm is restored to its

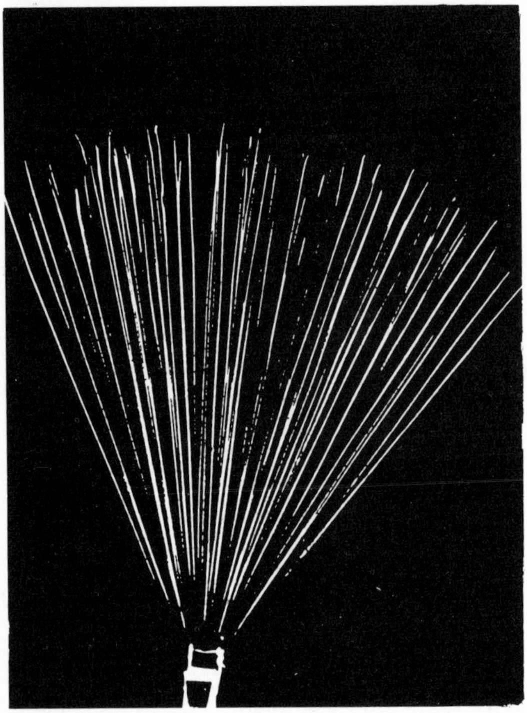

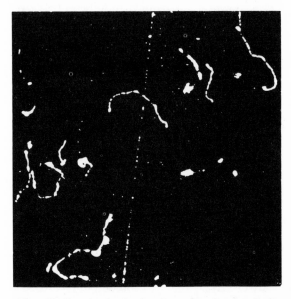

Fig. 11·9—*Photograph of α-particle tracks originating from a radioactive source in a cloud chamber*

original position thereby returning the pressure in the chamber to its original value and permitting the evaporation of the water droplets.

Charged particles or photons are passed into the chamber C through its side walls. Often it is necessary to provide a thin window in the wall to admit charged particles. After expansion, tracks formed by water droplets condensed on charged ions are illuminated by a light shone through the chamber from the side. They may be seen or photographed through the top glass plate. When an expansion has taken place and the resulting tracks have been photographed, it is desirable to

remove the ions from the sensitive volume of the chamber. This can be done by applying a potential difference of about 100 volt between a metal ring H immediately below the top glass plate and the base of the cloud chamber. The resultant electric field sweeps the ions from the chamber.

Air and water vapour are quite satisfactory in an expansion chamber but other gases and vapours can be used. Alcohol is commonly employed as the vapour. The expansion ratio required for satisfactory operation depends on the chamber filling.

The tracks left by charged particles traversing a cloud chamber allow different kinds of particles to be easily identified. Figure 11·9 shows the tracks left by α-particles. These particles generally proceed without deviation except near the end of their range, at which stage they have lost most of their energy. They ionise copiously so that their tracks are dense. α-particles of a given energy have a well-defined range. The diagram shows tracks of α-particles emitted from a small radioactive

Fig. 11·10—*A cloud chamber photograph of the tracks of fast and slow electrons. The thin line through the centre of the photograph is the track of a fast electron. Slow electrons leave heavy tortuous tracks*

source mounted inside the chamber. While such a source emits α-particles in all directions, the only tracks seen are those of particles which have passed through the illuminated region of the chamber.

Figure 11·10 shows the appearance of electron tracks in a cloud chamber. On account of their small mass, electrons are readily deflected by collisions with atoms. They produce less ionisation per unit length of track than do α-particles, so that their tracks are much thinner and become tortuous when the energy of the electrons is low. X-rays and γ-rays can cause the ejection of electrons from atoms and these produce characteristic electron tracks in the cloud chamber. The presence of a beam of X-rays or γ-rays is evident from the multiplicity of electron tracks originating in the gas of the cloud chamber as illustrated in Figure 11·11.

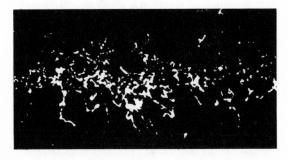

Fig. 11·11—*Cloud chamber tracks of electrons ejected by a γ-ray beam*

11·6 The Diffusion Chamber and the Bubble Chamber

In the diffusion cloud chamber, a vertical temperature gradient is maintained through a volume containing a gas and a condensible vapour. The vapour diffuses from the warmer region at the top of the chamber, where it is not at saturation pressure, down to the cold region at the bottom of the chamber. As it does so, it is cooled, and consequently the degree of saturation of the gas gradually increases. In the cooler region, suitable conditions of supersaturation can exist for the formation of droplets on ions as in the expansion chamber. A simple arrangement with alcohol vapour diffusing through air, with the bottom of the chamber held at 'dry ice' temperature is suitable for many purposes. A horizontal beam of light through the chamber serves to illuminate the tracks.

The theory of diffusion chambers was first put forward by Langsdorf[1] and was developed further by Shutt.[2] The diffusion chamber has the apparent advantage of being continuously sensitive. In practice, however, it may be rendered insensitive for some seconds by a heavy burst of tracks. A diffusion chamber must be operated in the horizontal plane which can be a disadvantage in some applications.

In an expansion or diffusion chamber, tracks are formed by condensation of a supersaturated vapour on ions formed in the chamber gas. Glaser[3] suggested that tracks might be produced by utilising the instability of superheated liquids, bubbles being formed along the path of a charged particle. In a bubble chamber superheating is produced by suddenly reducing the pressure imposed on a liquid. Bubbles form very rapidly along the path of a charged particle and must be photographed within a few microseconds of formation. At later times the bubbles become too large and eruptive boiling takes place.

Bubble chambers find their application in the study of nuclear processes involving extremely high energy particles. The use of a relatively dense detecting medium ensures a reasonable probability of a collision between a very fast nuclear particle and one of the atoms in the detector. A number of liquids can be used in bubble chambers but liquid hydrogen is by far the most popular. Hydrogen being the simplest atom of all, particle collisions with it are the simplest of all to interpret.

[1] Langsdorf, *Review of Scientific Instruments*, **10**, p91 (1939).
[2] Shutt, *Review of Scientific Instruments*, **22**, p730 (1951).
[3] Glaser, *Physical Review*, **87**, p665 (1952); *Scientific American*, **192**, No. 2, p46 (1955).

11·7   The Photographic Emulsion

As early as the beginning of this century it was known that the passage of ionising radiation through a photographic emulsion resulted in blackening after development. The effect was used extensively in the study of X-rays and it led Becquerel to the discovery of radioactivity.

Both light and ionising radiations result in the formation of free silver from its halogen salts such as silver bromide and silver iodide. In a normal photographic plate a very thin emulsion of silver halide grains in gelatin is deposited on a glass plate. 'Development' of the plate results in the blackening of the free silver and subsequent 'fixing' removes the unchanged silver halide grains so that further exposure cannot affect the plate. The tracks left by ionising particles in normal photographic plates are not well defined and, after some attempts by Rutherford to use plates as α-particle detectors, they were used only rarely.

In 1939, C. F. Powell* used a special type of emulsion, much thicker than usual, and containing some ten times the usual proportion of silver halide grains. Plates of this kind were found to show well-defined tracks after exposure to ionising particles and subsequent development. Nuclear emulsion plates are now produced commercially and are sensitive to all types of charged particle.

These plates provide a useful means of studying nuclear phenomena because they are continuously sensitive and produce a permanent record. They have been used very extensively in studying nuclear disintegrations produced by very high energy cosmic rays. These events are rare but often two or three observed in photographic emulsions suffice to identify a particular process with confidence. Some photographs obtained from nuclear emulsions are shown in Chapter 16.

The tracks produced in nuclear emulsions are generally very short due to the relatively high density of the emulsion. It is therefore

* Powell and Fertel, *Nature*, **144**, p115 (1939); Powell, *Nature*, **145**, p155 (1940).

necessary to study them under a high power microscope. As a consequence of this feature, it is often possible, using a particle accelerator, to obtain sufficient data on nuclear plates in a few minutes to keep an experimenter employed for months.

11·8   The Detection of Neutrons

A common feature of all the detectors so far described in this chapter is the production of ionisation by the particle being detected. γ-rays and neutrons do not themselves ionise, so their detection is only possible if they can initiate some process in which a charged particle is produced. In the case of γ-rays the electrons which they remove from atoms provide the agency for their detection.

There are two basic methods for neutron detection, the proton 'knock-on' technique and the nuclear reaction technique. Neutrons and protons have very nearly equal masses so that in a collision between a neutron and a proton, there can be a substantial transfer of energy from the one to the other. The process is the same as a collision between two billiard balls; thus anything from a 'glancing' collision to a 'head-on' collision is possible. In the latter case the proton moves off with a velocity equal to the initial neutron velocity. Since the *recoil* or knock-on protons are charged particles, they may be detected by any of the means previously described.

Fig. 11·12—*A cloud chamber photograph of 'knock-on' protons produced by neutrons in the chamber gas*

A hydrogen-filled ionisation chamber will detect neutrons since the recoil protons produced in the hydrogen gas then cause ionisation. A hydrogen-filled cloud chamber will show tracks *originating in the gas*, as shown in Figure 11·12, when neutrons pass through it. The tracks are not neutron tracks; they are the tracks left by the knock-on protons. While the neutron track is itself invisible, the telltale proton track allows a good deal of information to be obtained about the neutron which originated it. A nuclear emulsion can also be used to detect neutrons since the gelatin in it contains hydrogen. Again the track is a proton track and it originates in the emulsion.

The second basic neutron detection technique makes use of the fact that neutrons are capable of initiating a nuclear reaction (see Chapter 14). Of particular interest is the reaction in boron

$$_5B^{10} + _0n^1 \rightarrow _3Li^7 + _2He^4 .$$

This reaction occurs readily for slow neutrons and both the lithium nucleus and the α-particle can be detected by their ionisation. Ionisation chambers and Geiger counters filled with boron trifluoride gas form satisfactory neutron detectors. If the neutrons to be detected are fast, they can be slowed down by passing them through paraffin or water, in which collisions with hydrogen atoms reduce their energy very rapidly.

Neutrons can also be detected with a scintillation counter by using either a scintillator which contains hydrogenous material or one incorporating a suitable substance which undergoes a nuclear reaction when bombarded by neutrons.

CHAPTER 12

The First Shots are Fired with Alpha Particles

12·1 Collisions of α-Particles with Hydrogen

The dramatic results obtained when α-particles were scattered by metallic foils (Chapter 8) suggested that bombardment of other atoms by these energetic particles might prove to be an equally fruitful source of information. Marsden[1] soon showed that when α-particles passed through hydrogen, some of the atoms of this gas were knocked on and that the velocities given to these atoms were just those expected on the grounds of simple dynamical considerations. Suppose that a stationary hydrogen atom of mass m is struck by an α-particle of mass $4m$ and velocity u in such a way that it moves off with velocity v in the same straight line as the direction of motion of the incident α-particle. Then conservation of momentum and energy requires that

$$4\,m\,u = m\,v + 4\,m\,w\,,$$
and
$$\tfrac{1}{2}\,.\,4\,m\,u^2 = \tfrac{1}{2}\,m\,v^2 + \tfrac{1}{2}\,.\,4\,m\,w^2,$$

where w is the velocity of the α-particle after the impact. Solution of these equations gives

$$v = 1\cdot6\,u.$$

The corresponding energy of the hydrogen atom is then easily shown to be 64% of the original energy of the α-particle. This prediction was confirmed by Marsden's measurements.

It should be noted that, when a collision of this type occurs, the hydrogen atom is given so much energy that it immediately 'leaves

[1] Marsden, *Philosophical Magazine*, **27**, p824 (1914).

behind' its electron. It is the passage through the gas of this hydrogen nucleus, or *proton*, as it is called, which is observed. These energetic protons were detected by Marsden by the fact that their ranges in the gas were much greater than those of the α-particles, despite their somewhat lower energies. An approximate, but useful theory of the stopping of charged particles due to the energy they lose in producing ionisation along their tracks has been developed by Bohr.[2] For a heavy particle which is very little deviated in its passage through matter, the dependence of its range on its mass m, charge q and initial energy T_0 is mainly governed by a factor of the form T_0^2/q^2m. Thus the range of an α-particle of energy T_0 is about one quarter of that of a proton which has an energy of $0\cdot64\ T_0$.

In Marsden's experiments, the source of α-particles was a sample of the radioactive gas radon, enclosed in a thin-walled glass tube. This was placed some distance from a zinc sulphide screen and the intervening space filled with hydrogen gas in which the protons were produced. When the pressure of gas was more than sufficient to prevent the α-particles from reaching the screen, scintillations due to protons were observed. In a further investigation, however, Marsden and Lantsberry[3] observed some protons which appeared to originate from the radioactive source itself. This behaviour was not characteristic of the par-

[2] Bohr, *Philosophical Magazine*, **25**, p10 (1913); **30**, p518 (1915).
[3] Marsden and Lantsberry, *Philosophical Magazine*, **30**, p240 (1915).

ticular source used, since these protons were also observed, apparently, to be associated with other sources, such as a deposit of Radium C on a nickel foil. Thus there seemed to be a possibility that some radioactive transformations resulted in the formation of protons, as well as in the emission of α-, β- and γ-rays.

This important observation was investigated further by Rutherford. His work led to the conclusion that these protons were probably *not* emitted from the radioactive substances themselves. However, in the course of these experiments he came across a new phenomenon of the utmost importance.

12·2 The Discovery of Artificial Transmutation

The apparatus used by Rutherford* in these experiments is shown schematically in Figure 12·1. The disc D on which the radioactive source was deposited was mounted inside the rectangular brass chamber A. A small aperture in the plate at one end of the chamber was covered by a thin metal window, W. The thickness of this window was equivalent for the stopping of α-particles to about 5 cm of air. A zinc sulphide screen, Z, was fixed one

* Rutherford, *Philosophical Magazine*, **37**, pp537, 562, 571 and 581 (1919).

or two millimetres beyond the window and was viewed through the microscope, M. By means of the connecting tubes and taps the chamber could be filled with various gases to any desired pressure. The whole chamber was placed between the poles of a powerful electromagnet. In this way the numerous β-particles emitted by the source were made to travel in circular paths of such small radii that they were incapable of reaching the window W. Thus the only particles which could cause scintillations were those which were sufficiently massive to have only slightly curved paths in the magnetic field.

In a typical series of measurements, the rate at which scintillations appeared in the field of view of the microscope was studied as a function of the pressure of gas in the chamber and the thicknesses of absorbing foils which could be inserted between the window and the zinc sulphide screen. The total amount of absorbing material between source and screen was then known in each case. It was usual to express this amount of absorber in terms of an equivalent thickness of air at atmospheric pressure. The energy lost by a particular charged particle travelling between two points depends almost entirely on the mass per unit area of absorber between these points, as shown schematically in Figure 12·2. Since this energy loss is almost independent

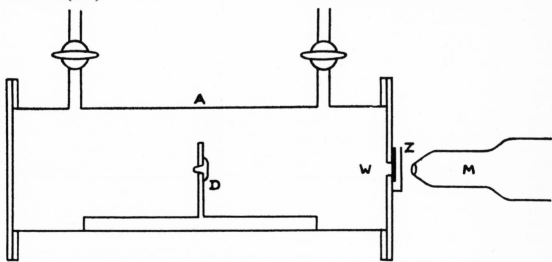

Fig. 12·1—*Rutherford's apparatus for the investigation of protons produced by α-particles*

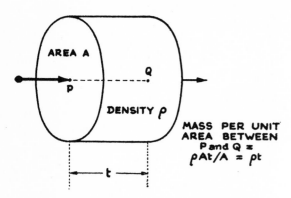

Fig. 12·2—*A charged particle passing through an absorber*

of the type of absorbing material employed, a thickness t_1 cm of a particular material whose density is ρ_1 is very closely equivalent to a thickness $\rho_1 t_1/\rho_2$ cm of air, ρ_2 being the density of air.

In his first experiments, Rutherford found that if the air was pumped out of the chamber and sufficient absorbing foils were inserted to stop the α-particles, scintillations were still observed. The number of these was proportional to the activity of the source. By inserting additional absorbers, it was found that the maximum range of the particles responsible for these scintillations was 28 cm of air. Now Marsden had found, in his studies of the collisions of α-particles with hydrogen, that the most energetic protons produced had just this range. Rutherford suggested that these 'natural' scintillations could possibly be due to the action of the α-particles on traces of hydrogen occluded on the source and its surroundings.

The absorption of these protons was also studied by introducing oxygen or carbon dioxide into the chamber at various pressures and the results obtained were quite consistent with the previous measurements using absorbing foils outside the chamber. However, when air was introduced instead, a surprising effect was observed—the number of scintillations increased! By carefully drying the air, Rutherford was able to exclude the possibility that these additional particles were protons produced from water vapour in the air, and

from a systematic series of observations he showed with certainty that the effect was due to the action of the α-particles on nitrogen.

Figure 12·3 shows the results of a typical series of experiments. Curve A is that obtained with varying pressures of carbon dioxide in the chamber. It therefore corresponds to a curve of the number of 'natural' scintillations as a function of absorber thickness. Curve B is the corresponding curve for air. The difference between these two results, given by curve C, shows that the number of additional particles due to the nitrogen in the air is about twice that of the 'natural' scintillations observed in the apparatus.

Three conclusions could be drawn about the particles produced in this way:

1. They could not be nitrogen atoms knocked on by the α-particles, since their ranges in the gas were far too long. In other experiments, the passage of α-particles through both nitrogen and oxygen had been observed to produce large numbers of scintillations due to such collisions, but the ranges of these atoms were about 9 cm of air equivalent.

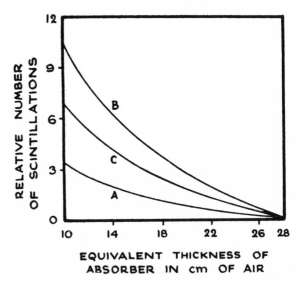

Fig. 12·3—*Absorption of protons observed with the apparatus of Fig. 12·1. The significance of the three curves is explained in the text*

2. To a trained observer there was a noticeable difference in the appearances of the scintillations produced in zinc sulphide by α-particles and protons. These long-range particles produced scintillations like those of protons.

3. If these particles were protons it was rather curious that their ranges were, as is clear from Figure 12·3, about equal to those of protons knocked on by collisions of α-particles in hydrogen.

In a further attempt to establish the nature of these particles, Rutherford tried to observe their deflections in a magnetic field. Such measurements require a degree of collimation of the particles, and the resulting reduction in their numbers meant that only very rough measurements were possible. However, Rutherford was able to satisfy himself that these particles had a mass which was certainly no more than twice that of the proton.

The significance of these experiments is clearly brought out in Rutherford's own discussion of his results. Here he points out that

... it is difficult to avoid the conclusion that the long-range atoms arising from collisions of α-particles with nitrogen are not nitrogen atoms but probably atoms of hydrogen or atoms of mass 2. If this be the case, we must conclude that the nitrogen atom is disintegrated under the intense forces developed in a close collision with a swift α-particle, and that the hydrogen atom which is liberated formed a constituent part of the nitrogen nucleus.

Two questions remained to be answered. What is the mechanism by which this disintegration takes place, and why do the emergent protons appear to have about the same energies as those knocked on by the α-particles from hydrogen itself? Rutherford was aware that these two questions were not independent of one another. Until further knowledge of the forces causing the disintegration was gained it was clearly not possible to predict the energy with which the proton would be expelled. Nevertheless, he realised — and our present knowledge confirms this conclusion — that it was probably just fortuitous that the protons resulting from this particular disintegration happened to have energies approximately equal to those of knock-on protons produced by the same α-particles.

12·3 Interpretation of this Disintegration Phenomenon

Two alternative mechanisms by which the disintegration of nitrogen by α-particles might proceed could readily be suggested. If the nitrogen nucleus can be thought of as an assembly of particles, some of which may be protons, then the α-particle could possibly knock one of these out of the nucleus. Although it would lose some of its energy in this process, the α-particle would then continue on, leaving behind a new nucleus of smaller mass than the original nitrogen nucleus. This residual nucleus would also have one unit of charge less than that of nitrogen because of the removal of a proton, and so would be expected to be a nucleus of carbon, the preceding element in the periodic table.

Such a *nuclear reaction* can be described using the symbolism introduced in Section 10·4. The α-particle and the proton are represented by the symbols $_2He^4$ and $_1H^1$ respectively, while the disintegration process suggested above would be represented by the equation

$$_7N^{14} + _2He^4 \rightarrow _6C^{13} + _1H^1 + _2He^4 . \quad (12·1)$$

Note that the law of conservation of electric charge requires that the sum of the atomic numbers should be the same on both sides of an 'equation' of this type. Similarly, the sum of the mass numbers of the reacting isotopes must equal the sum of the mass numbers of the products. This latter equality is not, as might at first be thought, directly associated with conservation of mass, but with another conservation law which we shall discuss later in Chapter 14.

It was stated above that there was a second possible mechanism for the production of protons from nitrogen. It was suggested that the α-particle was actually capable of entering the nitrogen nucleus itself. If this happens, the incident α-particle may lose its identity and be incorporated in the nucleus from which the proton is emitted. The residual nucleus would then be heavier than that of nitrogen.

If the sums of the atomic and mass numbers

are to remain constant, this residual nucleus must have a mass number of 17 and atomic number 8. The element whose atomic number is 8 is oxygen, so that this reaction would be represented by the equation

$$_7N^{14} + {_2}He^4 \rightarrow {_8}O^{17} + {_1}H^1 . \quad (12\cdot2)$$

Since $_8O^{17}$ is one of the known stable isotopes of oxygen, it would not then be necessary for any additional particles to be emitted.

Thus the important difference between the two suggested reactions described by equations (12·1) and (12·2) lies in the number of product nuclei. If some means could be found of showing whether one or two products were produced, in addition to the observed protons, one of these possibilities could be eliminated. The best way of investigating this point was to try to obtain a cloud chamber picture of

Fig. 12·4—*Disintegration of a nitrogen nucleus by an α-particle. The event is indicated by the arrow. The long track of an energetic proton and the short track of the residual oxygen nucleus are clearly visible*

such an event. This was achieved in 1925 by Blackett.* In a series of 23,000 cloud chamber photographs showing some 400,000 α-particle tracks, he found eight events of the type shown in Figure 12·4. In all cases only two particles, the proton and the residual nucleus, remained after the collision, so that equation (12·2) must be the one which correctly describes the reaction.

Many other experiments involving the α-particle bombardment of a target nucleus were performed by Rutherford and Chadwick. In several of these cases protons were emitted with greater energies than those of the incoming α-particles. Such reactions could not possibly be described by any mechanism of 'ejection' of a proton in which the α-particle retained its identity as a separate particle. Thus the view emerged that, in these events, the α-particle was absorbed into the structure of the target nucleus to form a so-called compound nucleus. This compound nucleus was unstable and almost instantaneously emitted a proton. The proton and the *final* nucleus then shared the energy given off when this unstable nucleus broke up. The compound nucleus concept is discussed further in Section 14·5.

Experiments of this kind gave support to the suggestion that the proton was a fundamental constituent of nuclear matter. However, it was equally clear that nuclei could not consist of protons alone. Any nucleus whose charge is equal to a certain number of proton charges has a mass which is, in general, about twice that number of proton masses. The key to the solution of this puzzle was provided by the discovery of the neutron, which is the subject of the later sections of this chapter.

12·4 Conservation of Energy in Nuclear Reactions

The law of conservation of energy must apply to nuclear reactions just as it does to any other physical or chemical process. It was shown in Chapter 10 that the masses of nuclei

* Blackett, *Proceedings of the Royal Society*, **A 107**, p349 (1925).

could be determined with great precision by mass spectroscopes. Using data obtained in this way, it is found that the total mass of the products of a nuclear reaction is never exactly equal to the sum of the masses of the initial nuclei. The differences are readily accounted for in terms of the theory of relativity. It was pointed out in Section 6·3 that one of the conclusions of this theory is that mass and energy should be regarded as merely different forms of the same quantity, measured in different units. In nuclear reactions, the energy changes which occur are so large that they amount to a measurable fraction of the masses of the reacting nuclei. The energies transferred between individual atoms in chemical reactions are, on the average, about a million times smaller. Therefore, for all practical purposes, mass may be regarded as being conserved in chemical processes.

This difference between the energy changes in nuclear and atomic processes provides the reason for the large discrepancy between the energy changes involved in radioactive and chemical transformations — a difference which had become obvious in the early days of measurements in radioactivity. This point has previously been referred to in Section 5·7.

In general, if the possibility of the emission of γ-rays is ignored, the energetics of a nuclear reaction involving only the nuclei A, B, C and D, such as

$$A + B \rightarrow C + D$$

must be described by the equation

(mass of A + mass of B)
+ (kinetic energy of A + kinetic energy of B)
= (mass of C + mass of D)
+ (kinetic energy of C + kinetic energy of D)
$$(12·3)$$

The masses concerned in this energy equation are, strictly speaking, the masses of the nuclei involved. At the same time, the energy equation will still hold if *atomic* masses are used instead of nuclear masses. Each atomic mass is equal to the mass of the nucleus of the atom plus the total mass of its electrons. Since the sums of the nuclear charges on each side of the reaction equation must be equal, the numbers of electrons whose masses are in-cluded in the atomic masses must be the same on each side of the energy equation. Hence the equality still holds.

In using this type of energy equation, both the masses and kinetic energies must be expressed in the same unit. For this purpose it is necessary to make use of the Einstein relation

$$E = m\,c^2.$$

The atomic masses are usually expressed in terms of the atomic mass unit. 1 a.m.u. is equal to $\frac{1}{12}$ of the mass of the isotope $_6C^{12}$. The most useful unit for kinetic energies is one million electron volt (1 MeV), and since 1 a.m.u. equals $1·660 \times 10^{-27}$ kgm, the Einstein relation gives

$$
\begin{aligned}
1 \text{ a.m.u.} &= 1·492 \times 10^{-10} \text{ joule} \\
&= \frac{1·492 \times 10^{-10}}{1·602 \times 10^{-19}} \text{ eV} \\
&= 931 \text{ MeV}.
\end{aligned}
$$

As an example of this type of calculation let us consider the reaction discussed in the previous section, namely

$$_7N^{14} + {_2He^4} \rightarrow {_8O^{17}} + {_1H^1}.$$

Since the nitrogen atom is at rest when struck by the α-particle, equation (12·3) as applied to this reaction can be rearranged to read

(k.e. of O^{17} nucleus) + (k.e. of proton)
= (mass of N^{14} + mass of He^4)
− (mass of O^{17} + mass of H^1)
+ (k.e. of α-particle).

Modern values* of the masses concerned are:

$$
\begin{array}{ll}
N^{14} : & 14·00307 \text{ a.m.u.} \\
He^4 : & \underline{4·00260 \text{ a.m.u.}} \\
& \overline{\overline{18·00567 \text{ a.m.u.}}} \\
\\
O^{17} : & 16·99913 \text{ a.m.u.} \\
H^1 : & \underline{1·00783 \text{ a.m.u.}} \\
& \overline{\overline{18·00696 \text{ a.m.u.}}}
\end{array}
$$

The difference between these two sums is thus 0·00129 a.m.u., corresponding to an energy of 1·2 MeV. Thus the energy shared between

---

* Everling, König, and Mattauch, *Nuclear Physics*, **18**, p529 (1960).

the proton and the recoil O^{17} nucleus is $1 \cdot 2$ MeV *less* than the kinetic energy of the incoming α-particle. From the source used by Rutherford the most energetic α-particles were those of RaC', having an energy of $7 \cdot 7$ MeV. Thus the combined energies of the two product particles was $6 \cdot 5$ MeV.

12·5   The Discovery of a Strange Type of Radiation

The bombardment of various substances with α-particles became a very popular form of experiment following Rutherford's discovery of the transmutation of nitrogen. However, nothing was found in the next eleven years which did not appear to be readily explicable. Then in 1930, Bothe and Becker[1] found that the bombardment of beryllium by α-particles gave rise to what appeared to be γ-radiation. Absorption experiments showed that this radiation was much more penetrating than that observed from any radioactive substance and, if it were γ-radiation, it must have a quantum energy of about 7 MeV. A remarkable discovery was then made by the French physicist Joliot and his wife, Mme. Joliot-Curie[2] (the daughter of the discoverers of radium).

In investigating the absorption of this radiation they used, as a detector, an ionisation chamber with a thin window. Between this and the beryllium target various absorbing materials could be placed. When paraffin wax, or any other material containing hydrogen was used as an 'absorber', the current in the ionisation chamber *increased*, sometimes by as much as a factor of two. They showed that this effect was due to the ejection of *protons* from the paraffin, and measurements of their ranges showed that they were emitted with energies of about $5\frac{1}{2}$ MeV.

Joliot and Joliot-Curie suggested that these protons might receive their energies from γ-ray photons produced by the α-particle bombardment of the beryllium. They assumed

a process analogous to that discovered by Compton[3] with electrons. It has been shown, in earlier chapters, that electromagnetic radiation can, in some circumstances, behave as though it were propagated in a succession of 'particles', or photons, each having an energy $h\nu$. Now the theory of relativity shows (see Section $6 \cdot 3$) that a particle travelling with velocity v has a *total* energy E, given by

$$E = m\,c^2,$$

where m, its *relativistic* mass, depends on v. It transpires that the appropriate relativistic expression for the momentum, p, of such a particle is

$$p = m\,v.$$

For a particle travelling with a speed which approaches the speed of light, its total energy and momentum are thus related, to a good approximation, by

$$p = E/c.$$

Compton assumed that a photon possessed momentum given by the corresponding expression

$$p = h\nu/c.$$

He considered an electron as being struck by a small particle having this momentum and an energy $h\nu$. From the laws of conservation of momentum and energy he calculated the change in the energy of the photon when it was deflected through a given angle in such a collision. These predictions were exactly borne out by experiment, so that the theory was outstandingly successful.

From the same theory it is possible to calculate the energy of the struck electron. This, again, has been found to be in agreement with experiment. Now this energy is a maximum when the electron is projected forwards in the direction of the incoming photon, and in this case, its kinetic energy is given by the expression

$$E' = \frac{2h\nu}{2 + m_0\,c^2/h\nu}, \qquad (12\cdot4)$$

where m_0 is the rest mass of the electron.

[1] Bothe and Becker, *Zeitschrift für Physik*, **66**, p289 (1930).
[2] Curie and Joliot, *Comptes Rendus*, **194**, p273 (1932).
[3] Compton, *Physical Review*, **21**, pp207, 483 (1923).

Joliot and Joliot-Curie applied this equation to the problem of the ejection of protons from paraffin by the beryllium radiation. In equation (12·4), if the energy of the proton is equated to E' and the proton mass is used for m_0, a value of $h\nu$ is obtained, corresponding to a photon energy of about 50 MeV. Thus if the Compton effect is responsible for the ejection of these protons, a γ-ray of this very large energy must be released in the bombardment of a beryllium nucleus by an α-particle.

At this stage, the matter was taken up by Chadwick.* He pointed out that there were two very serious objections to this γ-ray hypothesis. In the first place, if the process of ejection of the protons is basically the same as that of the interaction of X-rays with electrons, the theory governing the frequency with which the latter process occurs should also apply. However, the number of protons observed is many thousands of times greater than this theory would predict.

Secondly, it seems impossible that a γ-ray of such great energy could be emitted in the primary reaction in beryllium. The process most likely to lead to the emission of a high energy γ-ray is

$$_4\text{Be}^9 + _2\text{He}^4 \rightarrow _6\text{C}^{13} + \gamma.$$

* Chadwick, *Proceedings of the Royal Society*, **A 136** p692 (1932).

The energy of the γ-ray from this reaction will then be given by

$$E\gamma = (\text{mass of Be}^9 + \text{mass of He}^4 - \text{mass of C}^{13}) + (\text{k.e. of He}^4 - \text{k.e. of C}^{13}).$$

If the modern values of the masses are used and if the kinetic energy of the C^{13} nucleus is assumed to be negligible, it is found that, for an α-particle energy of 5 MeV,

$$E\gamma = [(9\cdot0132 + 4\cdot0026 - 13\cdot0034) \times 931 + 5] \text{ MeV}$$
$$= [0\cdot0114 \times 931 + 5] \text{ MeV}$$
$$\approx 15 \text{ MeV}.$$

Chadwick had available only approximate values of these atomic masses, but nevertheless he concluded that the γ-ray energy could not be greater than about 14 MeV.

It seemed impossible therefore, that the radiation ejecting protons from the paraffin could be γ-radiation.

12·6 Evidence for the Existence of the Neutron

Chadwick repeated the measurements of Joliot and Joliot-Curie using the apparatus shown schematically in Figure 12·5. α-particles from a polonium source passed through an evacuated region and thus struck the beryllium disc with their full energy. A sheet of paraffin wax, 2 mm thick, placed between the beryllium disc and an ionisation chamber provided

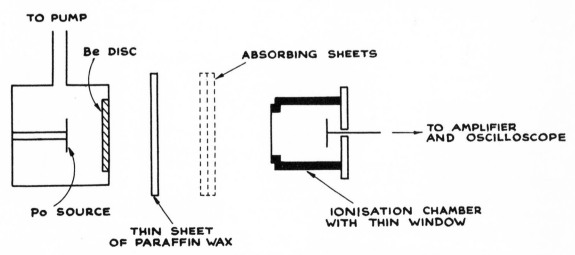

Fig. 12·5—*Apparatus used by Chadwick to investigate protons ejected from paraffin*

the source of protons produced by the 'radiation' from the beryllium. A thin window was necessary to allow the protons to enter the ionisation chamber. The energies of these protons were measured by finding the thickness of aluminium absorber necessary to prevent them from reaching the ionisation chamber. Chadwick found that these protons had a maximum velocity of $3 \cdot 3 \times 10^7$ m sec^{-1}, corresponding to an energy of $5 \cdot 7$ MeV, in agreement with the earlier measurements.

In a second experiment, performed in collaboration with Feather,[1] the same beryllium 'radiations' were allowed to enter a nitrogen-filled cloud chamber. Recoil tracks were observed, those with maximum range corresponding to nitrogen atoms having been knocked on with a velocity of $4 \cdot 7 \times 10^6$ m sec^{-1}.

On the basis of these measurements, Chadwick proposed that the 'radiation' emitted from the beryllium consisted not of γ-ray photons but of *particles* of mass very nearly equal to that of the proton. In order to account for the very great penetrating power of these particles it had to be assumed that they carried no electric charge. If this were the case, the interaction of such a particle with the atoms of the material it passed through would be a comparatively rare event and its range would be correspondingly large. Chadwick supposed that this new particle might be a combination of a proton and an electron. The existence of such a combination had been suggested twelve years earlier by Rutherford (see Section 9·13), who had proposed that it be called a *neutron*. This name was adopted by Chadwick. We now know that the neutron behaves in the nucleus as if it were a fundamental particle in its own right, rather than being a combination of two other particles.

Using this neutron hypothesis all the apparent contradictions in the experimental results disappeared. Consider first the measurements of the velocities of recoil atoms. If a particle of mass m and velocity v strikes

another particle of mass M in a head-on collision, a calculation based on the conservation of energy and momentum[2] shows that the particle of mass M will move off with a velocity V given by

$$V = \frac{2m}{m + M} \cdot v \ . \qquad (12 \cdot 5)$$

Now the same neutrons were shown to knock on hydrogen atoms with a velocity of $3 \cdot 3 \times 10^7$ m sec^{-1} and nitrogen atoms with a velocity of $4 \cdot 7 \times 10^6$ m sec^{-1}. Thus, if the masses of the particles are measured in terms of that of the hydrogen atom, we have

$$3 \cdot 3 \times 10^7 = \frac{2m}{m + 1} \cdot v$$

and

$$4 \cdot 7 \times 10^6 = \frac{2m}{m + 14} \cdot v,$$

where m is now the neutron mass. Division of these two equations gives

$$\frac{m + 14}{m + 1} = \frac{33}{4 \cdot 7},$$

whence $\qquad m = 1 \cdot 15.$

Chadwick discussed this result as follows:

The total error in the estimation of the velocity of the nitrogen recoil atom may easily be about 10 per cent, and it is legitimate to conclude that the mass of the neutron is very nearly the same as the mass of the proton.

To justify the neutron hypothesis, it was necessary for Chadwick to state a possible reaction for the production of neutrons from Be^9, and to show that such a reaction was consistent with observations of the reaction products. He suggested that the appropriate nuclear reaction might be

$$_4Be^9 + _2He^4 \rightarrow \ _6C^{12} + _0n^1 \ . \qquad (12 \cdot 6)$$

(The symbol $_0n^1$ is the one now in common use to represent a neutron.) If this equation were the correct one, the combined kinetic

[1] Feather, *Proceedings of the Royal Society*, **A 136**, p709 (1932).

[2] The velocities concerned are considered to be small enough for a simple non-relativistic calculation to be adequate.

energy E of the carbon nucleus and the neutron would be given by

$$E = \text{(mass of Be}^9 + \text{mass of He}^4)$$
$$- \text{(mass of C}^{12} + \text{mass of neutron)}$$
$$+ \text{(k.e. of He}^4). \qquad (12 \cdot 7)$$

Chadwick did not have available a value of the mass of Be^9, but he assumed, on grounds which seemed valid at the time, that it would be somewhat less than the sum of the masses of two α-particles and one neutron. On substituting this combination of masses for that of Be^9 in the above equation, the unknown mass of the neutron disappears from the expression for E. In this way, Chadwick estimated that the energy E would be no greater than 8 MeV.

As seen earlier in this section, the protons ejected by these neutrons in collision with hydrogen atoms had a maximum energy of 5·7 MeV. Now the maximum proton energy results from a head-on collision. Assuming the neutron to have a mass equal to that of the proton, conservation of momentum and energy required the observed neutrons to have an energy of 5·7 MeV. It was apparent that this was compatible with a total energy of the order of 8 MeV being available from the reaction.

If Chadwick's value of 8 MeV for the available energy E had been known to be strictly accurate, it would have been difficult to understand why the neutron was emitted with an energy of only 5·7 MeV Simple considerations of conservation of momentum show that, in this case, the more massive C^{12} nucleus should receive a much smaller fraction of the available energy than these figures would suggest. This difficulty is resolved by the availability of more accurate mass values and by more detailed knowledge of the reaction mechanism.

Using modern values of masses, the value of E which emerges from equation (12·7) is 11·0 MeV. However, this equation is incomplete. It is found that, in 90% of cases, the reaction is accompanied by the emission of a 4·4-MeV γ-ray. This leaves an energy of 6·6 MeV to be shared between the neutron and

the C^{12} nucleus. Conservation of momentum requires the neutron to have an energy of 6·2 MeV. Considering the accuracy attainable in measuring proton energies by the method used in this experiment, this value is in quite reasonable agreement with the observed energy of 5·7 MeV. This agreement indicates the basic correctness of the reaction given in equation (12·6).

Lastly, Chadwick performed another experiment which enabled him to obtain a much more accurate estimate of the mass of the neutron. It was known that the bombardment of boron by α-particles produced the same kind of radiation as did the bombardment of beryllium. Since the isotope B^{10} was known to emit protons from such a bombardment, Chadwick assumed that neutrons were produced when the other stable boron isotope, B^{11}, was the target of the α-particles. The appropriate reaction is thus

$$_5\text{B}^{11} + {}_2\text{He}^4 \rightarrow {}_7\text{N}^{14} + {}_0n^1 .$$

Using the same experimental technique, Chadwick found the maximum energy of protons knocked on by these neutrons, and hence the maximum energy and velocity of the neutrons themselves.

As has been seen earlier, the maximum neutron energy results from a head-on collision. In this case, both the neutron and the nitrogen nucleus must travel along the direction of motion of the incident α-particle. The law of conservation of momentum then allows the ratio of the energies of the neutron and nitrogen nucleus to be calculated. Hence from the one measurement, Chadwick could deduce the total kinetic energy of the neutron and the nitrogen nucleus.

As a result, the mass of the neutron could be calculated from the energy equation of this reaction, namely

$$\text{(mass of B}^{11} + \text{mass of He}^4 + \text{k.e. of He}^4)$$
$$= \text{(mass of N}^{14} + \text{mass of neutron}$$
$$+ \text{k.e. of N}^{14} + \text{k.e. of neutron).}$$

An accurate calculation was now possible, since accurate values of the masses of all three isotopes, B^{11}, He^4 and N^{14} were available from Aston's measurements with his mass spectrograph.

In this way, Chadwick obtained the value 1·0064 a.m.u.* for the mass of the neutron. Since the best available value of the proton mass was 1·0070 a.m.u.,* there was no doubt of the near equality of the masses of the two particles. It is rather important to note, however, that the present values of the masses of these two particles are somewhat different, namely

mass of neutron = 1·008665 a.m.u.

mass of proton = 1·007277 a.m.u.

Thus the neutron is actually heavier than the proton by an amount 0·001388 a.m.u.

* These values are in terms of the modern C^{12} mass scale. Chadwick in fact based his calculations on the O^{16} scale.

The discovery of the neutron as a new type of particle emitted in nuclear reactions immediately suggested that it is a fundamental particle which is a constituent of all nuclei. If a nucleus consists of a collection of protons and neutrons it is easy to see that its mass number will always be larger than its atomic number. Furthermore the existence of isotopes of an element is readily explained by proposing that nuclei with the same number of protons but containing different numbers of neutrons may exist. Our present ideas of nuclear structure are based on this picture of the composition of the nucleus, and this subject will be explored in more detail in Chapter 15.

CHAPTER 13

Particle Accelerators— The Development of Nuclear Artillery

13·1 Introduction

The early nuclear physics experiments discussed in the last chapter were carried out using α-particles emitted by radioactive materials. While this technique produced a considerable amount of information about the nuclei of atoms, it was extremely limited due to the difficulty of obtaining and handling sufficiently strong sources.

The 'activity' of a radioactive source is measured in terms of a unit called the *curie*. A source with an activity of one curie is one in which $3 \cdot 7 \times 10^{10}$ disintegrations occur per second. The particles resulting from these disintegrations are emitted uniformly in all directions. In many experiments a reasonably well collimated beam of particles is required. It is then difficult to arrange for more than about a quarter of one per cent. of the emitted particles to strike any target under examination. Thus a one-curie source might give about 10^8 particles per second arriving at the target. The probability of a nuclear reaction taking place is generally very small, so that α-particle bombardment from a one-curie source might produce only a few reactions per second. Since it is more usual to employ sources of a few millicuries,[1] the number of reactions which can be studied in a reasonable time under these conditions may be extremely small.

To overcome this difficulty, *particle accelerators* have been built which are capable of generating high speed atomic particles in

large numbers. In an accelerator, it is often possible to obtain a beam of charged particles which is equivalent to a current of a few microampere. Since each ion carries one or two electronic charges ($e = 1 \cdot 6 \times 10^{-19}$ coulomb), a current of one microampere represents about 10^{13} particles per second. This is about one thousand times the total number of particles produced per second by a one-curie radioactive source. Furthermore, since accelerators produce particles travelling in one direction, the number hitting a target may easily be about 10^5 or 10^6 times greater than can be obtained from a one-curie source.

A second great advantage of particle accelerators is that they can produce high speed electrons, protons, deuterons, α-particles or, for that matter, high speed nuclei of many heavier atoms. Radioactive sources only produce α-particles or electrons. The availability of a variety of projectiles permits a greater range of experiments to be performed.

Any one radioactive source can only produce α-particles of a few discrete energies and the highest α-particle energy from any radioactive substance is about 9 MeV. Accelerators, on the other hand, can produce particles of almost any desired energy from a few thousand electron volt up to thousands of millions of electron volt.

The first particle accelerator used for nuclear physics research was built in 1932 by Cockcroft and Walton[2] at the Cavendish Laboratory in Cambridge. Since that time, a

[1] 1 millicurie $= 10^{-3}$ curie.

[2] Cockcroft and Walton, *Proceedings of the Royal Society*, **A 136**, p619 (1932).

large number of accelerators has been constructed, culminating in the present-day giants capable of producing particles with energies in excess of 10^{10} eV.

13·2   Electrostatic Accelerators

If positively charged particles are introduced into a tube with two electrodes between which a potential difference is maintained, they will be accelerated from the region of the positive electrode to the region of the negative electrode. If such a particle has a charge ne where n is an integer, and e the electronic charge, its energy after passing through a potential difference V volt will be nV electron volt.

It is not possible to maintain a potential difference much greater than 200,000 volt between two electrodes in an evacuated tube, so that for acceleration to energies greater than one or two hundred thousand electron volt special multistage accelerator tubes are employed. Figure 13·1 shows one type of tube. A potential difference of 50 to 100 kV is maintained between each pair of electrodes in the tube and a total potential difference

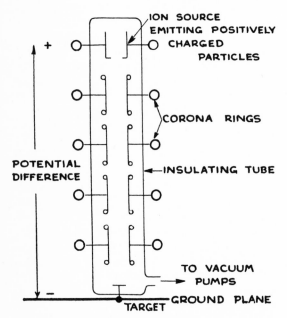

ION SOURCE
EMITTING POSITIVELY
CHARGED
PARTICLES

CORONA RINGS

INSULATING TUBE

POTENTIAL
DIFFERENCE

TO VACUUM
PUMPS

GROUND PLANE
TARGET

Fig. 13·1—*One type of multistage accelerator tube*

of up to 5 million volt may be applied. Metal *corona rings* are connected to each electrode outside the insulating wall of the tube. These rings ensure that the electric field within the tube is parallel to its axis so that particles will not receive a velocity component towards the tube surface. This is essential to prevent particle bombardment of the tube which can cause overheating and deterioration of the tube wall.

The electrodes themselves must be smooth and free from sharp corners so that high local electric fields are not produced. The accelerator tube is normally evacuated to a pressure of about 10^{-5} mm of mercury or better, this being necessary to reduce, as far as possible, collisions between the accelerated particles and the residual gas molecules in the tube. Such collisions would result in loss by scattering of the particles being accelerated, and in the production of gas ions and electrons, both of which would themselves be accelerated.

Successive acceleration between cylindrical electrodes has the further advantage that it produces a focusing effect which tends to confine the accelerated particles to a compact beam along the axis of the tube. The focusing action of a pair of cylinders can be understood by reference to Figure 13·2. The dotted lines represent lines of force due to the electrostatic field between the cylinders, which are maintained at a potential difference V.

Suppose that a positively charged particle, travelling downwards, arrives at the gap between the two cylinders. If its path is slightly off the axis of the system it will experience a force which has a component towards the axis of the system. The particle will therefore be accelerated towards this axis. Because of the shape of the electrostatic field the acceleration experienced by the particle in the lower half of the gap will have a component away from the axis. However, its velocity parallel to the axis of the tube is increasing as it passes through the gap so that the acceleration away from the axis in the lower half acts for a shorter time than that towards the axis in the upper half. The result is that the particle leaves the gap with

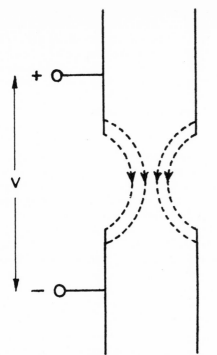

Fig. 13·2—*Some of the lines of force due to the electric field between two coaxial cylinders*

the positive electrode and ion source then being at a high voltage with respect to earth. In the ion source, an electric discharge is maintained in a gas. This discharge causes ionisation and the positive ions are drawn out of the source into the accelerator tube by a relatively small potential difference of a few thousand volt.

The potential difference required in an electrostatic accelerator is produced either by the Van de Graaff principle or by electronic rectifiers producing a steady voltage from an alternating supply.

13·3   The Van de Graaff Generator

In 1931, Van de Graaff* invented a machine for producing very high voltages. The principle of the Van de Graaff generator is illustrated in Figure 13·3. A belt of insulating

*Van de Graaff, *Physical Review*, **38**, p1919 (1931).

a net velocity component towards the axis and a focusing effect occurs.

With accelerator tubes of the type shown in Figure 13·1, there is often only a single source of potential difference connected between the first and last electrodes in the tube. The electrodes in between are held at the appropriate potentials by the combined effect of the capacitances between them (the tube is equivalent to a number of equal condensers in series) and by corona discharges from the corona rings.

A complete electrostatic accelerator consists of an accelerator tube, a high voltage generator to maintain the potential difference across the tube, an ion source to produce the particles which are to be accelerated, and ancillary equipment such as vacuum pumps and control gear. In an accelerator designed for positive ions, the ion source will be at the positive potential end of the tube and the experimental targets at the negative end. It is usually convenient to earth the target end,

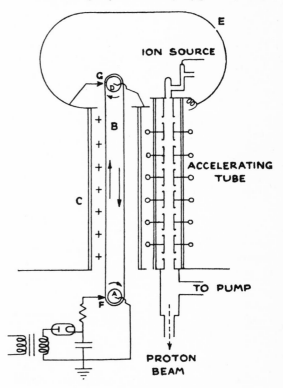

Fig. 13·3—*Van de Graaff generator and accelerating tube*

material B runs between two pulleys A and D, the lower one being earthed and the upper one being enclosed in a large electrode E, which is supported and insulated by a column C. A number of sharp points in the form of a metallic comb F, is located near the lower pulley and a potential difference of a few tens of kilovolts is maintained between this comb and the pulley. Because of the sharp points on the comb, a high electric field is produced through the belt from comb to pulley and a corona discharge takes place. This discharge removes electrons from the insulated belt leaving it positively charged.

The moving belt carries the positive charge up to the region of the top pulley where the belt passes a second comb G, connected to the high voltage electrode E. A corona discharge again occurs, a stream of electrons leaving comb G to neutralise the positive charge on the belt. This process leaves the outside of the high voltage electrode positively charged. When the machine is first started, charge builds up on the electrode E, and as a result its potential with respect to earth increases. The voltage rises rapidly until equilibrium is established, the rate of loss of charge from the high voltage electrode just equalling the current carried by the moving belt. Charge is lost from this electrode due to leakage across the insulators supporting it, by corona discharges from the electrode to its surroundings and by acceleration of the particle beam down any accelerator tube which may be connected between E and earth.

The operating potential of a Van de Graaff generator may be adjusted by controlling the corona current leaving the high voltage electrode. This is often achieved by moving a sharp earthed point to a controllable distance from the electrode. The energy required to carry the charge to the top electrode is supplied by an electric motor driving the pulley A. The voltage obtainable with a Van de Graaff generator is limited by charge leakage from the high voltage electrode. If the machine is enclosed in a pressure tank containing a gas such as freon, which has better insulating properties than air, it is possible to generate potential differences of up to 7 million volt.

13·4 The Cockcroft and Walton Voltage Multiplier

It is also possible to generate high voltages using a voltage multiplier circuit developed by Cockcroft and Walton.* In this circuit, an alternating potential difference is converted into a steady and higher voltage. Consider firstly the circuit of the *voltage doubler* given in Figure 13·4. The transformer T has a secondary winding producing a peak voltage E. Thus the voltage of the point A with respect to that of point B varies in a sinusoidal fashion, taking alternately the extreme values of $+E$ and $-E$.

In the description of the operation of this circuit, it will be assumed that the diodes

* See reference 2, page 135.

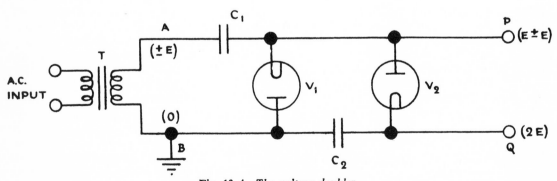

Fig. 13·4—*The voltage doubler*

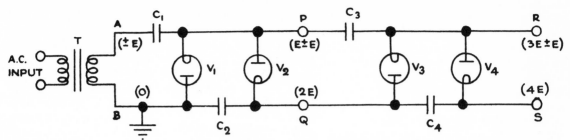

Fig. 13·5—*The voltage quadrupler*

behave like perfect switches, conducting only when their plates are positive with respect to their cathodes.

Assume for the moment that the diode V_2 is removed from the circuit. The simple circuit formed by the diode V_1, the condenser C_1 and the transformer is a form of half wave rectifier. Consequently, as the potential of point A becomes negative, the diode V_1 conducts so that when A reaches a potential of $-E$ a potential difference of magnitude E is established across C_1. Then, as the potential of A rises, the diode V_1 no longer conducts and the potential difference across C_1 remains constant. Thus the potential of point P (the cathode of V_1) will *always* be higher by an amount $+E$ than that of point A. That is, the potential of point P must vary between the limits 0 and $2E$ with respect to point B.

Assume now that the circuit is complete as shown in Figure 13·4. As the potential of point P rises, the diode V_2 begins to conduct with the result that the charge of condenser C_1 is shared with condenser C_2. After a number of cycles of the applied alternating voltage, an equilibrium condition will be reached. The necessity for the existence of this equilibrium may be seen from the following arguments. Since there are no loops in the circuit which do not contain a condenser, no steady current can flow. As a result the condensers will both be charged to potentials such that there is no current flowing through either diode.

The charge on condenser C_2 can never *decrease* during the charging process, since the diode V_2 can never conduct current away from point Q. Thus the voltage at Q must increase until, at equilibrium, it is equal to the greatest voltage ever attained by point P. Only under this condition can diode V_2 never conduct. If diode V_2 does not conduct, this, from the point of view of C_1, is just the same as if V_2 were not in the circuit. Therefore the voltage at point P behaves in just the same way as was described in the preliminary part of this discussion, that is, it varies between the limits 0 and $2E$. Thus Q must reach a potential $2E$ with respect to B under equilibrium conditions. It can be seen that if the diodes act as perfect switches and if no current flows in any part of the circuit, a steady voltage equal to twice the transformer secondary peak voltage appears across C_2. In practice, the diodes have some resistance associated with them and some current leaks across the condenser insulation, with the result that the voltage across C_2 is slightly less than $2E$.

Two voltage doublers may be cascaded to form the voltage quadrupler shown in Figure 13·5. The section to the right of P and Q formed by C_3, C_4, V_3 and V_4, is identical with the original voltage doubler. If no current is being drawn, points P and Q have the potentials deduced for the case of Figure 13·4. Q is at a potential $2E$ with respect to B while at P there is a sinusoidally varying potential of peak amplitude E superimposed on a steady voltage E with respect to B. The important point is that the *same alternating potential* appears between P and Q as is generated across the transformer secondary terminals A and B. The second part of the circuit can therefore rectify and double the alternating voltage between P and Q in exactly the same

139

manner as the first part rectifies and doubles the alternating voltage between A and B. In consequence, a voltage $2E$ is developed across C_4. Since C_4 is in series with C_2, the potential of point S rises to $4E$ volt with respect to B. Once again an alternating potential, of peak value E, appears between points R and S so that a third section could be connected to these points to produce a six-fold multiplier. Notice that each successive pair of diodes and condensers adds $2E$ to the steady potential difference between B and the last of the points Q, S, ... in the lower line of the circuit.

The original Cockcroft and Walton generator, built in 1932, used a voltage quadrupler and achieved an output voltage of 700 kV corresponding to a peak voltage of 175 kV across the transformer secondary. Some modern cascade voltage multipliers have more stages and can be used to generate up to two million volt. While it may appear practicable to extend the cascade process indefinitely, leakage across the condensers and resistance associated with the diodes makes the circuit unattractive for potentials much in excess of one or two million volt.

A cascade generator may be connected to an accelerator tube of the kind described in Section 13·2 to form a complete particle accelerator.

13·5   The Tandem Accelerator Principle

Electrostatic generators are limited to a maximum output of about 7 million volt in the case of the Van de Graaff type and rather less for the Cockcroft and Walton type. The High Voltage Engineering Corporation in the United States of America has produced a *tandem* accelerator which can produce singly charged particles whose energies are as high as 14 MeV. The principle of the tandem accelerator is illustrated in Figure 13·6.

Negative ions are produced in an ion source S, at earth potential and are accelerated through the first accelerator tube into the high voltage electrode E, which is at a positive potential V with respect to earth. At this stage the ions have an energy V electron volt if they are singly charged. Inside the electrode E, the ions are stripped of two electrons and emerge *positively charged*. They then accelerate away from E towards the target, gaining an additional energy V electron volt. Thus an ion can be accelerated twice through the same potential difference to give twice the energy possible with a simple electrostatic accelerator.

Machines to accelerate protons to any energy up to 14 MeV have been successfully constructed using a Van de Graaff generator to produce a potential difference of 7 million

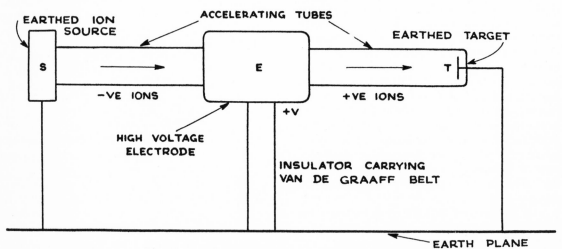

Fig. 13·6—*Schematic diagram of a tandem accelerator*

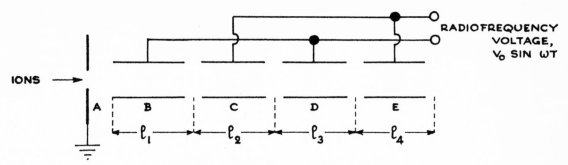

Fig. 13·7—The principle of a linear accelerator

volt between the high voltage electrode and earth. The tandem principle could of course be used with cascade generators, but since such an arrangement would give less than 5 MeV, no advantage over a single Van de Graaff generator would be obtained. In the acceleration of protons ($_1H^1$) or deuterons ($_1H^2$), the initial ions are hydrogen atoms each carrying one excess electron. These ions then lose two electrons in the high voltage electrode and become protons or deuterons, depending on whether the initial ions are formed from ordinary or heavy hydrogen respectively.

13·6 The Linear Accelerator

In 1928, Wideröe* showed that it was possible to accelerate particles to relatively high energies without the use of very high potential differences between electrodes. He suggested the principle of *synchronous acceleration* which is illustrated in Figure 13·7. In the Wideröe machine a series of hollow cylinders, B to E, of increasing length are arranged along the axis of an evacuated tube. Alternate cylinders are electrically connected together, and the two sets of electrodes so formed are coupled to a source of high frequency alternating potential difference, $V_0 \sin \omega t$. There is an alternating potential difference between each pair of adjacent cylinders and therefore electric fields in the gaps between them. In describing the action of this *linear accelerator*, it will be assumed that the gaps between the cylinders are very short.

* Wideröe, *Archiv für Elektrotech*, **21**, p387 (1928).

Suppose that a positive ion of charge q is produced at the ion source and passes through the earthed plate A at the instant when the potential difference between cylinder B and the plate A is at its maximum value, with B negative with respect to A. The ion will be accelerated across the gap between A and B. If this gap is small, the transit time of the ion can be neglected and it will gain energy corresponding to an acceleration through a potential difference V_0. The ion therefore enters B with a velocity v_1 given by

$$\tfrac{1}{2}mv_1^2 = qV_0, \qquad (13\cdot1)$$

where m is the mass of the particle. Inside B, there is no electric field and the ion travels at constant velocity, taking a time $t_1 = l_1/v_1$ to travel the length of the cylinder. If this time interval is made equal to one half of the period of the alternating voltage, the ion will emerge into the gap between B and C at the instant when the voltage is again a maximum, with C now negative with respect to B. The particle will again accelerate through the potential difference V_0. Thus it gains another increment of energy qV_0 and enters C with a velocity v_2, given by

$$\tfrac{1}{2}mv_2^2 = 2\,qV_0. \qquad (13\cdot2)$$

If the frequency of the alternating voltage is

$$f = \omega/2\pi \qquad (13\cdot3)$$

its period will be $1/f$, and thus the second acceleration will take place if

$$l_1/v_1 = 1/2f. \qquad (13\cdot4)$$

Exactly the same argument applies to each successive cylinder. Synchronous acceleration will take place at each gap provided the lengths of the cylinders are correctly related to the particle velocity in each, so that the length of the nth cylinder must be

$$l_n = \frac{v_n}{2f} . \qquad (13\cdot5)$$

In the nth cylinder, the particle has an energy

$$W_n = \tfrac{1}{2}mv_n{}^2 = nqV_0 . \qquad (13\cdot6)$$

From this

$$v_n = \left(2\,n\,\frac{q}{m}\,V_0\right)^{\frac{1}{2}} = \left(\frac{2\,W_n}{m}\right)^{\frac{1}{2}}, \qquad (13\cdot7)$$

and hence

$$l_n = \frac{1}{f}\left(\frac{n\,q}{2\,m}V_0\right)^{\frac{1}{2}} = \frac{1}{f}\left(\frac{W_n}{2m}\right)^{\frac{1}{2}}. \qquad (13\cdot8)$$

Equation (13·8) shows that the lengths of the cylinders must be made proportional to $n^{\frac{1}{2}}$. In linear accelerators, it is rarely possible to vary the frequency f of the alternating voltage. For constant f, equation (13·8) shows that the energy of a given type of particle cannot be changed once the tube lengths have been selected. It is possible to accelerate different types of particle in the one machine but equation (13·8) indicates that, for a fixed frequency, the energy will be proportional to the mass of the particle. It is therefore easier to accelerate heavy rather than light ions to high energies. In fact, unless the frequency f can be made large, the tubes become prohibitively long for particles of small mass.

In the original linear accelerator, Wideröe produced potassium ions. In 1931, Sloan and Lawrence[1] built a linear accelerator which produced mercury ions with energies of 1·26 MeV. At that time it was not possible to generate high alternating voltages at very high frequencies. Thus, as may be seen from equation (13·6), a large number of accelerating gaps was needed to attain high energies. Furthermore, equation (13·8) shows that each tube had to be very long except for heavy ions. In consequence, the linear accelerator fell into disuse until after the Second World War. By then radio-frequency techniques had

been improved greatly and in 1947, Alvarez[2] produced a proton linear accelerator with an output energy of 32 MeV. Since then, several such machines have been built and proposals have been made for a 600 MeV machine.

13·7 The Cyclotron

In 1930, Lawrence[3] suggested the principle of the cyclotron. His proposal used the Wideröe technique of synchronous acceleration but added a magnetic field which constrained the accelerating particles to a spiral path so that they crossed and re-crossed the same gap between two electrodes. The soundness of this technique was quickly verified by Edlefson.

Suppose a charged particle moves with a velocity v at right angles to a magnetic field of induction B. Its path is then circular as shown in Figure 13·8. If the ion has a charge ne, where n is an integer, and e the electronic charge, it will experience a force $F = nevB$

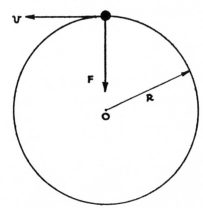

Fig. 13·8—*Path of a positively charged particle in a magnetic field directed into the paper*

in the magnetic field, the force being normal to v. This force provides the centripetal force mv^2/R necessary to hold the particle of mass m in its circular arc of radius R. It follows that

$$mv = ne\,BR . \qquad (13\cdot9)$$

The time, T, taken for the particle to make

[1] Sloan and Lawrence, *Physical Review*, **38**, p2021 (1931).

[2] Alvarez, *et al.*, *Science*, **106**, p506 (1947).
[3] Lawrence and Edlefson, *Science*, **72**, p376 (1930).

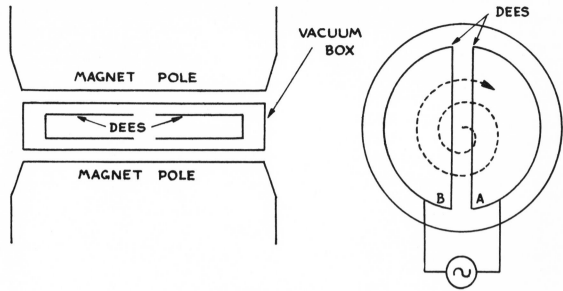

Fig. 13·9—*Schematic diagram of a cyclotron*

one complete revolution will be $2\pi R/v$, and from equation (13·9), it follows that

$$T = \frac{2\pi R}{v} = \frac{2\pi m}{ne B} \qquad (13 \cdot 10)$$

and the angular velocity of the particle is

$$\omega = \frac{2\pi}{T} = \frac{ne B}{m} \,. \qquad (13 \cdot 11)$$

It can be seen that the period and angular velocity of the particle in the magnetic field are independent of its velocity and the radius of its path, and depend only on the charge-to-mass ratio of the particle and the value of the magnetic induction. In consequence, if the velocity of a particle can be increased while it moves in a magnetic field, the radius of its orbit will increase but the time taken for one revolution will remain the same.

In a cyclotron, a uniform magnetic field is maintained in the gap between the two cylindrical poles of an electromagnet. In the gap, two hollow D-shaped electrodes, known as *dees*, are arranged inside a highly evacuated box as shown in Figure 13·9. The plane of the dees is made parallel to the faces of the magnet poles and therefore normal to the lines of magnetic induction. An alternating

potential difference is maintained between the dees so that an alternating electric field is set up in the gap between them. At the same time, the region inside the dees is free of electric fields.

Suppose that a positive ion leaves the ion source, which is at the centre of the machine, when dee A is negative with respect to B. The ion accelerates into A and travels through a half circle inside this dee since, in this region, it is under the action of the magnetic field alone. If the machine is properly adjusted, the ion returns to the gap between the dees when B is negative with respect to A. In this case, the ion accelerates again and enters dee B, where it once more executes a half circle due to the magnetic field. In this way the particle may be accelerated repeatedly provided it always arrives at the gap when the field is such as to produce a force which accelerates it towards the dee which it is entering. This condition will be fulfilled if the alternating voltage applied to the dees executes exactly one half-cycle in the time taken for the particle to travel through half a revolution. This requires the period of the alternating voltage to equal the period of the particle. Thus, if *f* is the frequency of the alternating voltage, the condition of resonance is, from equation (13·10),

$$f = \frac{1}{T} = \frac{neB}{2\pi m}. \qquad (13\cdot12)$$

To tune the machine and allow acceleration to take place, either the frequency of the alternating voltage or the value of the magnetic field may be adjusted.

As the ion gains energy at each successive crossing of the gap, the radius of its path in the magnetic field increases. From (13·9), the particle energy at any radius R is given by

$$E = \tfrac{1}{2}mv^2 = \tfrac{1}{2} \cdot \frac{n^2e^2B^2R^2}{m}. \qquad (13\cdot13)$$

The maximum energy which can be obtained depends on the radius available in the magnetic field and the maximum value of the field which can be achieved. When the beam of particles reaches the largest radius possible in the machine, it is usually allowed to enter a channel between two plates, the *splitter* and the *deflector*, as shown in Figure 13·10. The deflector is held at a negative potential of about 50 kilovolt with respect to the splitter. The particles experience an outward radial force due to the electric field and are drawn clear of the magnetic field so that they leave the machine before striking the target under investigation.

The first cyclotron, built by Lawrence and

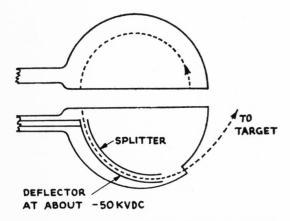

Fig. 13·10—*The extraction system of a cyclotron*

Livingston[*] came into operation in 1931. It was very small by modern standards and accelerated protons to an energy of 80 keV. Once the cyclotron principle was proven, this type of machine was developed very rapidly and by 1939, Lawrence's cyclotron with magnet poles 60″ in diameter was operating, producing protons and α-particles with energies of 8 MeV and 32 MeV respectively.

Until recently, cyclotrons have been capable of producing particles of one energy only. This was due to the difficulty of altering the magnetic field and the frequency of the voltage applied to the dees. In 1953, the Universities of Rochester in the U.S.A. and Melbourne in Australia both proposed plans for variable energy cyclotrons. These are now operating, together with additional machines in several other laboratories. Variable energy cyclotrons can produce particles with any energy down to about one quarter of the maximum attainable energy and they are consequently competitive with tandem electrostatic generators as convenient research machines for energies below about 20 MeV.

At first sight it would appear that cyclotrons could produce particles of any energy provided the magnet cost was not prohibitive. In fact this is not the case. In practice, it is necessary to use a magnetic field which decreases slightly with increasing radius. This field fall-off results in a slight curvature of the lines of magnetic induction between the magnet poles and provides *vertical focusing* as illustrated in Figure 13·11. A positively charged particle at some point such as P, travelling into the plane of the diagram, experiences a force towards the median plane due to the horizontal component B_{H} of the magnetic field. In fact, the field curvature results in all particles which are not moving in the median plane receiving accelerations tending to return them to this plane. This focusing action is essential to prevent particles striking the top and bottom surfaces of the dees and thus being lost.

Unfortunately, if the magnetic field de-

* Lawrence and Livingston, *Physical Review*, **37**, p1707 (1931); **38**, p834 (1931); **40**, p19 (1932).

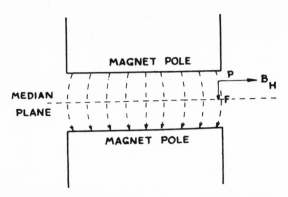

MAGNET POLE

MEDIAN
PLANE

MAGNET POLE

Fig. 13·11—*Focusing action of a non-uniform magnetic field which decreases with increasing radius*

creases with radius, the relation for synchronous acceleration (13·12) can be strictly satisfied only at one radius. In consequence, acceleration is not exactly synchronous in a practical machine. Nevertheless it is still possible for acceleration to take place at as many as one hundred gap crossings before the degree of synchronisation between the motion of the particle and the alternating voltage deteriorates to such an extent that no effective acceleration results. Thus it is desirable to use voltages between the dees such that the particle receives about 1% of its final energy at each acceleration, so that a 10-MeV machine would require a dee voltage of about 100kV. Very high energy machines are not possible since sufficiently large dee voltages cannot be obtained. The situation is further aggravated by the relativistic increase in mass which takes place as the particles gain energy. An increasing value of m in equation (13·12) upsets synchronism in a manner which adds to the effect of a decreasing value of B. These effects place a practical limit of about 20 MeV to the energies to which singly charged particles can be accelerated.

13·8 Developments from the Cyclotron

Between 1943 and 1945, suggestions were made by Oliphant[1] in England, McMillan[2]

[1] Oliphant, Gooden and Hide, *Proceedings of the Physical Society*, **59**, p666 (1947).
[2] McMillan, *Physical Review*, **68**, p143 (1945).

in the United States of America and Veksler[3] in Russia that the energy limitations of a cyclotron might be overcome by varying, during the acceleration process, the frequency of the accelerating voltage, the strength of the magnetic field, or both. These suggestions gave rise to two different machines, the *synchrocyclotron* and the *synchrotron*.

In a synchrocyclotron, the machine layout is similar to that of a conventional cyclotron but the frequency of the accelerating voltage is swept from a relatively high value to a lower one and then back. The relativistic increase in the mass of the particle as it spirals outwards and the decreasing magnetic field which it then encounters both result, as may be seen from equation (13·12), in a lower value of frequency of the accelerating voltage being needed to preserve synchronism. Thus, particles emitted from the ion source at a time when the frequency is high can be accelerated at each successive gap crossing between the dees as the frequency decreases. Provided the variation in frequency is smooth and not too rapid, the accelerating ions automatically adjust their energies to a value in resonance with the frequency of the applied voltage. With this mode of operation, quite small dee voltages (10 or 20 kV) can be used. The frequency is usually swept a few hundred times a second and at each sweep a bunch of ions is accelerated to the maximum energy allowed by the radius of the guiding magnetic field. While the average beam current attainable is considerably less than that produced by cyclotrons, the energy limitation set by resonance requirements is removed and synchrocyclotrons with output energies in excess of 600 MeV have been built.

The synchrocyclotron technique was first tested at Berkeley in California in 1946, where an early type of 37″ cyclotron was modified for synchrocyclotron operation. At the time, a cyclotron of 184″ diameter was in the course of construction in the same laboratory. It is doubtful whether the enormously high dee

[3] Veksler, *Journal of Physics, Academy of Science, U.S.S.R.*, **9**, p153 (1945).

voltages needed for such a huge cyclotron could ever have been produced. However, as soon as the principles of synchrocyclotron operation had been verified, the larger machine was converted to allow a variable frequency to be used. It came into operation late in the same year and produced deuterons with an energy of 190 MeV.

In 1946 in Birmingham, England, physicists working under Oliphant began the design of a different type of machine called a proton synchrotron. In this machine, both the magnetic field and the accelerating frequency are varied with time so as to produce both synchronous acceleration and a particle orbit of constant radius. Acceleration at constant radius has many advantages. Since the magnetic guide field is required only around an annular ring and not at small radii, a ring magnet may be used. Furthermore, only a ring-shaped vacuum box of relatively small cross section is required. The reduction in the cost of the magnet and its associated equipment makes possible machines which produce particles of even higher energies than are economically possible with synchrocyclotrons.

In a synchrotron, particles are accelerated to an energy of the order of 1 to 50 MeV in a small *injector* accelerator, usually of the linear or electrostatic type. The relatively low energy particles are injected into the vacuum chamber of the synchrotron proper at the instant when the magnetic field and accelerating voltage frequency have low values. It is necessary to inject at exactly the right instant so that the magnetic field has the correct magnitude to hold the particles in a circular orbit of the desired radius.

After injection, the magnetic field and the frequency of the accelerating voltage are both increased smoothly, maintaining the resonance condition, equation (13·12) at all times. The particles then accelerate at each revolution while remaining in an orbit of constant radius until the magnetic field reaches its maximum value. In a synchrotron, the particles are accelerated twice per revolution as they enter and leave a hollow electrode to which the high frequency voltage is applied. The upward sweep of magnetic field and accelerating voltage frequency usually takes about one second and is repeated once every few seconds. At each sweep a bunch of particles is accelerated to full energy. During the acceleration period the particles execute many million revolutions at speeds approaching that of light and they may travel hundreds of thousands of miles before attaining their maximum energy.

Because of the long acceleration period, the average beam current in a synchrotron is extremely small. However, the energy attainable is very great.

The first synchrotron to come into operation was the Brookhaven *Cosmotron* in the U.S.A. The building of this machine commenced after the start of the Birmingham synchrotron, but progress was more rapid and the *Cosmotron* produced particles of 900 MeV energy in May 1952. In July of the following year the Birmingham machine operated at about the same energy and in January 1954 the Brookhaven machine's energy was increased to 2,900 MeV. Later in the same year, a second American machine, the Berkeley *Bevatron*, came into operation with an energy of 6,000 MeV and this was followed a year or so later by the Russian 10,000 MeV machine. An internationally owned machine with an energy of nearly 30,000 MeV is now operating in Geneva. The proton synchrotron is the largest accelerating machine at present in existence. There appears to be no fundamental limitation to the particle energies attainable with these giants weighing thousands of tons, apart from the extremely difficult engineering problems encountered in their construction. There is, in addition, a serious economic limit. Even a relatively modest proton synchrotron costs over a million pounds and the largest ones cost tens of millions of pounds. There is, therefore, a never ceasing quest for cheaper ways of producing charged particles with these very high energies.

13·9 The Betatron

This chapter has been concerned so far with machines designed to accelerate heavy particles — protons, deuterons, α-particles and so on. There is also an important group of machines designed to accelerate the much lighter electron. While high speed electrons are not themselves used very often in the study of nuclei, they produce γ-rays whenever they are allowed to collide with a target. These γ-rays can cause nuclear disintegrations, and machines for their generation form an essential part of the artillery of nuclear physics. One of the most important electron accelerators is the *betatron*, developed in 1940 by Kerst.*

In a betatron, electrons are accelerated in an orbit of *constant radius*, the accelerating force being provided by the effect of a changing magnetic field. Faraday's law of electromagnetic induction states that, whenever a magnetic field linking a circuit changes, an electromotive force is generated around the circuit, and this e.m.f. is equal in magnitude to the time rate of change of the magnetic flux threading the circuit. In the statement of the law, the term 'circuit' is not restricted to a metallic ring. An e.m.f. is in fact generated around any *closed* path enclosing a changing flux. If an e.m.f. exists around any circuit, a charged particle moving round the circuit will be accelerated.

In a betatron, electrons are accelerated by electromagnetic induction within a doughnut-

* Kerst, *Physical Review*, **60**, p47 (1941).

shaped vacuum tube as illustrated in Figure 13·12. The vacuum tube is mounted between the specially shaped poles of an electromagnet which is energised with an alternating current. The frequency of this alternating current is usually from 50 to 200 cycles per second and is constant in any individual betatron. The magnetic field is normal to the plane of the 'doughnut' so that a changing magnetic flux threads the *equilibrium orbit* whose radius is R_0. As the magnetic field increases during part of the alternating current cycle, an e.m.f. is generated around the orbit and electrons, injected into the doughnut when the field is low, are accelerated. To maintain acceleration at constant radius, the changing magnetic field must provide both a tangential accelerating force due to electromagnetic induction, and the appropriate centripetal force to maintain a circular orbit.

Let the instantaneous magnetic field at the equilibrium orbit radius R_0 be B_0. Then the momentum of a particle of mass m and charge e travelling around this orbit with tangential velocity v is, from equation (13·9),

$$mv = e B_0 R_0 . \qquad (13 \cdot 14)$$

If Φ is the total magnetic flux threading the equilibrium orbit, the e.m.f. around the orbit is given by the time rate of change of flux, $d\Phi/dt$. The e.m.f. per unit length around the orbit will therefore be $\dfrac{1}{2\pi R_0} \dfrac{d\Phi}{dt}$. In moving unit distance, the electron gains energy equal

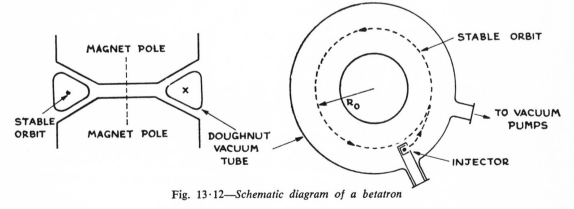

Fig. 13·12—*Schematic diagram of a betatron*

to its charge multiplied by the e.m.f. per unit length. That is,

$$\text{energy gain per unit path length} = \frac{e}{2\pi R_0}\frac{d\Phi}{dt}.$$

$$(13\cdot15)$$

However, if a force acts on a body during a movement through a given distance, work equal to the force times the distance is done on the body and it gains this amount of energy. Therefore the energy gain per unit length must equal the accelerating force exerted on the electron due to electromagnetic induction. Since Newton's second law of motion equates force with time rate of change of momentum, the rate of change of momentum is equal to the energy gain per unit length. Thus from (13·15)

$$\frac{d(mv)}{dt} = \frac{e}{2\pi R_0}\frac{d\Phi}{dt}. \qquad (13\cdot16)$$

Integrating this relation with respect to time and assuming the momentum to be zero at time $t = 0$, yields

$$mv = \frac{e}{2\pi R_0}\Phi. \qquad (13\cdot17)$$

This is then the momentum of an electron which has been accelerated by the increase in magnetic flux from zero to a value Φ. If this acceleration is to take place in an orbit of *constant* radius R_0, equations (13·14) and (13·17) must both be satisfied simultaneously. This requires the flux Φ threading the stable orbit and the magnetic induction B_0 at the orbit to be related by

$$e\,B_0\,R_0 = \frac{e}{2\pi R_0}\Phi,$$

or $$\Phi = 2\pi R_0{}^2 B_0. \qquad (13\cdot18)$$

This is a fundamental design relation for the betatron. It is clear that B must *vary* with distance from the centre of the orbit. For example, if B were constant and equal to B_0 (its value at the equilibrium orbit), the magnitude of the flux threading the orbit would be just $\pi R_0{}^2 B_0$, and the fundamental relation would not be satisfied. The changing magnetic field must be arranged to vary with radius from the centre of the magnet so as to satisfy equation (13·18) at all times during the acceleration cycle.

While this is a necessary condition for betatron acceleration, it is not a sufficient one. If acceleration is to take place in a stable orbit, there must be a tendency for particles with too large or too small an orbit radius to return to the desired orbit. Similarly, if they travel a little high or a little low in the doughnut they must also return to the selected orbit. The necessary focusing forces can be provided by the magnetic field. It can be shown that the field must satisfy equation (13·18) simultaneously with the requirement that the *field index n* should lie between the limits of 0 and 1. This field index refers to the rate at which the magnetic field at any instant decreases with increasing radius in the vicinity of the stable orbit. It is defined by the equation

$$B = B_0\left(\frac{R_0}{R}\right)^n, \qquad (13\cdot19)$$

where B is the magnetic induction at a radius R near the stable radius R_0. To satisfy the two conditions for correct betatron acceleration, the magnet pole pieces are shaped somewhat as indicated in Figure 13·12.

In the betatron, a hot filament in the *injector* provides electrons which are shot into the doughnut when the magnetic field has a low value and is increasing. Because of their very low mass, electrons of relatively small kinetic energy have achieved high speeds. Therefore Newtonian mechanics cannot be used to compute their energies, and the equations of relativistic mechanics (see Chapter 6) must be used. For example, an electron with a kinetic energy of 2 MeV travels with a speed which is 98% of the speed of light. As a result of this factor, the masses of electrons accelerated to kinetic energies of, say, 20 MeV, become several times greater than the rest mass.

However it so happens that the simple equations used in the theory outlined above turn out to have exactly the same form using relativistic mechanics, provided one replaces the product mv, wherever it occurs, by the correct relativistic expression for the momentum of the particle. Thus the final result, equation (13·18), remains unchanged, as does the stability requirement, equation (13·19).

Nevertheless relativistic expressions must be used to calculate the energies of the electrons, and from these it can be shown that the maximum total electron energy (kinetic energy + rest mass energy) in a betatron is given to a good approximation by

$$E_{max} = e \, c \, R_0 \, B_{0\,max}, \qquad (13·20)$$

where c is the velocity of light and $B_{0\,max}$ is the largest value of the magnetic induction at the stable orbit. The electrons reach their maximum energy one quarter cycle of the magnetic field after injection. If at this moment, the magnetic field is disturbed slightly, the orbit radius can be changed and the electrons can be made to strike a target where they produce γ-rays.

The original Kerst betatron produced electrons with an energy of 2·3 MeV. There is now quite a large number of betatrons in operation in physics laboratories around the world. The largest machines accelerate electrons to energies of about three hundred MeV.

While the betatron is perhaps the most interesting electron accelerator, there are electron synchrotrons, electron linear accelerators and microtrons (bearing some resemblance to a cyclotron) which operate in much the same way as similar machines for the acceleration of heavier particles. The major differences occur due to the low mass of the electron and the resulting fact that its high velocity at moderate energies makes it a particle which does not, even approximately, obey the simple laws of Newtonian mechanics. That electron accelerators do work is, in itself, a verification of some of the predictions of Einstein's theory of relativity.

CHAPTER 14

Nuclear Reactions

14·1 Introduction

The central aim of all work in nuclear physics is to find out the details of the forces that hold the nucleus together. The philosophy behind the study of the nucleus is basically that of a small boy who has been presented with a new toy. If he is of an enquiring turn of mind he will want to know how it works. There are then two courses open, both of which are eventually followed. Firstly, he will inspect the object closely and find out all he can from simple observation. Secondly, having learned some but not all of the story in this way, he will then proceed to try to take the toy to pieces. The same attitude has been adopted in the study of the atomic nucleus. Scientists have learned a great deal about the nucleus as a result of pondering on its properties, and they have also learned much from the process of 'trying to take it to pieces' — that is, from nuclear disintegrations.

14·2 Cockcroft and Walton's Experiment

The first nuclear disintegrations induced by accelerated charged particles were made in the Cavendish Laboratory by Cockcroft and Walton,* who were working under the direction of Lord Rutherford. They used an electrostatic accelerator, of the type described in Section 13·4, to produce monoenergetic beams of protons with energies up to 600 keV. The first disintegration observed was that of lithium.

The experimental apparatus used by Cockcroft and Walton is shown in Figure 14·1. The proton beam D moving down the evacu-

* Cockcroft and Walton, *Proceedings of the Royal Society*, **A 137**, p229 (1932).

ated tube F of the electrostatic accelerator struck a lithium target A and particles emitted from the foil at right angles to the proton beam caused scintillations in a zinc sulphide screen B. These scintillations were detected by the observer by means of the microscope E.

Cockcroft and Walton realised that many protons would be scattered from the lithium and therefore took steps to prevent protons of energy up to 600 keV from reaching the zinc sulphide screen. This was done by placing a sheet of mica C between the target and the screen.

For incident protons having kinetic energies in excess of 125 keV, it was found that scintillations were observed on the screen, their number being proportional to the proton beam current. By increasing the thickness of

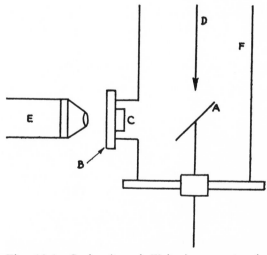

Fig. 14·1—*Cockcroft and Walton's apparatus for detecting α-particles emitted in the proton bombardment of lithium*

the absorber C, Cockcroft and Walton were able to obtain an estimate of the range of the product particles from the nuclear disintegration. They found that this range was approximately constant for accelerating voltages between 125 and 600 kV.

Further information was obtained by replacing the zinc sulphide screen by a thin window, through which the product particles entered a Wilson cloud chamber. In this, tracks of the particles were photographed. In a third experiment, the detector used was an ionisation chamber, and the range was again estimated by inserting absorbers between the target and the detector. In this last case, the behaviour of the particles was compared with that of the α-particles from polonium and found to be similar. This result, together with the observation that the range of the particles and the ionisation produced by them were both uniform and independent of the accelerating voltage, was sufficient to exclude the possibility that they were protons.

Thus Cockcroft and Walton were led to the conclusion that the products of the reaction were α-particles, and this view was supported by the cloud chamber photographs. They then wrote the equation for the reaction produced as

$$_3\text{Li}^7 + {}_1\text{H}^1 \rightarrow {}_2\text{He}^4 + {}_2\text{He}^4 .$$

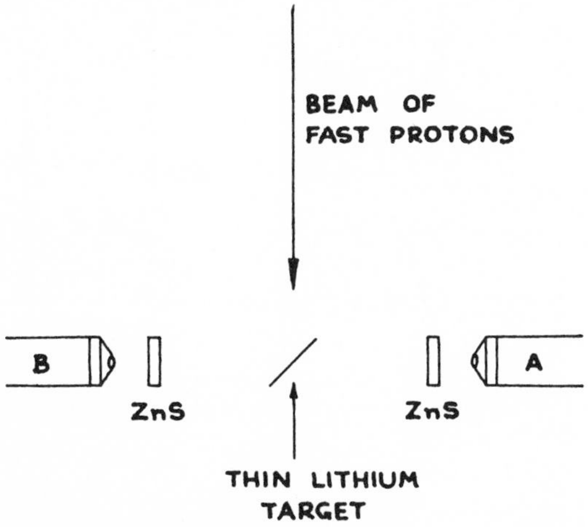

BEAM OF FAST PROTONS

B ZnS   ZnS A

THIN LITHIUM TARGET

Fig. 14·2—*Schematic diagram of Cockcroft and Walton's experimental arrangement for the detection of two α-particles in coincidence from the reaction* Li⁷ (p, α) He⁴

However, since they observed the α-particles singly, it had not been proved that there were *two* α-particles emitted per disintegration process.

They then argued that if momentum was conserved in the reaction process, the two α-particles must take away equal quantities of energy and must be ejected in practically opposite directions. That the first point is consistent with experiment is shown by the observation that the ionisation and ranges of the particles were uniform. Therefore Cockcroft and Walton set out to demonstrate that two alpha particles were emitted simultaneously in the one disintegration, and that they did travel in opposite directions. They set up the apparatus illustrated in Figure 14·2 and were able to observe simultaneous scintillations on the two ZnS screens. This result indicated quite conclusively that two α-particles were emitted 'in coincidence'.

Using the measurements of atomic masses made by Aston and his collaborators, Cockcroft and Walton were able to show that a considerable amount of energy should be released in this reaction. Recent values for the atomic masses* are:

Li⁷	7·016005 a.m.u.
H¹	1·007825 a.m.u.
	8·023830 a.m.u.
2He⁴	8·005208 a.m.u.

Thus the combination of (Li⁷ + H¹) has a mass of 0·018622 a.m.u. in excess of that of the two α-particles. According to the Einstein mass-energy relation, this is equivalent to an energy of 17·35 MeV. This energy appears as the kinetic energy of the reaction products. In fact, the best estimate of this energy release, which could be made on the basis of the mass values available at the time of the experiment, was 14·3 ± 2·7 MeV. To calculate the total kinetic energy of the α-particle pair one should add the energy brought in by the incident proton (say, 300 keV).

Now Cockcroft and Walton had measured

* Everling, König, and Mattauch, *Nuclear Physics*, **18**, p529 (1960).

the kinetic energies of the emitted α-particles to be each 8·6 MeV, this value being based on a comparison of the range and ionisation of α-particles from Po^{210} with those observed in the reaction. Thus their measured value of the total energy release was 17·2 MeV per reaction. This is seen to be in excellent agreement with the calculated value of about 17·6 MeV based on present day mass values. Furthermore, the agreement with the value of $14·6 \pm 2·7$ MeV, estimated from the mass values available at the time, was sufficiently good for Cockcroft and Walton to conclude that their interpretation of the mechanism of the nuclear reaction was correct.

Apart from being the first observation of a nuclear reaction produced by artificially accelerated particles, this experiment had the additional significance of providing the first direct confirmation of the validity of Einstein's prediction concerning the equivalence of mass and energy.

14·3 Nuclear Structure and Conservation Laws

The discovery of the neutron by Chadwick (see Chapter 12) was followed immediately by the proposal of Heisenberg that nuclei are made up of neutrons and protons. This represented an alternative to the early suggestion of Rutherford that protons and electrons were the constituents of atomic nuclei.

The proton-electron picture was put forward because, before the discovery of the neutron, the simplest way of 'making up' a nucleus of mass number A and atomic number Z was to combine A protons, to give the correct mass, with $(A - Z)$ electrons. The atomic number, that is, the net nuclear charge, would then be $A - (A - Z) = Z$, as required. Apparent support for this picture was provided by the fact that electrons, in the form of β-particles, are emitted in radioactive decay. This process is known to be one involving the nucleus of the atom.

However, there are a number of compelling reasons why electrons *cannot* exist in a nucleus. The arguments supporting this view lie beyond the scope of the present discussion.

Here we must be content to accept the view that the atomic nucleus is composed of protons and neutrons as being an inescapable conclusion from our present knowledge of the properties of nuclei. On this picture, a nucleus with atomic number Z and mass number A is made up of Z protons and $N = (A - Z)$ neutrons. The term *nucleon* has been introduced as a 'family name' to describe *either* a proton or a neutron. It follows that a nucleus with mass number A contains A nucleons.

With this picture of the nucleus in mind, we are now in a position to summarise four important conservation laws applicable to all nuclear reactions.

Conservation of mass-energy must apply. As indicated in the previous Section, this law was verified, although not with any great accuracy, by the Cockcroft-Walton experiment. Today, it has been verified* to an accuracy of 2 parts in 10^4. Thus we may say that *energy is conserved in any individual nuclear reaction, provided that mass is taken as a form of energy, according to the relation $E = mc^2$.*

The important principle of *conservation of momentum* holds for a nuclear reaction just as it must for any mechanical system. This is illustrated by the detection of two α-particles travelling in opposite directions from the disintegration of Li^7 by a proton.

The *conservation of charge* is a general law which applies throughout all physics. In the case of nuclear reactions, this requires that the sum of the atomic numbers of the initial nuclei must equal that of the products. We have seen several applications of this law in the reactions discussed in previous Sections.

In the nuclear reactions so far discussed use has been made of the rule that the sum of the mass numbers on both sides of the reaction equation are equal. The neutron-proton picture of the nucleus now provides a justification for this rule as being a consequence of the *conservation of nucleons*. Thus, while the individual numbers of neutrons and protons present may alter as a result of a

---

* Wapstra, 'Atomic Masses of Nuclides', *Handbuch der Physik*, **38/1**, p1 (Springer, 1958).

nuclear reaction, the *total* number of these nucleons remains unchanged. This law is a direct result of the study of such reactions, rather than an extension to nuclear dynamics of a previously known law.

14·4 The Q-Value of a Nuclear Reaction

In order to take account of the conservation of mass-energy, the equation for a typical nuclear reaction involving nuclei A, B, C and D may be written

$$A + B \rightarrow C + D + Q.$$

Here, Q is the energy *released* in the reaction due to the difference between the sum of the masses of particles A and B and the sum of the masses of C and D. Thus in the reaction

$$_3Li^7 + {_1}H^1 \rightarrow {_2}He^4 + {_2}He^4 + Q,$$

the energy release, or *Q-value*, is $+17·35$ MeV. The Q-value of a reaction may be either positive or negative.

A reaction which has a positive Q-value is one in which energy is released. Thus such a reaction would, in principle, take place even for zero kinetic energy of the bombarding particle. The reaction is then said to be *exoergic*, and the amount of energy given by the Q-value appears, together with any kinetic energy of the incident particle, as kinetic energy of the reaction products. The reaction studied by Cockcroft and Walton is a good example of an exoergic reaction.

If a reaction has a Q-value which is negative, the total mass on the right-hand, or product side of the equation is greater than that on the left-hand side. Sufficient energy must be supplied to make up this deficiency before the reaction can occur. The energy which must be supplied is, in magnitude, equal to the Q-value. Such reactions are *endoergic*, and are said to have a *threshold* or *threshold energy*. The energy which must be supplied is carried in by the bombarding particle as kinetic energy, or by an incident quantum of electromagnetic radiation. In this case, the kinetic energy of the reaction products is given by the difference between the

kinetic energy of the incident particle and the magnitude of the Q-value.

This definition of the Q-value is modified slightly when a γ-ray is emitted as a result of a nuclear reaction. In this case a typical reaction may be written as

$$A + B \rightarrow C + D + \gamma + Q.$$

Thus the Q-value is defined as the difference between the combined mass of A and B and the result of adding the energy of the γ-ray to the sum of the masses of C and D.

14·5 A Picture of Nuclear Reactions

The experiments discussed so far illustrate that a nuclear reaction involves a rearrangement of nuclear constituents, in the same way as a chemical reaction involves a rearrangement of atoms. It has been pointed out earlier in this book that the energies involved in nuclear transmutations are very much larger than those in chemical reactions.

Neutrons, protons, deuterons, α-particles and photons are the most common bombarding particles used in the study of nuclear reactions. The neutron and photon have one distinct advantage as bombarding 'particles'. They carry no charge and therefore do not have to overcome an electrostatic repulsion in order to interact with an atomic nucleus. Any charged particles have to overcome this Coulomb repulsion before they can penetrate the nucleus and interact with its constituents.

In 1936, Bohr* proposed a theory which pictured a nuclear reaction as taking place in two completely independent steps. First, the incident or bombarding particle is absorbed by the initial, or target nucleus to form a *compound nucleus*. Second, the compound nucleus disintegrates by ejecting one or more particles (proton, neutron, deuteron or α-particle) or a photon, leaving the final, or product nucleus. Bohr assumed that the mode of disintegration of the compound nucleus was independent of the way it was formed, and that the disintegration process

* N. Bohr, *Nature*, **137**, p344 (1936).

depended only on the properties of the compound nucleus.

The two steps of the reaction can thus be considered as separate processes:

1. Incident particle + target nucleus → compound nucleus.
2. Compound nucleus → product nucleus + outgoing particles.

The compound nucleus need not necessarily be one which is stable in nature. Whether it is or not, the stage 2 is due to the fact that the compound nucleus is formed in an unstable, high-energy state.

In the same paper Bohr introduced a theory which likened the nucleus to a liquid droplet. The virtue of this theory was that it gave scientists a physical picture of the way a nucleus *might* behave, and it was a picture which provided a basis for predictions which could be checked by experiment.

The point relevant to the present discussion is that the emission of the outgoing particle from the compound nucleus may be likened to the process of evaporation of a molecule from a liquid droplet. As a result of this statement, no definite prediction can be made as to which, or what type of particle will escape from the nucleus; it may be a proton or a neutron or a composite particle such as the deuteron or α-particle. What happens is governed by statistical laws, just as is the phenomenon of radioactive decay. This theory is in accord with many facts relating to nuclear reactions.

If a given target is bombarded with particles of a single type, many reactions may occur. For example

$$_{13}\text{Al}^{27} + _{1}\text{H}^{1} \rightarrow [_{14}\text{Si}^{28}] \rightarrow {}_{14}\text{Si}^{28} + \gamma$$
$$\rightarrow {}_{13}\text{Al}^{27} + {}_{1}\text{H}^{1}$$
$$\rightarrow {}_{13}\text{Al}^{26} + {}_{1}\text{H}^{2}$$
$$\rightarrow {}_{12}\text{Mg}^{24} + {}_{2}\text{He}^{4}$$
$$\rightarrow {}_{14}\text{Si}^{27} + {}_{0}n^{1}.$$
$$(14 \cdot 1)$$

Thus we may say that once the compound nucleus has been formed, its mode of disintegration cannot be definitely specified. It may decay in any one of a number of ways, the

only limitations placed on this decay being due to the conservation laws discussed in Section 14·3. In practice, it will often be found that one of the possible decay processes is much more probable than any of the others. Thus the reaction will proceed principally by this particular mode of decay of the compound nucleus.

14·6 Nomenclature of Nuclear Reactions: Proton-Induced Reactions

We have seen how bombardment of a target by one type of incident particle may produce a number of nuclear reactions leading to a number of final nuclei and outgoing particles. However if, in addition to the target, both the incident and outgoing particles are specified, the nuclear reaction is completely defined from considerations of the conservation of atomic numbers and mass numbers. Thus it is possible to adopt an 'in-out' specification of nuclear reactions. This is expressed in a shorthand notation, in which the target nucleus is written before a bracket and the final nucleus after it. Inside the bracket the incident and out-going particles are written together, using the symbols p for proton, n for neutron, α for α-particle, d for deuteron and γ for γ-ray. Thus, the reaction whose equation is

$$_{13}\text{Al}^{27} + _{1}\text{H}^{1} \rightarrow {}_{14}\text{Si}^{27} + {}_{0}n^{1} + Q$$

may be written as $_{13}\text{Al}^{27}(p, n)_{14}\text{Si}^{27}$. Alternatively the bombardment of $_{13}\text{Al}^{27}$ with protons may lead to (p, γ), (p, p), (p, d) or (p, α) reactions provided sufficient energy is available. (Compare equations 14·1.)

We have considered the reactions in the special case of the target nucleus $_{13}\text{Al}^{27}$. However, *proton-induced* reactions of one or another of these types may take place with any target nucleus. Let us now classify these reaction types. In the first case, the proton is absorbed into the target nucleus, and the compound nucleus does not emit a particle. Rather, it returns to its lowest energy state by emission of a photon. This process is known as *simple capture* or *radiative capture*.

In the cases where a particle of the same type as the bombarding particle is emitted, the process of *scattering* is said to occur. If the conservation of *kinetic* energy holds in this reaction, the scattering is said to be *elastic*, and the reaction type is designated, as above, by (p, p). If however, the conservation of kinetic energy does *not* hold in this reaction, the scattering is said to be *inelastic*. This reaction type is then represented by (p, p'), the dash above the second p signifying that the emitted proton has less kinetic energy than the bombarding proton.

The other three reactions noted above may be classified together as true *reactions*, in which the final nucleus is different from the target nucleus, and the outgoing particle is not a photon.

One feature of proton-induced reactions of all types is that the incident proton, as it nears the nucleus, experiences a repulsive force due to the interaction of its charge with the positive charge of the nucleus. The higher the energy of the bombarding proton, the greater is the probability that it will penetrate through to the nucleus. This is demonstrated by the fact that probability of a proton-induced reaction taking place in general increases as the proton energy rises. This is especially true for the heavier target nuclei, where the Coulomb repulsion effect is most marked because of the large nuclear charge.

14·7 Deuteron-Induced and Alpha-Induced Reactions

Very shortly after Cockcroft and Walton's classic experiment on the proton bombardment of Li^7, other workers* in the Cavendish Laboratory demonstrated that nuclear reactions could also be initiated by deuterons, that is by the ions of heavy hydrogen which had recently been discovered. An early reaction of this type which also led to the production of two α-particles was

$$_3Li^6 + {_1}H^2 \rightarrow {_2}He^4 + {_2}He^4 + 22 \cdot 37 \text{ MeV}.$$

* Oliphant, Kinsey and Rutherford, *Proceedings of the Royal Society*, **A 141**, p722 (1933).

In the terminology discussed earlier a restatement of this equation would be that the $_3Li^6(d, \alpha)_2He^4$ reaction has a Q-value of $+22 \cdot 37$ MeV. Bohr's compound nucleus theory provides a very satisfactory explanation for the appearance of the two α-particles in this reaction, since the compound nucleus, $_4Be^8$, formed in this case is just the same as that produced by $_3Li^7 + {_1}H^1$ in the Cockcroft-Walton experiment.

As may be expected from the discussion in Section 14·5, the interaction of a deuteron with $_3Li^6$ does not always produce two α-particles, and reactions may lead to the emission of protons, neutrons, γ-rays and so on.

Two important (d, n) reactions are those in which the target nuclei are respectively deuterium and the third hydrogen isotope which has been given the name *tritium*. The nucleus of this isotope consists of a proton and two neutrons. These reactions are written

$$_1H^2(d, n)_2He^3 \quad (Q = +3 \cdot 27 \text{ MeV}),$$
$$_1H^3(d, n)_2He^4 \quad (Q = +17 \cdot 59 \text{ MeV}).$$

These reactions are important because they form very useful sources of neutrons for use in the laboratory. The energies of these neutrons can be accurately controlled by control of the energy of the bombarding deuterons.

Deuterons are extremely efficient in initiating nuclear reactions. In fact, relatively low energy deuterons have caused reactions to take place in quite heavy nuclei, despite the presence of the repulsive Coulomb forces which would be expected to prevent the deuteron from interacting with these nuclei. The explanation of this apparent anomaly follows from the fact that in the deuteron the proton and the neutron are relatively loosely bound to one another. So loosely are these particles bound that in this case we may consider them to interact with the nucleus almost as separate particles. Thus the Coulomb repulsion will occur between the target nucleus and the proton of the deuteron structure, and this nucleon may be deflected. The neutron, being uncharged, is not deflected and has a good probability of being absorbed into the nucleus. The resulting (d, p) reaction appears to the observer in the laboratory as if a deuteron has been absorbed and a proton emitted. The (d, n) reaction, in which the neutron 'misses' the nucleus and the proton is absorbed is, as would be expected, much less probable, except among the very lightest target nuclei.

The first nuclear reaction produced in the laboratory, Rutherford's pioneer reaction $_7N^{14}(\alpha, p)_8O^{17}$, is a typical α-induced reaction. Reactions of this class are usually endoergic because of an unfavourable mass-energy balance. That is, energy must be supplied in the form of kinetic energy of the bombarding particle in order to make the reaction take place. Further, since the α-particle carries a charge of two fundamental units, the Coulomb repulsion effect will be twice as great as for protons or deuterons, and this acts as a further discouragement to the occurrence of this type of reaction.

14·8 Photon-Induced Reactions

Nuclear disintegrations can be brought about by bombarding targets with electromagnetic radiation. The best way to picture a reaction of this kind is to use the analogy of the photo-electric effect. In that process, a particle (an electron) can be removed from the metal surface if it absorbs all the energy of a photon and thereby gains enough kinetic energy to escape. In the 'nuclear photo-effect', as it is called, a nucleus absorbs the energy of the photon and, for example, a neutron is emitted. As in the photoelectric effect, there is a threshold frequency of the radiation below which the disintegration process will not take place. This is equivalent to saying that the photon energy must exceed a certain threshold value. Photon-induced reactions are always endoergic, reflecting the fact that energy has to be supplied to break up a stable nucleus.

The first 'photodisintegration' reaction was discovered by Chadwick and Goldhaber[*] in 1934. It was the disintegration of the deu-

[*] Chadwick and Goldhaber, *Nature*, **134**, p237 (1934).

teron, under photon bombardment, into a neutron and a proton. That is

$$_1H^2 + \gamma \rightarrow {}_1H^1 + {}_0n^1 + Q\,.$$

It is important, because it was one of the first means used for an accurate determination of the mass of the neutron. Chadwick and Goldhaber used ThC″ as the source of γ-rays — in this case, of energy 2·62 MeV. The conservation of mass-energy equation for this reaction is

$$\text{mass of } _1H^2 + 2\cdot62 \text{ MeV}$$
$$= (\text{mass of } _1H^1 + \text{mass of } _0n^1)$$
$$+ (\text{k.e. of proton} + \text{k.e. of neutron}).$$

Since the proton and neutron have nearly equal masses, these two particles will leave the disintegration with approximately equal momenta, and hence approximately equal kinetic energies. The kinetic energy of the proton is readily measured from its range in air. This is then doubled, to account for the energy carried away by the neutron. Recent measurements of this combined kinetic energy give the value as 0·39 MeV. Converting the energies to atomic mass units using the Einstein equation, the mass-energy equation above becomes

$$2\cdot01410 + 0\cdot00281 = 1\cdot00783 + \text{mass of}$$
$$\text{neutron} + 0\cdot00042.$$

This leads to

$$\text{mass of neutron} = 1\cdot00866 \text{ a.m.u.}$$

All known stable nuclei may be photodisintegrated today, because the development of the betatron and synchrotron allow γ-ray beams of high energy to be produced. The most commonly observed reactions are, as might be expected, (γ, n) and (γ, p) reactions.

14·9 Neutron-Induced Reactions

Soon after the discovery of the neutron, its importance in the study of nuclear disintegrations was realised. The neutron, being an uncharged particle, can penetrate relatively easily into the nucleus since it experiences no Coulomb repulsive force due to the nuclear charge. For this reason, it is possible for neutrons of all energies, even to the lowest possible, to initiate nuclear reactions. The probability of occurrence of a particular type of neutron-induced reaction usually depends markedly on the energy of the incident neutron. For this reason, it is often useful to classify neutrons as being either 'slow' or 'fast', the division between these categories being at an energy of the order of 1 keV.

When a neutron comes close to a nucleus, it may be attracted by the strong, but short range nuclear forces, and be captured. The compound nucleus so formed has a surplus of energy and may divest itself of this excess energy in a number of ways. For slow incident neutrons, the most common way is by the emission of electromagnetic radiation. This is a radiative capture reaction. For example, the neutron capture reaction

$$_{48}Cd^{113} + _0n^1 \rightarrow _{48}Cd^{114} + \gamma$$

occurs with very high probability for slow neutrons. The excess energy is carried off by a photon at the instant the Cd^{114} is formed.

It is also possible for the neutron to be emitted with the same kinetic energy in an elastic scattering process, and in some light nuclei the emission of charged particles from the compound nucleus is possible. For example the reaction

$$_5B^{10} + _0n^1 \rightarrow _3Li^7 + _2He^4 + 2.79 \text{ MeV}$$

occurs with high probability for slow neutrons. For this reason, an ionisation chamber or counter filled with the gas boron trifluoride provides a commonly used form of neutron detector (see Section 11·8).

When the kinetic energy of the incident neutron is increased, the radiative capture reaction becomes progressively less probable. By contrast, the probability of scattering increases, and for sufficiently high neutron energies the emission of charged particles from the compound nucleus becomes possible. Thus for neutron energies above about 0·5 MeV, (n, p) and (n, α) reactions occur, in most cases with negative Q-values. There are only few exceptions to this statement.

14.10 Probability of a Nuclear Reaction: Cross Section

The concept of the probability of occurrence of a nuclear reaction is most simply discussed by considering neutron induced reactions, since here there is no complicating effect due to the Coulomb force between the nucleus and incident particle. Thus the problem reduces more closely to a simple geometrical one.

Suppose a uniform beam, in which there are I neutrons per metre^2, impinges perpendicularly in a given time on a target layer of thickness dx, containing N atoms per metre^3. Let dI be the number of individual processes occurring in that time per metre^2 of the target. Note that all these assumptions refer to conditions external to the target nuclei. The nuclear property which specifies the probability that a reaction will occur is called the *cross section* and is defined as the average number of individual processes per target nucleus occurring per incident neutron in the beam. Since in this example I neutrons have passed through a region of the target containing $N\,dx$ nuclei, the cross section is

$$\sigma = \frac{dI}{N\,dx\,I} \text{ metre}^2 \text{ per nucleus.} \quad (14\cdot2)$$

Nuclear cross sections range from 10^{-24} to 10^{-34} metre^2, and are commonly expressed in terms of a unit of 10^{-28} metre^2, which is known as the *barn*.

In the case of fast neutrons the reaction may be considered as a 'hit or miss' proposition. That is, if the neutron makes a head-on collision with a nucleus, a reaction takes place, but otherwise the neutron passes by without interaction. Let us now use the concept of cross section in its strict geometrical sense and apply it to this special case. Consider 1 metre^2 of target area and the thickness of the target to be dx as above. Then the number of nuclei per unit area in this target is $N\,dx$. If each of these nuclei had cross sectional area σ, and we consider them to be put together side by side at the front of the target, they would cover an area $N\,dx\,\sigma$. Now consider this 1 metre^2 area bombarded with a beam of fast neutrons of intensity I neutrons per square metre, uniformly spread over that area. Then those neutrons which impinge on the selected area $N\,dx\,\sigma$ will initiate reactions, but the others will not do so. Writing in the symbols used above, the fraction of neutrons removed from the beam, $d\,I/I$, is just equal to the proportion of the 1 metre^2 area presented by the nuclei. That is,

$$\frac{d\,I}{I} = N\,dx\,\sigma, \qquad (14\cdot3)$$

which is just a rearrangement of the equation (14·2).

In the cases of reactions other than those induced by fast neutrons, the cross section σ is taken to represent the *effective area* presented by each target nucleus. It is also possible to subdivide the total reaction cross section and to speak of partial cross sections. Thus, when the cross section for the $_{13}\mathrm{Al}^{27}(n,\,p)_{12}\mathrm{Mg}^{27}$ reaction is quoted as 2 barn for neutrons of 4-MeV energy, it means that σ is the effective nuclear area which would be presented to the incident neutron beam if proton emission were the only possible process of decay of the compound nucleus Al^{28}.

CHAPTER 15

Radioactivity and Nuclear Structure

15·1 Artificial Radioactivity

In Chapter 5, the fascinating history of the discovery and the early studies of radioactivity were described. In particular, the following facts concerning radioactive decay should be borne in mind, as they will be added to, and some discussion given of the reasons behind them. First, the naturally radioactive substances may emit α-particles, β-particles or γ-rays. Next, the α-particles and γ-rays are emitted in monoenergetic groups, while the β-particles exhibit a continuous spectrum, that is they have a finite probability of being emitted with any energy between zero and some maximum possible energy. Further, the half-lives of the radioactive elements cover a very considerable range, the extremes being 10^{-6} second and 10^{10} year. Finally, the heavy elements, such as uranium, decay into other elements which are themselves radioactive, thus giving rise to the formation of radioactive decay series.

The knowledge of these facts raised many questions which remained unanswered until the late 1920's. Some of these were referred to at the end of Chapter 5. Before examining radioactive decay from the point of view of our present knowledge of nuclear structure and fundamental particles, it is necessary to complete the picture of radioactivity by discussing the very important contribution made by Frederic Joliot and his wife Irene Joliot-Curie.

While Cockcroft and Walton's experiment demonstrated the utility of artificially accelerated particles, there was still considerable interest in reactions produced by α-particles

from natural radioactive substances. In the course of this work the Joliots,[*] in 1934, studied the products resulting from the α-particle bombardment of aluminium. They observed both neutrons and protons among the products, as well as *positrons*. These latter are particles of the same mass as the electron, but with a positive charge equal in magnitude to that of the electron. They had been discovered in studies of cosmic radiation by Anderson in 1932 (see Chapter 17). This new discovery by the Joliots raised the question, 'where did these positrons originate?'

The Joliots then found that, upon removing the source of α-particles, the emission of protons and neutrons ceased but the emission of positrons persisted. In fact, they observed that the number of positrons emitted per unit time decreased exponentially with time in the same way as did the radiations from naturally radioactive substances. They measured the half-life of this *artificial radioactivity* to be about 3 minutes.

The facts which have been related were accounted for in the following way. The protons arise from the nuclear reaction.

$$_{13}Al^{27} + _2He^4 \rightarrow \ _{15}P^{31} \rightarrow \ _{14}Si^{30} + _1H^1 + 2 \cdot 38 \text{ MeV}.$$

Note that Si^{30} is one of the isotopes of silicon which occurs in nature and is stable. The neutrons, from the same type of reasoning must be emitted in the reaction

$$_{13}Al^{27} + _2He^4 \rightarrow \ _{15}P^{31} \rightarrow \ _{15}P^{30} + _0n^1 - 2 \cdot 69 \text{ MeV}.$$

Now P^{30} does not appear on the list of stable nuclei, and the Joliots suggested that the posi-

[*] Curie and Joliot, *Comptes Rendus*, **198**, p254 (1934).

trons observed were products of the radio-active decay of the P^{30}, as follows:*

$$_{15}P^{30} \rightarrow _{-1}e^0 + _{14}Si^{30},$$

yielding the stable Si^{30} as the final product nucleus. To justify their postulate, they irradiated aluminium for a long period and then separated the phosphorus chemically. They found that the phosphorus fraction contained whatever was emitting the posi-trons. More recent work has fully confirmed the correctness of this explanation and yielded the more accurate value of 2·55 minute for the half-life of the phosphorus isotope of mass number 30.

The Joliots also reported that the α-particle bombardment of boron led to the formation of a positron-emitting product. This result is accounted for in terms of the reaction

$$_5B^{10} + _2He^4 \rightarrow _7N^{14} \rightarrow _0n^1 + _7N^{13}$$
$$_7N^{13} \rightarrow _{+1}e^0 + _6C^{13}$$

(N^{13} half life = 10·1 minute).

For their discovery of artificial radioactivity, the Joliots were awarded the Nobel Prize for Chemistry in 1935. The study of artificial radioactivity has today proceeded to such an extent that many hundreds of radioactive species have been produced in the laboratory.

Further work on the radioactive decay pro-cess in which positrons were emitted demon-strated that there are many common features between positron decay and the β-particle decay already known among the heavy nuclei. For example, the positrons are emitted with a continuous spectrum of energies. Thus the same queries which were raised concerning β-particle decays in the heavy elements are now relevant to the positron decay process. We shall therefore discuss these together later.

15·2 Alpha Radioactivity

As has been mentioned previously, the α-particles which are emitted from radio-active substances have discrete energies, and

* Throughout this chapter use will be made of the symbols $_{-1}e^0$ and $_{+1}e^0$ to represent an electron and a positron respectively. The symbolism is a natural extension of that used to specify a particular isotope.

the decay processes have half-lives which vary from about 10^{-6} second to 10^{10} year. The energies of the emitted α-particles from differ-ent isotopes vary by only a factor of two, in contrast to the variation of a factor of about 10^{24} in the half-lives.

When an α-particle is emitted, the ejected particle removes charge equal in magnitude to two electronic charges and also removes four atomic units of mass. That is, the nucleus formed as a result of α-decay of a nucleus with atomic number Z and mass number A has atomic number $(Z - 2)$ and mass number $(A - 4)$. For example, the decay of radium proceeds as follows

$$_{88}Ra^{226} \rightarrow _{86}Rn^{222} + _2He^4 .$$

As in the nuclear reactions discussed in Chapter 14, the law of conservation of mass-energy applies here. Thus the mass of Ra^{226} must equal the sum of the masses of Rn^{222} and the α-particle plus the mass equivalent of the total kinetic energy of the α-particle and the product nucleus. In cases such as this where the product nucleus is very much more massive than the α-particle, conservation of momentum results in the α-particle carrying off virtually all of the available kinetic energy.

In this type of decay reaction no energy is supplied to the system. The fact that the break-up of the original nucleus is a spontane-ous process must mean that the nucleons have rearranged themselves into a new system which, when the two product nuclei are brought to rest, has a lower energy than the original one. In the same way as the water falling to the bottom of a waterfall seeks the state of lowest potential energy, so the nuclear system seeks the state of lowest possible energy. In the example quoted above, the final state of the $(_{86}Rn^{222} + _2He^4)$ system is a state of lower energy than that of the original $_{88}Ra^{226}$, and the excess energy carried by the $_{88}Ra^{226}$ nucleus appears, almost wholly, as the kinetic energy of the α-particle in the final system. This process of radioactive decay continues until the product nucleus reached in the final system is a stable one.

Since this process of decay is pictured as

one of transition between two well-defined energy states, radioactive substances may be expected to decay with the emission of α-particles which all have the same energy. In a series of very careful experiments in 1929, Rosenblum[1] was able to show that this was not so. Rather, the energy spectrum of emitted α-particles from the substance known as Thorium C, for example, was found to consist of six 'lines', corresponding to six monoenergetic α-particle groups, whose energies are 6·086, 6·047, 5·765, 5·622, 5·603 and 5·481 MeV.

This existence of *fine structure* in α-particle spectra can be understood if it is possible for the product nucleus to exist in more than one energy state. It will be remembered that an *atom* can be excited to discrete states of energy higher than that of the stable or *ground state*, in which it normally exists. The emission of the photons observed in optical spectra is interpreted as the result of transitions of an atomic system from one of these *excited states* to a state of lower energy. It is not unreasonable to suggest that a *nucleus* may have excited states as well as its ground state.

In talking of the emission of an α-particle, we have implicitly assumed that the residual nucleus is left in its lowest energy state or ground state. If now it is postulated that the

[1] Rosenblum, *Comptes Rendus*, **188**, p1401 (1929).

residual nucleus may be left in a state of energy higher than the ground state, then it follows that there will be less energy available to appear as kinetic energy of the α-particle. That is, all but the highest energy α-particles in a series of discrete lines represent α-decays in which the residual nucleus is left in an excited state. Figure 15·1 shows an 'energy level diagram' illustrating the formation of fine structure in α-decay.

If the residual nucleus is left in an excited state it will immediately undergo a transition to a state of lower energy. This behaviour is analogous to that of an atomic system except that the energies involved in such transitions are quite different. The energy differences between the allowed states in the nuclear case are far greater than the corresponding differences for an atomic system. Thus the energies of photons of electromagnetic radiation which are emitted as a result of transitions between these states are very much higher. When a nucleus falls from a state of higher energy to one of lower energy, a γ-ray rather than radiation of optical wavelength is emitted. It is in this way that the γ-rays emitted by radioactive substances arise, and this mechanism also explains why the γ-rays have discrete energies and not a continuous spectrum.

In the introductory paragraph it was mentioned that the half-lives of the α-decay processes varied from 10^{-6} second to over 10^{10} year, while the energies of the emitted α-particles varied by a factor of about two from 8·8 MeV to 4·2 MeV.

In 1911 Geiger and Nuttall[2] noted that the high energy α-particles were always given off in decays which had short half-lives, and the lower energy α-particles came in decays which had long half-lives. They were able to find an empirical relation, the Geiger-Nuttall rule, connecting the range in air R, of the emitted α-particle with the decay constant λ, of the parent nucleus. This relation is

$$\log R = A + B \log \lambda .$$

In this expression A and B are constants

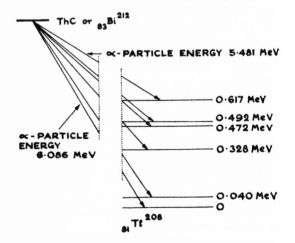

Fig. 15·1—*Illustration of fine structure in the α-decay of $_{83}Bi^{212} \rightarrow {}_{81}Tl^{208} + {}_{2}He^{4}$*

[2] Geiger and Nuttall, *Philosophical Magazine* **22**, p613 (1911); **23**, p439 (1912).

which have different values for the different radioactive series (see Section 15·4).

The provision of a satsifactory theory of α-particle decay which, amongst other things, predicted the exact form of the Geiger-Nuttall rule was one of the early triumphs of wave mechanics.[1]

15·3   The Beta-Disintegration Process

In discussing the decay of radioactive isotopes which emit either positrons or electrons, both of these particles are often referred to as β-particles. Since the β-particle has an extremely small mass compared with even a proton, the emission of such a particle will result in a product nucleus which has the same mass number as that of the initial nucleus. Because of the charge carried by the β-particle, the emission of a positron will leave a product nucleus having atomic number one less than that of the initial nucleus, while emission of a negatively charged electron leaves a product nucleus having Z one unit greater than the initial nucleus Examples of these two types of β-decay are:

$$_7N^{13} \rightarrow {}_6C^{13} + {}_{+1}e^0, \quad \text{(Half life 10·1 min)}$$

$$_{82}Pb^{210} \rightarrow {}_{83}Bi^{210} + {}_{-1}e^0. \quad \text{(Half life 19 yr)}.$$

The other features which any satisfactory explanation of the process must provide are the continuous energy spectrum of the emitted β-particles, and a relation between the half-life for the β-decay and the maximum energy of emitted β-particles. The problem of the continuous energy spectrum of the electrons is a very interesting example of the scientific 'detective story'.

By analogy with the case of α-decay, it might be expected that the emission of a β-particle of energy less than the maximum possible would be followed by the emission of a γ-ray which took with it the rest of the available energy. If this were correct, then it

would be expected that a continuous spectrum of γ-rays would be given off from a β-emitter, because the β-spectrum is continuous. However, it is known that this continuous γ-ray spectrum is not observed in β-decay processes. In fact, a number of β-emitters are known which do not emit any γ-rays at all. $_{83}Bi^{210}$ is an example of such a case.

The implications of this situation present serious difficulties. There is no doubt that the β-decay process involves a transition between two well defined nuclear systems — the initial and final nuclei. It is therefore to be expected that such a transition would result in the release of a single definite amount of energy. This definite amount of energy cannot be less than the *maximum* energy of the β-particle spectrum. Now, if no γ-ray accompanies the emission of any β-particle, it is difficult to see how such a particle could ever be emitted with an energy less than the maximum available.

The only possibility seemed to be that some other mechanism, hitherto undetected, was responsible for the removal of some energy. In a search for this missing energy, Ellis and Wooster[2] undertook to measure the average energy emitted per β-disintegration of $_{83}Bi^{210}$ (Radium E). They placed the disintegrating substance inside a lead filter which was capable of absorbing all the β-particles emitted in the decay process. The energy absorbed in the filter caused it to heat up. From the observed temperature rise it was possible to calculate the energy absorbed in the filter. It was argued by these authors that if the *average* energy of decay as measured in this 'calorimeter' was equal to that computed from the energy spectrum of the β-particles, then all the energy of the β-decay process had been accounted for. The figures obtained for Radium E were 0·35 MeV from the calorimeter, and 0·34 MeV as computed from the β-particle spectrum. Thus it appeared that all the observable energy was accounted for by consideration of the β-par-

[1] Gamow, *Zeitschrift für Physik*, **51**, p204 (1928); Gurney and Condon, *Nature*, **122**, p439 (1928).

[2] Ellis and Wooster, *Proceedings of the Royal Society*, **A 117**, p109 (1927).

ticles only. This was consistent with the fact that Radium E was known to emit no γ-rays. Thus the conclusion was that the energy carried off by the electrons represented the total energy released in β-decay.

Then what was the cause of the continuous energy spectrum of β-particles? If the β-particles took all the energy in the decay of Radium E, why were they only rarely emitted with the maximum possible energy? Where did the missing energy go? In fact, was energy conserved in the β-decay process? It appeared that the principle of conservation of energy — one of the very foundations of physics — might not apply in nuclear processes. A further interesting discovery followed from very careful measurements of the momenta of the emitted β-particles and of the recoiling nuclei. It was found that, apparently, the principle of conservation of momentum was also violated in this two-body system. So it seemed as though the two basic principles of dynamics were doomed! However, these principles work so well in all other branches of physics that it is difficult to see why they should fail here.

They were saved by a daring postulate which was put forward by the Swiss theoretical physicist Pauli.[1] This was simply that in the β-decay process, a second particle was emitted. In order that charge should still be conserved in the β-decay process, it was necessary to assume that this new particle had zero charge. This assumption was backed up by the fact that no such particle had been observed. Further, the β-particle itself is capable, on occasions, of carrying off all the available energy. Therefore this new particle had to be able to carry off very little kinetic energy, and in fact would have to have an exceedingly small rest mass. Pauli postulated that the new particle had zero rest mass as well as zero charge. It was not long before this particle was given the name *neutrino*, 'the little neutral one'. Clearly, the neutrino would be even harder to detect than a neu-

tron, and Pauli recognised the possibility that his postulate might never be proved to be correct.

Fermi[2] used this postulate of Pauli's to work out a complete theory of the β-decay process, including the required relation between the half-life for the decay and the maximum possible β-particle energy. As a result of the successes of this theory, evidence began to accumulate in favour of Pauli's neutral particle, the neutrino. However, until it was certain that a neutrino had been detected, it could not be said that Pauli's hypothesis was surely right. As with other neutral particles, the only hope of detecting the neutrino was to make it initiate a reaction and to detect the products. This was successfully carried through by Cowan and Reines[3] in 1956.

To detect the neutrino, these physicists placed a very large detector near a nuclear reactor. Since the products of fission are radioactive, and decay by β-emission, they argued that there should be a large flux of neutrinos in the vicinity of a reactor. The detector, which acted as a scintillator, consisted of 10 cubic feet of an organic liquid, and thus contained a good deal of hydrogen. A cadmium salt was dissolved in this liquid. The reaction which Cowan and Reines sought to observe was (writing the neutrino as ν)

$$_0\nu^0 + {}_1H^1 \rightarrow {}_0n^1 + {}_{+1}e^0 .$$

The apparatus was required to detect that a positron and a neutron were emitted simultaneously. Since the positron is charged it may be detected directly. The neutron, to be detected, had to be captured by the cadmium and the γ-rays following the reaction

$$_0n^1 + {}_{48}Cd^{113} \rightarrow {}_{48}Cd^{114} + \gamma$$

were then detected in the scintillator, as has been discussed in Chapter 11. It will be noted that this is not a usual method for detecting neutrons, but it is a method which is favour-

[1] Pauli, in *Rapports du Septième Conseil de Physique, Solvay*, 1933. (Gauthier-Villars 1934.)

[2] Fermi, *Zeitschrift für Physik*, **88**, p161 (1934).
[3] Cowan and Reines, *Nature*, **178**, p446 (1958).

able in those cases where large detectors need to be employed.

Using this method, Cowan and Reines were able to produce positive evidence that the interaction of a neutrino with a proton did give a neutron plus a positron, and the existence of the neutrino was thus verified.

15·4 Radioactive Series

It was seen in Chapter 5 that when a natural radioactive disintegration occurred, the original atom, called the *parent*, changed into another nucleus, called the *daughter*. The nature of the differences between the parent and daughter nuclei was first suggested by Rutherford and Soddy. The same conclusions are reached by the application of the conser-

vation laws for nuclear reactions discussed in Section 14·3.

It is known that when certain radioactive substances disintegrate they give rise to daughter substances which are themselves radioactive and decay further. Thus we know that uranium produces radium, which decays and produces radon, and this too is radioactive. The radioactive nuclei which constitute such a decay chain are called the members of a *radioactive series*.

It is to be noted that, amongst the naturally occurring radioactive substances, the only decay products are α-particles ($Z = 2$, $A = 4$), negative β-particles ($Z = -1$, $A = 0$), and γ-rays. Because of this, if the mass of a daughter nucleus is different from that of the

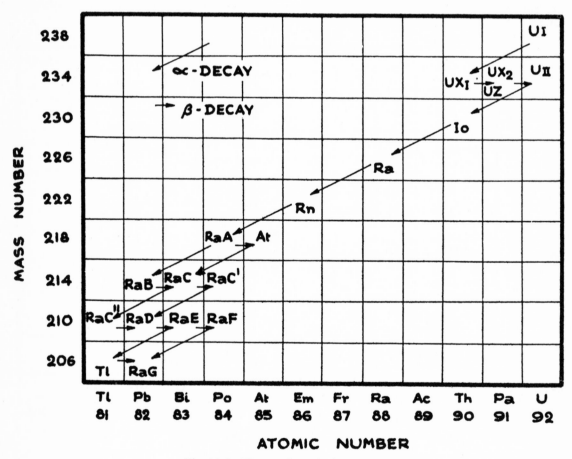

Fig. 15·2—*The uranium (4n + 2) series*

parent nucleus, it must differ by 4 units in mass number. Therefore if the first member of a radioactive series has a mass number which is exactly divisible by four, then so does every following member of the series.

Three radioactive series occur in nature. They are the uranium, the thorium and the actinium series. These are also called the $(4n + 2)$, the $(4n)$, and the $(4n + 3)$ series respectively, because the mass numbers of the nuclei in them are given by those formulae. The quantity n is an integer, and decreases by unity between parent and daughter nuclei in an α-particle decay. The value of n is not the same for the first element of each series.

There is a fourth series which is now known, called the neptunium series, or $(4n + 1)$ series, and it became known only

after the plutonium isotope of mass 241 had been produced artificially. It is a special series in another sense, since it is the only one of the four which does not finish with an isotope of lead. This series does not occur in nature because its longest-lived member has a half-life of only 2×10^6 year, which is small compared with the age of the earth — about 4×10^9 year.

The four radioactive series are shown in Figures 15·2 to 15·5 and more data are given in Appendix C. One feature is that some nuclei can emit *either* an α- or a β-particle. No single nucleus can emit both, but some nuclei of the substance concerned decay one way, some the other. Then if this parent nucleus decays in either of these ways, its daughter decays in the other, so that after two decays the branches join up again.

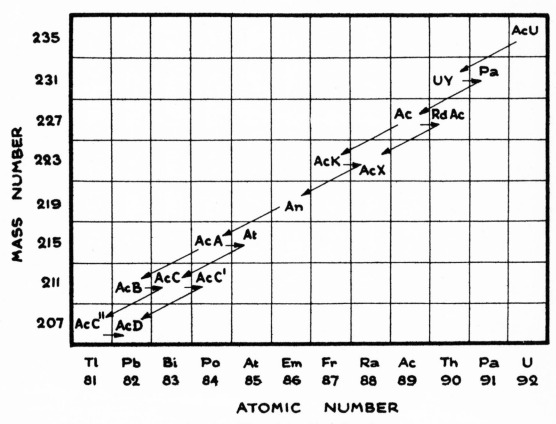

Fig. 15·3—*The actinium (4n + 3) series*

15·5 Nuclear Binding Energy

Aston (see Chapter 10) found in the 1920's that the masses of atoms were not exact integers when these masses were expressed in terms of the mass of C^{12} taken as exactly 12. He postulated correctly that this difference was an effect due to the binding together of the particles into the nucleus. Aston's discovery may be restated, in the light of later knowledge, in the following terms: the mass of any combination of neutrons and protons forming a nucleus is less than the sum of the masses of the individual particles.

The use of mass spectrographs of high precision has made possible the accumulation of much accurate data on the masses of atomic species. It is convenient here to introduce a new term, the *mass excess* δ, defined by $\delta = M - A$. M is the exact *atomic* mass, and A the integer nearest M, that is the atomic mass number. For example, the mass excess of $_3Li^7$ is $\delta_{Li} = (7 \cdot 016005 - 7)$ atomic mass units or $0 \cdot 016005$ a.m.u.*

* All atomic mass data used in this chapter are taken from Everling, König, and Mattauch, *Nuclear Physics*, **18**, p 529 (1960).

The *packing fraction*, which was defined by Aston as $f = \dfrac{M - A}{A}$, is related to the mass excess, since

$$f = \frac{\delta}{A} \ .$$

It turns out that the mass excess is a much more useful quantity in discussions of the energetics of nuclear reactions and we shall therefore not use the packing fraction concept further.

In our discussion of Cockcroft and Walton's experiment, the mass-energy balance equation was written

$$(\text{Mass of } {}_3Li^7) + (\text{Mass of } {}_1H^1)$$
$$= 2 \times (\text{Mass of } {}_2He^4) + Q.$$

This may be rewritten as

$$(A + \delta)(Li^7) + (A + \delta)(H^1)$$
$$= 2 \times (A + \delta)(He^4) + Q.$$

Since atomic mass number is a quantity which is conserved, the A's on either side of this equation may be cancelled, and the reaction

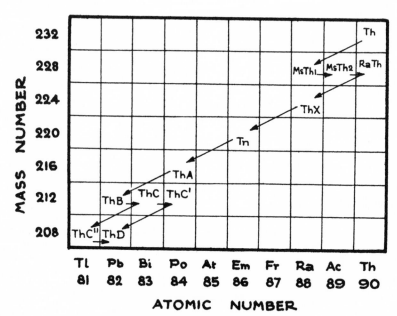

Fig. 15·4—*The thorium (4n) series*

equation rewritten in terms of mass excesses only. Thus

$$\delta(\mathrm{Li^7}) + \delta(\mathrm{H^1}) = 2 \times \delta(\mathrm{He^4}) + Q.$$

The concept of mass excess is thus useful in working out the mass-energy balance which determines the Q-value of a reaction. However, it is not able to tell us a great deal about the binding together of particles within an individual nucleus.

A much more useful quantity in this regard is the *binding energy* Δ, which is defined as

$$\Delta = W - M, \qquad (15 \cdot 1)$$

where W is the sum of the masses of the individual hydrogen atoms and neutrons which go to make up the atom, and M is the measured atomic mass. Note that the mass of the hydrogen atoms is included here rather than the mass simply of the protons. This is for convenience, as M is the measured *atomic* mass and therefore includes the mass of Z electrons. Thus in the equation (15·1) above, the mass of the Z electrons is included in both terms on the right-hand side, and Δ is thus independent of this quantity. Table 15·1 gives examples of the computations of the binding energies of two nuclei. On the left side of the table this computation is shown for $_2\mathrm{He^4}$, one of the most stable nuclei known. The mass of the $_2\mathrm{He^4}$ atom is subtracted from the sum of the masses of two hydrogen atoms and two neutrons. The result is 0·03038 atomic mass units, which may be converted to energy units using the fact that 1 a.m.u. is equivalent to 931 MeV. The second example computes the binding energy of the $_{20}\mathrm{Ca^{40}}$

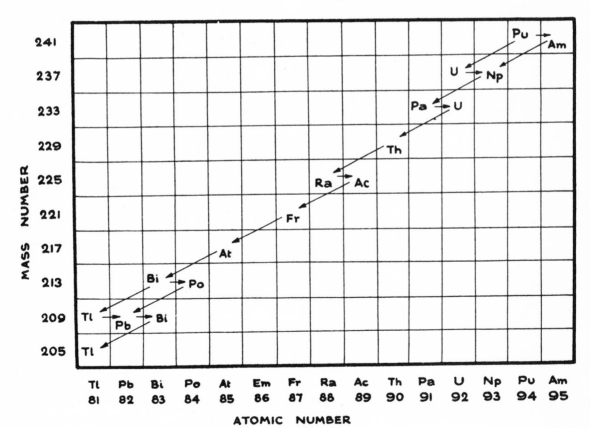

Fig. 15·5—*The neptunium (4n + 1) series*

Table 15·1 — *Binding energies of $_2He^4$ and $_{20}Ca^{40}$*

$_2He^4$		$_{20}Ca^{40}$	
$2 \times _0n^1 =$	2·01732 a.m.u.	$20 \times _0n^1 =$	20·1732 a.m.u.
$2 \times _1H^1 =$	2·01566 a.m.u.	$20 \times _1H^1 =$	20·1566 a.m.u.
	4·03298 a.m.u.		40·3298 a.m.u.
$_2He^4 \quad =$	4·00260 a.m.u.	$_{20}Ca^{40} \quad =$	39·9626 a.m.u.
Binding Energy:	0·03038 a.m.u.	Binding Energy:	0·3672 a.m.u.
	= 28·29 MeV.		= 342·0 MeV.

nucleus in exactly the same way. One point to notice about this latter result is that the binding energy is very much larger than was the case for $_2He^4$. The binding energy increases as the mass number A increases.

What does this binding energy mean? Consider again the case of $_2He^4$. If we were able to fuse together two neutrons and two protons to form an α-particle, this resulting nucleus would be *lighter* than the mass of the original nucleons. Thus, in this fusing process mass would be lost. However, since mass-energy is conserved, this 'lost' mass would appear as another form of energy — for example, radiation. This amount of energy would be exactly *equal to the binding energy* that holds the four nucleons together as an α-particle. If we

consider the converse process of the break-up of $_2He^4$ into two protons and two neutrons, it is apparent that energy would have to be supplied from outside to make up the deficiency in the mass of the α-particle as compared to the sum of the masses of its component particles.

An important quantity is the *binding energy per nucleon*, which is defined as Δ/A. A graph of this quantity plotted against A is shown in Figure 15·6. Note that the curve of binding energy per nucleon rises to a flat maximum at about $A = 50$ or 60 and then decreases very slowly for further increase in A. These features of this curve are important in discussions on nuclear energy (see Chapter 16). A noticeable feature of this curve of

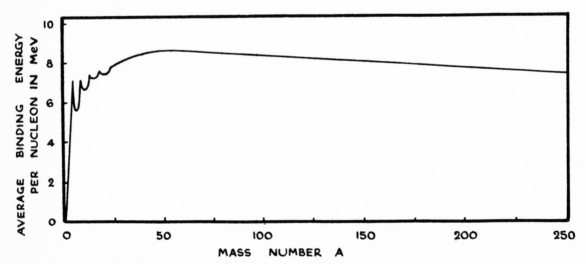

Fig. 15·6—*Average binding energy per nucleon as a function of mass number*

binding energy per nucleon is that below $A = 30$, it is marked by severe irregularities. If we revert to our description of binding energy as being a measure of the work which must be done to break up a nucleus into its constituent particles, it is clear that a nucleus which is particularly stable will be characterised by a high binding energy per nucleon. A natural deduction from this is that certain of the lighter nuclei are rather more stable than their neighbours. Closer investigation shows that those nuclei whose atomic mass numbers are multiples of four are the most stable of the light nuclei. This is suggestive of a tendency of the nucleons to form into α-particle sub-groups in light nuclei.

15·6   Nuclear Stability

Why are some nuclei stable, and some radioactive? Can we tell whether a radioactive nucleus will decay by α-particle or β-particle emission? We are now in a position to try to answer these questions.

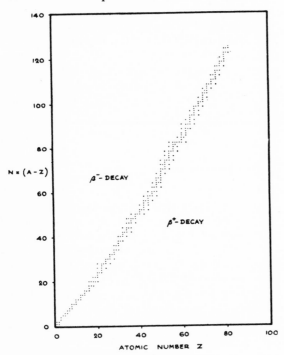

Fig. 15·7—*Plot of the neutron number* N *versus atomic number* Z *for stable nuclei*

As a first guide to this problem of nuclear stability, a plot of the *stable* nuclei is shown in Figure 15·7. The plot is of $N = A - Z$, the *neutron number*, versus Z, the atomic number for each nucleus. This graph shows that for mass numbers up to 40, the preference is to form nuclei with $N = Z$. After that mass number, there tend to be more neutrons than protons in nuclei, but the relative proportions of neutrons and protons remain within fairly narrow limits for the stable nuclei.

Any nucleus which would be plotted to either side of this narrow region will be radioactive. Consider, for example, the radioactive isotope $_{13}\mathrm{Al}^{25}$, which would fall on the low side of the stable region in Figure 15·7. Its instability may be regarded as a consequence of there being insufficient neutrons present to make a stable structure with 13 protons. Therefore the nucleus $_{13}\mathrm{Al}^{25}$ can be made more stable by the transformation of one of its protons into a neutron. This may be done, in effect, by the emission of a positron in the process of β-decay. Thus

$$_{13}\mathrm{Al}^{25} \rightarrow {}_{12}\mathrm{Mg}^{25} + {}_{+1}e^0 + {}_0\nu^0 ,$$

the neutrino being included in the equation in order to satisfy the two conservation laws of dynamics, as discussed above. Thus, all nuclei which, when plotted in Figure 15·7, fall below the stability region, will decay by positron emission.

Conversely, any nucleus which would be plotted on Figure 15·7 above the stability region will have too many neutrons for the number of protons present, and will approach stability by transforming a neutron into a proton, that is, by emitting a negative electron. For example, $_{13}\mathrm{Al}^{29}$ decays by emitting an electron, according to the equation

$$_{13}\mathrm{Al}^{29} \rightarrow {}_{14}\mathrm{Si}^{29} + {}_{-1}e^0 + {}_0\nu^0 .$$

The reasons for these rules emerge from a study of the variations in mass from one nucleus to another. If two nuclei of neighbouring elements have the same mass number but different actual masses, it is clear that it must be energetically possible for the more massive nucleus to decay into the lighter one. Let us consider a set of nuclei all having the same mass number. Such nuclei are called *isobars*. If the points corresponding to such a set of isobars were plotted on Figure 15·7, they would lie on a line intersecting the 'line of stability' almost at right angles. Now it is found that, in general, the masses of these isobars increase as the nuclei concerned become further removed from the line of stability and that this increase occurs on both sides of this line. Thus, of two neighbouring isobars, the one further from the line of stability will have the greater mass and will decay into the one closer to this line. Below the line of stability, this process results in a decrease of atomic number and hence positron decay, while above the line it results in negative β-decay.

This behaviour is illustrated by the four isobars of mass number 24 whose masses are shown in Table 15·2.

Table 15·2 – *Atomic masses of a set of isobars*

Isobar	Atomic Mass (a.m.u.)	Mode of Decay
$_{10}Ne^{24}$	23·9936	$_{11}Na^{24} + {_{-1}}e^0 + {_0}\nu^0$
$_{11}Na^{24}$	23·9910	$_{12}Mg^{24} + {_{-1}}e^0 + {_0}\nu^0$
$_{12}Mg^{24}$	23·9850	Stable
$_{13}Al^{24}$	24·0000	$_{12}Mg^{24} + {_{+1}}e^0 + {_0}\nu^0$

Without any further information, it is clear that $_{12}Mg^{24}$ must be stable against β-decay since its mass is less than those of its neighbouring isobars.

Let us now look at the question of nuclear stability from the point of view of the possibility of emission of nucleons. Consider the case of the isotope $_{20}Ca^{40}$. Instead of computing the binding energy of $_{20}Ca^{40}$ by comparing its mass with those of its basic constituents, as we did above, we could have made a comparison with a combination such as $(_{19}K^{39} + {_1}H^1)$. That is, the energy of binding

a proton into $_{19}K^{39}$ to give $_{20}Ca^{40}$ could have been computed. Of course, many other combinations, such as $(_{20}Ca^{39} + {_0}n^1)$, $(_{19}K^{38} + {_1}H^2)$, $(_{18}A^{36} + {_2}He^4)$ and so on, could have been used. *All* of these combinations would be found to lead to total masses greater than that of the $_{20}Ca^{40}$. This is related to an important point about the stability of nuclei. If the mass of any combination of this type is greater than that of the nucleus under consideration, this nucleus must be stable against such a possible break-up. In fact all stable nuclei have masses such that they cannot spontaneously break up by the emission of a proton or a neutron.

However, in the region of heavy nuclei, α-particle emission becomes energetically possible. Consider the four heavy atoms whose masses are set out in Table 15·3.

Table 15·3 – *Atomic masses of four heavy elements together with possible decay products*

Nucleus	Atomic Mass (a.m.u.)
$_{88}Ra^{224}$	224·020
$_{88}Ra^{223}$	223·019
$_{87}Fr^{223}$	223·020
$_{86}Em^{220}$	220·011
$_1H^1$	1·008
$_0n^1$	1·009
$_2He^4$	4·003

The combinations $(_{88}Ra^{223} + {_0}n^1)$ and $(_{87}Fr^{223} + {_1}H^1)$ both have the same numbers of protons and neutrons as $_{88}Ra^{224}$. However, the masses of these two combinations are, from the values given in the table, 224·028 a.m.u. and 224·028 a.m.u. respectively. Clearly the break-up of $_{88}Ra^{224}$ by proton or neutron emission is impossible just as it is for all stable nuclei. However, the combination $(_{86}Em^{220} + {_2}He^4)$ has a mass of 224·014 a.m.u. Since this is less than that of $_{88}Ra^{224}$, α-particle decay is possible. This is the type of situation which always exists when α-particle decay is observed. It is interesting to note that from Table 15·3, one would expect the nucleus $_{87}\text{Fr}^{223}$ to be unstable against negative β-decay to its isobar $_{88}\text{Ra}^{223}$. This β-decay is in fact observed.

One interesting special case of β-decay is evident from a comparison of the masses of the neutron and *proton* (not the hydrogen atom). The mass of the neutron is greater than that of the proton plus that of the electron, and, using the arguments given above, the logical deduction is that a neutron will decay into a proton plus a (negative) electron plus a neutrino, thus:

$$_{0}n^{1} \rightarrow {}_{1}p^{1} + {}_{-1}e^{0} + {}_{0}\nu^{0} .$$

For free neutrons, that is neutrons which are *not* combined in nuclei with other nucleons, this process is indeed found to occur. Robson[1] succeeded in measuring the half-life for this decay. The currently accepted value is 12·8 minute.

To sum up, if the disintegration of a nucleus into two nuclear species is energetically possible, it will in general occur. Exceptions to this rule are to be found at the branch-points in the natural radioactive decay series (Section 15·4).

If a nucleus has an isobar with a smaller mass, and is itself stable against disintegration into two new nuclear species, then it will decay by emission of an electron or positron.[2]

15·7 Nuclear Forces

We have seen in the previous two sections that the binding energies of nuclei are very large. This one fact leads to the inference that the forces between nucleons in nuclei are very strong. Can anything be said about the forces that act within nuclei?

Firstly, since the protons carry positive charges, there exist between them electrostatic forces. Further, since the charges are all of the same sign, these forces are repulsive, and

thus, if no other forces were acting, the nucleus would not remain stable. Stable atomic nuclei *do* exist, and this means that there is some other force at work in the nucleus, that it is an attractive force, and that its magnitude exceeds that of the repulsive electrostatic forces.

Secondly, it might be assumed that the attractive forces are gravitational. Putting the mass of the proton equal to $1 \cdot 6 \times 10^{-27}$ kgm, the gravitational force of attraction between two protons may be calculated readily for a typical separation of 10^{-15} metre. It turns out to be $1 \cdot 7 \times 10^{-34}$ newton. For the two protons the repulsive electrostatic force for the same separation is about $2 \cdot 3 \times 10^{2}$ newton, that is, about 10^{36} times the gravitational attraction. Clearly, then, gravitational forces are far too weak to account for the stability of nuclei.

It is thus necesary to assume that the force between nucleons is of a type not previously found in physics, and a great deal of research is being undertaken in an effort to discover more about, and finally to understand the *nuclear forces*. Quite a number of the properties of these forces can be written down from presently available data. First, the nuclear force is an *attractive force*. If this were not true, no nuclei at all would exist because the Coulomb force would cause them to fly apart. Second, nuclear forces are not strongly dependent on the nature of the interacting nucleons. That is, the attractive force between a neutron and a proton is approximately the same as that acting between two neutrons.

The approximate constancy of the binding energy per nucleon (Figure 15·7) for values of mass number above about 50 is a clue to a very important property of nuclear forces. It indicates that the nuclear force is a *short-range force*. If this is so, each nucleon can be attracted only to the other nucleons in its immediate vicinity, and not to all nucleons in the nucleus. If this latter condition held, the total binding energy of each nucleon would be approximately proportional to

---

[1] Robson, *Physical Review*, **83**, p349 (1951).
[2] An alternative process to positron emission, called *electron capture*, often occurs. For further details see, for example, Richtmeyer *et al.*, Appendix A.

$(A - 1)$ since there would be $(A - 1)$ separate attractive forces on the nucleon concerned. This is not observed, and thus the nuclear force cannot have a range sufficient for each nucleon to interact with all others in a heavy nucleus. This then sets an *upper limit* of about 10^{-14} metre for the range of the nuclear force. Experiments on the interaction of neutrons with protons give the information that the range is less than 3×10^{-15} metre.

In spite of the fact that the results of huge quantities of experimental work have allowed statements such as the above to be made, there is still a very long way to go before the nature of the nuclear force is understood. Its origin and indeed many of its characteristics are far from well established. As we shall see in Chapter 17, the existence of the *meson* was postulated by Yukawa during his attempt to work out the nature of the nuclear force, but even theories based on this hypothesis experience difficulties. Much work is going on in further attempts to understand more about the force acting between nucleons.

CHAPTER 16

Nuclear Energy

16·1 The Possibility of Obtaining Energy from the Nucleus

As has been discussed in Section 15·5, the mass of any nucleus is always less than the sum of the masses of its constituent protons and neutrons. The energy equivalent of this mass difference is the *binding energy* of the nucleus. Thus the average binding energy per nucleon of a nucleus of mass number A is given by

Binding Energy per nucleon

$$= \frac{1}{A}(\text{mass of the } A \text{ nucleons}$$
$$- \text{ mass of the nucleus}).$$

Figure 15·6 shows the average binding energy per nucleon as a function of mass number A. It will be noticed that the binding energy per nucleon is least for very low mass numbers and highest for mass numbers around 50 to 60.

Suppose two nuclei with low mass numbers could be joined together to form a single heavier nucleus with higher binding energy per nucleon. This re-arrangement of a fixed number of nucleons, resulting in an increase in the binding energy per nucleon of the system, must be accompanied by a decrease in the total mass of the system and hence a release of energy. This process of joining together two nuclei to form a heavier nucleus is called *fusion*.

On the other hand, if a nucleus with very high mass number is split into two or more nuclei of smaller masses and consequently higher binding energies per nucleon, there is again a release of energy. A splitting process of this kind is called *fission*.

If either fusion or fission reactions can be induced, energy can be obtained from the nuclei of atoms. The fission process has been demonstrated to be possible both in the 'atomic' bomb and in controlled reactions which have been developed as a source of industrial power. Fusion reactions have been dramatically demonstrated by the 'hydrogen' bomb, but sources of controlled fusion power have not yet been developed.

16·2 The Discovery of Fission

In 1934, Fermi[1] bombarded thorium and uranium with neutrons and found that radioactive products were formed. The half-lives of these products did not agree with those of any known radioactive isotopes with atomic numbers close to those of thorium or uranium. Since all types of reaction known at the time gave products with atomic numbers close to that of the parent nucleus, Fermi concluded that new elements, with atomic numbers greater than 92, had been formed. A number of other workers produced similar results, although the reported half-lives of the products differed greatly and it did not seem possible to fit the experimental results into any general scheme.

In 1939, the German chemists Hahn and Strassmann[2] made a very thorough chemical analysis of the radioactive substances formed by the bombardment of uranium with neutrons. They were able to show that barium, whose atomic number is 56, was one of the products resulting from the bombardment.

[1] Fermi, *Nature*, **133**, p898 (1934).
[2] Hahn and Strassmann, *Die Naturwissenschaften*, **27**, p11 (1939).

This was a very striking discovery since the atomic number of barium is very far removed from that of uranium (92). It became obvious that a hitherto unknown process occurred in the uranium as a result of neutron bombardment. Hahn and Strassmann advanced the hypothesis that after absorbing a neutron, the uranium nucleus may break into two or more large fragments each the size of a nucleus with atomic number somewhere near the middle of the periodic table. The barium nuclei they interpreted as being fragments resulting from the splitting of uranium nuclei in this way.

Once this hypothesis was understood, its validity was quickly confirmed. The process was called *fission* by Meitner and Frisch[1] and within a few months it was known that neutron bombardment produced fission in uranium, thorium and protactinum. Further careful chemical analyses showed that besides barium, other elements of medium atomic number such as bromine, molybdenum, rubidium, antimony, iodine and caesium were formed from the fission of uranium. Cloud chamber photographs of the process showed two heavy fragments travelling in opposite directions at high speeds, confirming the fission hypothesis.

Frisch and Meitner estimated that the energy released by the fission of a single U^{235} nucleus amounts to about 200 MeV. Thus the fission process is a source of a relatively large amount of energy per nuclear disintegration. The energy released at fission appears mainly as kinetic energy of the particles produced. When this kinetic energy is dissipated by collisions with surrounding atoms, the fission energy is transformed into heat energy.

Von Halban, Joliot and Kowarski,[2] working in France, made the vital discovery that at the instant of fission two or three high speed neutrons are emitted. It was immediately realised that there was a theoretical possibility of a self-sustaining or *chain reaction*. Since one neutron can cause fission in a nucleus resulting in the production of two or three new neutrons, the process can proceed without any additional external stimulus, provided these neutrons can be induced to cause fission. The question of the conditions necessary for a chain reaction will be discussed later in this chapter. For the present it will suffice to say that by 1940 the theoretical possibility of the large-scale generation of energy by fission was realised but many technical problems remained unsolved.

16·3 The Fission Reaction

It is now known that fission can be induced in several nuclear species and that neutrons, α-particles, protons, deuterons and γ-rays can all cause fission. However, by far the most important fission reactions for practical purposes are those induced by neutrons.

A typical equation for the fission reaction is

$$_{92}U^{235} + _{0}n^{1} \rightarrow _{92}U^{236} \rightarrow X + Y . \quad (16·1)$$

U^{236}, formed when U^{235} captures a neutron, is unstable and splits into two heavy fragments X and Y. Since there are *two* unknown products, the laws of conservation of atomic number and mass number are insuf-

[1] Meitner and Frisch, *Nature*, **143**, p239 (1939).
[2] Von Halban, Joliot and Kowarski, *Nature*, **143**, pp470, 680 (1939).

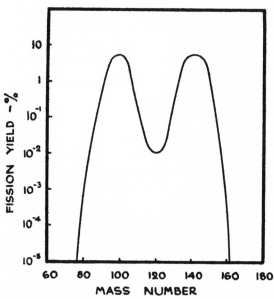

Fig. 16·1—*Relative yield of fission fragments as a function of mass number*

ficient to determine the *primary fission fragments* X and Y uniquely. On the other hand, if one were known the other could be determined. Many different nuclear species may be produced in fission. This is illustrated by Figure 16·1 which shows the distribution by atomic mass number of the fission fragments resulting from the neutron-induced fission of U^{235}. It will be noticed that symmetrical fission (the break-up into two nuclei of equal mass) is quite rare. The most common event is the production of two fragments with mass numbers in the vicinity of 96 and 140 respectively. The curve must be symmetrical about its central minimum since every relatively heavy nucleus must be accompanied by a relatively light one in such a way as to conserve the total number of nucleons involved in any one reaction. There is as yet no satisfactory theoretical explanation for the observed mass asymmetry of the fission products.

At least one of the two primary fission fragments is always unstable and frequently they both are. The reason for this is that stable nuclei of high atomic number have a relatively large excess of neutrons over protons while nuclei of lower atomic number have more nearly equal numbers of neutrons and protons. Thus in the case of fission, one or both the primary fission fragments will be over-rich in neutrons. This neutron excess may be removed in two ways. Firstly, a few neutrons (two or three) are emitted from the fission fragments within a very short time (of order 10^{-14} second) after fission. These *prompt* neutrons, emitted almost at the instant of fission, are often included explicitly on the right-hand side of the fission equation (16·1). After some fission events, a neutron may be emitted from a fission fragment as long as several minutes after the initial reaction. On the average, these *delayed* neutrons account for about 0·75% of all neutrons produced by fission, the remaining 99% being prompt.

The second way in which the neutron excess of the fission fragments is reduced, is by β-decay. A neutron-rich nucleus emitting a negative β-particle will increase its atomic number without change of mass number. Each β-decay process results in relatively more protons and fewer neutrons being present in the nucleus, and after several decay processes a stable nucleus results. The decays follow chain-like sequences, a typical example of which is

$$_{54}Xe^{140} \xrightarrow[16s]{\beta^-} {}_{55}Cs^{140} \xrightarrow[66s]{\beta^-} {}_{56}Ba^{140} \xrightarrow[12 \cdot 8d]{\beta^-}$$

$$_{57}La^{140} \xrightarrow[40h]{\beta^-} {}_{58}Ce^{140} \text{ (stable)}.$$

The first nucleus of such a chain, which is the one produced after prompt neutron emission has ceased, and those which follow it, are often referred to as the *fission products*. More than 60 chains, involving over 200 different radioactive nuclei, have been identified. γ-radiation accompanies the β-decay in many cases, and neutrinos are, of course, always produced in such decays.

While the majority of the energy released at fission appears as kinetic energy of the heavy fission fragments, a significant contribution to the total energy is made by the fission neutrons, β-particles, γ-rays and neutrinos. The total balance-sheet for the energy released by the fission of a nucleus of U^{235} by a neutron is given in Table 16·1.

Table 16·1 — *Energy released in the fission of U^{235} by neutrons*

	MeV
Kinetic energy of fission fragments	167
Kinetic energy of fission neutrons	5
β-particle energy	5
γ-ray energy	10
Neutrino energy	11
	——
Total fission energy	198

16·4 The Chain Reaction in Uranium

If, on average, at least one neutron from a fission event produces a new fission, a self-sustained reaction is possible. The process is illustrated in Figure 16·2. In U^{235} each fission produced by a slow neutron gives, on average, 2 to 4 neutrons so that a chain reaction is possible even if only one neutron causes a new fission event and the remainder are absorbed or lost without producing fission. While at first sight, this seems to be a generous allowance, it is in practice relatively difficult to produce a satisfactory neutron economy. The reasons for this are to be found in a study of the possible neutron-induced reactions in uranium.

Natural uranium is a mixture of three isotopes, U^{234} (0·006%), U^{235} (0·718%) and U^{238} (99·28%). U^{234} is present in such small proportions as to be insignificant for the present discussion. Each of the other isotopes undergoes two different types of reaction when subjected to an 'atmosphere' of neutrons. Absorption of a neutron by U^{235} leads to the formation of the compound nucleus U^{236} with an excess of energy. This nucleus may either undergo fission according to the equation

$$_{92}U^{235} + {_0}n^1 \rightarrow {_{92}}U^{236} \rightarrow 2 \text{ fission fragments,}$$

or it may emit a γ-ray and remain as U^{236}. This latter process is called *radiative capture* and the equation for it is

$$_{92}U^{235} + {_0}n^1 \rightarrow {_{92}}U^{236} + \gamma.$$

Both these neutron-induced reactions in U^{235} have cross sections (or probabilities of occurrence) which depend strongly on the velocity

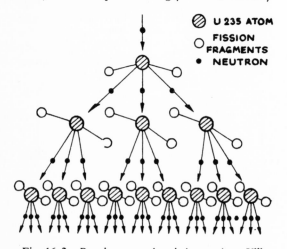

U 235 ATOM
FISSION FRAGMENTS
NEUTRON

Fig. 16·2—*Development of a chain reaction* $_{92}U^{235}$

of the incident neutron, being proportional to the reciprocal of this velocity. At *thermal* energies, that is, when the average energy of the neutrons is equal to the average thermal energy of the atoms of the medium (an energy, at 20°C, of 0·025 eV), about 85% of the reactions in U^{235} are fission reactions. The neutrons emitted from U^{235} by fission have a range of energies up to about 10 MeV with a most probable energy slightly less than 1 MeV.

U^{238} also undergoes both fission and radiative capture according to the equations

$$_{92}U^{238} + {_0}n^1 \rightarrow {_{92}}U^{239} \begin{cases} 2 \text{ fission fragments} \\ _{92}U^{239} + \gamma. \end{cases}$$

While the reactions appear similar to those for U^{235}, there are very important differences due to the variations of the cross sections with energy. In U^{238}, fission can occur only for incident neutrons with energies in excess of about 1 MeV. Thus U^{238} is said to undergo *fast fission*, while U^{235} suffers both fast and *slow fission*. The radiative capture reaction in U^{238} is velocity dependent and the cross section follows, in general, a reciprocal velocity law as for U^{235}. However, there are some important departures from the general trend in the energy region between 5 and 500 eV. Here the capture cross section becomes exceedingly large at a number of fairly well-defined energy values. At these *resonance capture* peaks the cross section may be as much as 1000 times above the normal level.

Now let us consider the 'history' of the neutrons produced in the fission of U^{235}. These neutrons have a range of energies up to 10 MeV, but their most probable energy is slightly less than 1 MeV. It can now be seen that a chain reaction cannot be sustained in an isolated specimen of natural uranium. The majority of fission neutrons have energies which are too low to cause further fission in U^{238}. At these relatively high energies, the probability of capture in U^{238} exceeds the probability of fission in U^{235}. In addition, there are about 140 U^{238} atoms present for every one of U^{235}, and thus most of the fission neutrons fail to produce further fissions. It is true that collisions rapidly reduce the neutron energy and that the fission probability in U^{235} increases greatly at low energies, but the resonance capture peaks in U^{238} cause a serious neutron loss as the slowing down process occurs.

Thus few neutrons reach the thermal energy region in which the probability of U^{235} fission, even allowing for the low abundance of this isotope, exceeds that of U^{238} capture by a factor of about two. The net result is that little more than 5% of the fission neutrons ultimately produce further fission.

There are two ways in which a chain reaction can be achieved. The first method is to 'enrich' the uranium so that it contains an increased percentage of U^{235}. In this way the overall probability of fission is increased, relative to that of capture. This method is used in 'fast' reactors for the production of nuclear energy and in the so-called 'atomic' bomb, where the fuel is almost entirely material which undergoes fission rather than capture. The second method of achieving a chain reaction is to cause the fission neutrons to slow down very rapidly to energies less than 5 eV. In this way, a large percentage can escape capture in U^{238} and cause fission in U^{235}. This technique is used in the *thermal reactor* for the production of nuclear power.

16·5   The Thermal Reactor

In a thermal reactor, fission neutrons are allowed to collide with the atoms of a substance of low mass number called a *moderator*, throughout which natural uranium is dispersed. At each collision with a moderator atom, the neutrons lose energy until they finally end up with thermal energies. For a lower mass number of the moderator, the average energy lost by a neutron in each collision is increased. Hence fewer collisions are necessary to reduce the neutron energy to a fraction of an electron volt. In a thermal or slow reactor, the neutrons travel a relatively short distance through the uranium fuel before emerging into the moderator. Consequently, the probability of capture by U^{238} is small.

When the neutrons have reached thermal energies, they diffuse through the reactor like a gas and when they once again enter a uranium *fuel element* their energies are so low that the probability of fission in U^{235} greatly exceeds the capture probability in U^{238}. It is of course essential that the moderator itself does not absorb a large percentage of the fission neutrons. This requirement limits the choice of moderator materials considerably. The most commonly used moderators are carbon, in the form of graphite blocks, or 'heavy water' (deuterium oxide).

It is of course essential to provide some means of reactor control. If, on the average, more than one fission neutron per event causes a new fission, the chain reaction will increase in intensity. If less than one fission neutron causes a new fission the reaction will die down. To maintain a stable rate of reaction, exactly one new fission must occur for each preceding fission event. In a practical reactor control rods of materials such as boron or cadmium, which absorb neutrons strongly, are inserted into the reactor. By moving these in or out, the percentage of neutrons available to produce fission, and consequently the rate of increase or decrease of the reaction, can be controlled.

Figure 16·3 shows a sketch of a typical thermal reactor arrangement. To protect the

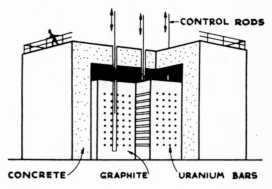

Fig. 16·3—*Essential features of a graphite-moderated nuclear reactor*

reactor staff from the intense neutron and γ-radiation, a thick shield wall encloses the reactor. In any power reactor a great deal of heat is generated and this must be removed by a suitable cooling system.

The first demonstration of a controlled, self-sustained nuclear reaction took place in a converted squash court of the University of Chicago on December 2, 1942. In this first reactor, constructed by Professor Enrico Fermi and his colleagues, the moderator consisted of 385 ton of graphite in the form of bricks. These formed a lattice at the corners of which the uranium fuel was located. Six ton of uranium metal and 40 ton of uranium oxide were employed, there being insufficient pure metal available in the world at that time. Control was achieved by the use of cadmium absorbing rods. The power attained in the totally unshielded reactor was initially only half a watt, but the experiment showed that the generation of nuclear power was possible.

Since that time, the techniques of reactor construction have developed considerably, although the basic design principles remain the same. Graphite moderated reactors have been built in quite large numbers and are in operation in the United Kingdom, the United States of America, the U.S.S.R. and several other countries. For example, reactors using gas cooling with carbon dioxide and capable of generating powers of about 200 megawatt have been constructed in the United Kingdom.

Heavy water, that is water formed from the hydrogen isotope of mass two, has also been employed as a moderator with great success. Reactors of this type are smaller but the moderator is expensive. Heavy water reactors are operating in several countries, including Australia. Ordinary water would appear to be a suitable moderator since it is cheap and it contains atoms of very low mass. However, ordinary hydrogen produces a significant absorption of neutrons and a chain reaction cannot be maintained in a reactor employing a 'light' water moderator and natural uranium fuel. If the uranium is slightly enriched in U^{235}, a chain reaction is possible and this type of reactor has been used with success in nuclear-powered submarines.

When a reactor is used to generate electricity, it replaces the usual boiler in a conventional power station. The reactor generates heat energy which is removed by the cooling fluid or *coolant*. This heat energy is then used to boil water, producing steam which drives turbines in the usual way.

The attraction of nuclear reactors lies in the immense amount of energy which can be released from a relatively small quantity of fuel. In the fission of a nucleus of U^{235}, approximately 0·09% of its mass is converted to energy. Now the energy equivalent of 1 kgm of mass is 9×10^{16} joule. It follows that 1 kgm of natural uranium, which contains 0·75% of U^{235}, is capable of releasing fission energy amounting to

$$(9 \times 10^{-4}) \times (7 \cdot 5 \times 10^{-3}) \times (9 \times 10^{16}) \text{ joule,}$$

or approximately 6×10^{11} joule. This amounts to nearly 200 megawatt days or enough energy to supply an average city of half a million people for about a day. To generate the same energy by burning coal with 100% efficiency, it would be necessary to consume nearly 50 tons of coal.

Thermal reactors are used for purposes other than power production. In fact, until recently most reactors were used for research or for the production of the new element, *plutonium*. It is possible to design a thermal reactor which is self-sustaining due to fission in U^{235} but in which there is still an appreciable capture of neutrons by U^{238} to form U^{239}. U^{239} is itself unstable and decays by β-emission to the first of the *transuranic elements, neptunium*. In a further β-decay, neptunium is converted to plutonium. These reactions are described by the equations

$$_{92}U^{238} + _{0}n^{1} \rightarrow _{92}U^{239} \rightarrow _{93}Np^{239} + _{-1}e^{0} ;$$
$$_{93}Np^{239} \rightarrow _{94}Pu^{239} + _{-1}e^{0} .$$

The half-life of U^{239} is 23·5 minute while that

of Np^{239} is 2·3 day. Both neptunium and plutonium are elements which do not occur naturally on earth. Plutonium is relatively stable having a half-life of 24,000 year and, being a different element, it can be separated from uranium by chemical means. Plutonium is itself a material which undergoes fission for slow neutrons and its behaviour in this respect is very similar to that of U^{235}. Thus, the manufacture of plutonium in a thermal reactor, followed by chemical separation, leads to a pure nuclear fuel with none of the disadvantages of natural uranium.

16·6 The 'Atomic' Bomb

While the first nuclear chain reaction was in fact a controlled one, most of the scientific effort of the following few years was devoted to the development of an *uncontrolled* re-action. Once the fission process was understood, it was clear that an immense explosion could be produced by a chain reaction spreading rapidly through any pure fuel capable of undergoing fission. Both U^{235} and Pu^{239} are ideal for this purpose. It is possible to separate U^{235} from natural uranium by gaseous diffusion processes and it has been shown that Pu^{239} can be produced in thermal reactors. Both these sources of *fissile material* were rapidly developed during the war years. In 1945, a test bomb was exploded in the New Mexico desert in the U.S.A., and shortly afterwards bombs were dropped on Hiroshima and Nagasaki. The success of this form of chain reaction is sufficiently well known to call for no further comment.

In pure *fissile* material, that is, material capable of undergoing fission by slow neu-trons,* the only requirement for a sustained chain reaction is that there should be enough of the material present. In a small piece, many neutrons can escape from the bounding surface without causing fission. Consider, for example, a spherical sample of radius r. The

---

* Although fissile material, defined in this sense, is used in a bomb, the explosion results from fissions produced by neutrons of all energies.

volume, and therefore the number of fission-able atoms in the sample, increases as r^3, while the surface area increases only as r^2. Thus, a larger piece of material will lose a smaller proportion of its fission neutrons. There is therefore a *critical size* below which a chain reaction will not take place and above which it will. In a bomb, two or more pieces of fissile material, each smaller than the critical size, are kept some distance apart. At the instant of detonation, the pieces are forced together by a subsidiary chemical explosive. Combined, their size exceeds the critical size and a chain reaction spreads with devastating rapidity. There is a reasonable limit to the explosive power of bombs of this type owing to the difficulty of arranging the collision of many pieces of material at the same instant. 'Atomic' bombs, using the fission process in U^{235} or Pu^{239}, produce an effect equivalent to that of a few tens of thousands of tons of chemical explosive. Hence the term 'a 20 kiloton bomb' means that such a weapon has the same explosive effect as 20,000 ton of chemical explosive.

16·7 Fast Reactors and Breeding

If pure Pu^{239} is used in a reactor, it is possible to dispense with the moderator. A fast reactor is very like a controlled atomic bomb and consists in essence of an array of plutonium rods, each below critical size. These fuel rods are supported by an enclosing structure of natural uranium. A coolant is necessary to remove the intense heat gene-rated, but it does not, in principle, slow down the fission neutrons. In the fuel section of the fast reactor, there is very little neutron capture as distinct from fission which takes place for neutrons of all energies. In conse-quence, losses of neutrons are smaller than for a thermal reactor. Most of the neutrons which fail to cause fission are captured by the U^{238} in the surrounding uranium container and produce plutonium. Control of a fast reactor can be achieved by moving one of the container walls nearer or further away from the fuel rods. In this type of reactor, a very large percentage of the fission neutrons either cause fission in the fuel rods or produce plutonium in the surrounding case.

The fission of plutonium produces an average of 2·88 neutrons per fission. A small fraction of these is lost by radiative capture in plutonium, and one is required to produce a further fission so that the chain reaction can be maintained. The remainder (about one per event) are available to produce plutonium in the uranium case. The plutonium so produced can be chemically extracted when the U^{238} is removed from the reactor. It can then be used as further fuel, so that such a reactor has a high fuel efficiency. Indeed, if the number of neutrons per fission available for capture by U^{238}, and therefore for plutonium production, exceeds one by even a small amount, the system produces more fuel than it consumes and is said to *breed*. Fast reactors have been constructed but it is doubtful whether a fast reactor using plutonium fuel can actually be made to breed. This is because the fission process in plutonium has to compete with a large amount of neutron capture in the plutonium itself. Because of this, the number of neutrons available for capture by U^{238} is reduced.

Another attractive material for use in a fast reactor is thorium. Thorium exists in nature as a single isotope Th^{232}. This does not itself undergo fission by slow neutrons and behaves in a manner similar to U^{238}. However, Th^{232} captures neutrons to form Th^{233}, which is radioactive and decays by two stages to U^{233}. The scheme is

$$_{90}Th^{232} + _{0}n^{1} \rightarrow _{90}Th^{233} + \gamma$$
$$_{90}Th^{233} \rightarrow _{91}Pa^{233} + _{-1}e^{0} \quad \text{(half-life 23·5min.)}$$
$$_{91}Pa^{233} \rightarrow _{92}U^{233} + _{-1}e^{0} \quad \text{(half-life 27·4 day).}$$

U^{233} does not occur naturally on earth but like Pu^{239} it is a relatively long-lived isotope which undergoes fission for neutrons of all energies. It can be separated from thorium by chemical means and can be used as a fissile fuel. A fast reactor surrounded by thorium can produce U^{233} fuel.

U^{233} produces an average of 2·54 neutrons per fission, slightly fewer than does Pu^{239}. However, its capture to fission ratio is also smaller and using U^{233} as fuel there should be more than one spare neutron per fission available for breeding. At least in theory, a U^{233}-fuelled fast reactor can breed U^{233} from a thorium case. This is a very attractive proposition. However, the achievement of the system in practice presents difficulties. Firstly it is necessary to produce enough U^{233} in a Pu^{239}-fuelled reactor, the Pu^{239} having in turn been produced in a thermal reactor. Secondly, a fast reactor is very much smaller than a thermal reactor and consequently the heat transfer problems are very much greater. Liquid metal coolants appear to offer the most promising solution. A high power fast reactor is under construction in Scotland, but it is not yet certain whether fast reactors will finally prove to be an attractive proposition.

The production of power by fission is a problem which has been studied very actively for more than fifteen years and very large sums of money have been invested in experimental and power reactors. There are, however, many problems which remain unsolved and it is impossible at this stage to predict which type of reactor will provide the most economic source of power.

16·8 Fusion and the Future

It was mentioned at the start of this chapter that energy can be released by the fusion of light atoms into heavier atoms. This process is employed with conspicuous success in the so-called 'hydrogen' bomb. However, despite a great deal of research, it has not been possible as yet to produce a self-sustained reaction under controlled conditions.

In the sun, fusion reactions are responsible for its enormous heat output. The main reactions result in the production of helium from hydrogen with energy release due to the resulting loss of mass. There are two main reaction cycles, the *carbon cycle* and the *proton-proton cycle*. The reactions in the carbon cycle are as follows:

Reaction	Energy Release
$_1H^1 + _6C^{12} \rightarrow _7N^{13}$	1·9 MeV
$_7N^{13} \rightarrow _6C^{13} + _{+1}e^0$	2·2 MeV*
$_1H^1 + _6C^{13} \rightarrow _7N^{14}$	7·5 MeV
$_1H^1 + _7N^{14} \rightarrow _8O^{15}$	7·3 MeV
$_8O^{15} \rightarrow _7N^{15} + _{+1}e^0$	2·8 MeV*
$_1H^1 + _7N^{15} \rightarrow _6C^{12} + _2He^4$	5·0 MeV.

The net result of this cycle is that four protons are consumed and one helium atom plus two positrons are produced. The total energy release is 26·7 MeV. It should be noticed that C^{12} behaves rather like a catalyst. It is converted successively into C^{13}, N^{14}, O^{15}, N^{15} and finally back to C^{12}. In order that the reactions involved in this type of fusion chain should take place with a reasonable frequency, it is necessary that the protons should have velocities which are very much higher than, for example, those of hydrogen molecules in a gas at any temperature usually encountered in the laboratory. In the sun, there is plenty of hydrogen and the very high temperatures present result in high thermal velocities of the particles and conditions suitable for the fusion chain of reactions to take place. Because these reactions take place at high temperatures they are often called *thermonuclear reactions*.

The reactions involved in the proton-proton cycle are:

$$_1H^1 + _1H^1 \rightarrow _1H^2 + _{+1}e^0 + \text{energy}$$

$$_1H^2 + _1H^1 \rightarrow _2He^3 + \text{energy}$$

$$_2He^3 + _2He^3 \rightarrow _2He^4 + _1H^1 + _1H^1 + \text{energy}.$$

In a complete *p-p* cycle, the first two reactions must occur twice to provide the two $_2He^3$ nuclei for the third reaction. Six protons are thus employed in the production of a single helium nucleus and two positrons. Four of

* This includes the energy resulting from the annihilation of the positron.

these protons are consumed while the remaining two are available for further reactions. If the energies given out in the reactions of the cycle are computed, and the energy resulting from the annihilation of the two positrons is added, the total energy release per cycle is again found to be 26·7 MeV.

While these two helium building cycles can proceed in the interior of the sun, it is very doubtful whether they can be achieved on earth. It should be stressed that any of the so-called fusion or thermonuclear reactions can be produced using bombarding particles from accelerators. But this does not constitute a self-sustaining reaction since more energy is consumed in the accelerator than is released by the nuclear reaction. What is required is a reaction, or a set thereof, which can be made self-perpetuating. While the sun's reactions appear unsuitable for the controlled release of energy on earth, there are reactions involving deuterium and tritium which appear to be possible. The most promising of these are:

$$_1H^2 + _1H^2 \rightarrow _2He^3 + _0n^1 + \quad 3·27 \text{ MeV}$$
$$_1H^2 + _1H^2 \rightarrow _1H^3 + _1H^1 + \quad 4·03 \text{ MeV}$$
$$_1H^2 + _1H^3 \rightarrow _2He^4 + _0n^1 + 17·59 \text{ MeV}.$$

In practical systems it is difficult to harness the kinetic energy of the neutrons and in consequence, the *available* energy release in the first and third reactions is very much smaller than the total energy indicated.

Reactions involving deuterium are most attractive as a source of energy. Deuterium occurs in heavy water which forms about one part in 6000 of ordinary water and it can be extracted by electrolysis techniques for about £1000 per kilogram. To get a very rough estimate of fuel cost for a thermonuclear reactor, suppose that 1 MeV of energy can be *utilised* for each two deuterons reacting. One a.m.u. is equivalent to $1·66 \times 10^{-27}$ kgm so that each reaction using two deuterons, of total mass 4 a.m.u., consumes $6·64 \times 10^{-27}$ kgm of mass. At £1000 per kgm this costs £$6·64 \times 10^{-24}$ per reaction and therefore per MeV released. But 1 MeV is equal to $1·6 \times 10^{-13}$ joule so that one joule of released energy costs £6·64 × 10^{-24}/1·6 × 10^{-13}. This is about £4 × 10^{-11} per joule. Electric power is usually metered in kilowatt hours. Since 1 kw hr = 3·6 × 10^6 joule, the fuel cost per kw hr would be very roughly £1·4 × 10^{-4} or 0·03 pence. This is a very low figure as it stands and, even so, it might well be too high. Thus thermonuclear power is attractive from the point of view of fuel costs.

Similar assumptions regarding usable energy per reaction lead to a fuel consumption figure of about 1 kgm of deuterium per megawatt year. Thus one ton of fuel would last a large city for the best part of a year and fuel transport costs would be negligible. A further attraction of thermonuclear power is the absence of radioactive waste products. These present a serious disposal problem in the case of fission power stations.

The attraction of thermonuclear power is therefore very great, but so are the problems involved in its development. Unfortunately, reactions of the type described above require temperatures as high as two or three hundred million degrees centigrade before the particles achieve a satisfactory velocity. It is also necessary for the particle density in the gas to be large so that a high gas pressure is required. The problem then is to produce very high temperatures and pressures in deuterium gas. The necessary temperatures can only be attained if the gas atoms are prevented from hitting the container walls since this process results in cooling of the gas.

Heating of ionised gases to very high temperatures has been achieved by the passage of very large electric currents through them. It has been possible to use magnetic fields to contain the ionised gas or *plasma* in a 'magnetic bottle' or region clear from the container walls. However, the temperatures and pressures so far attained have not been adequate to produce a true thermonuclear reaction.

In the 'hydrogen' bomb, thermonuclear reactions do take place, the necessary high temperatures being produced by a plutonium fission bomb acting as a detonator. Since thermonuclear reactions do not depend on the quantity of material present, there is no theoretical limit to the size of a hydrogen bomb and most thermonuclear weapons have an explosive effect in the megaton range.

While the hydrogen bomb is a thermonuclear process, it is certainly not a controlled one and despite intensive research in the United States, Britain and Russia during the last few years, there is as yet no sign of a controlled thermonuclear reaction being achieved. The prize for success in this field is enormous. It is estimated that there is enough deuterium on earth to supply power for the entire world for 20,000 million years at present rates of consumption and the power would be cheap and plentiful. How it is to be harnessed, if indeed it can be, remains one of the greatest scientific challenges of all time.

CHAPTER 17

More Fundamental Particles are Discovered

17·1 Cosmic Radiation

In the previous chapters, some of the so-called *fundamental particles* of physics have been discussed and some of their properties have been enumerated. Among these are included the proton, the electron, the neutron and the neutrino. In the years since 1930, many other fundamental particles have been discovered, and the task of fitting these into a rational structure is proving to be a challenging, but very difficult one.

The earliest experimental work which indicated the existence of more than three fundamental particles (we shall exclude the neutrino, since its existence was not verified experimentally until 1956) came from studies of the *cosmic radiation* and we shall therefore discuss briefly this field of work.

In the early part of this century, at a time when gold-leaf electroscopes were in relatively common use for measuring the intensity of radiations, a great deal of careful work was done in searching for the cause of residual ionisation in such detectors. This *natural leak*, as it was called, was always present, and was found to be too large to be accounted for in terms of leakage due to imperfect insulation between the leaves and the case. The cause of the natural leak was eventually traced to ionising particles which were, in the first instance, assumed to come from radioactive substances in the earth's crust. On this assumption, the intensity of this ionising radiation should decrease with height above the earth's surface.

The German physicist, Hess, made ascents in balloons to check this point, and found large *increases* in the intensity of the radiation for altitudes up to 5 kilometre. Similar measurements were made by Kolhörster for heights up to 9 kilometre. These results led Hess to propose that the source of this radiation was beyond our atmosphere, that the radiation was very penetrating and that it fell upon the atmosphere uniformly from all directions. More recent work has indicated that the intensity of this cosmic radiation increases with height up to 22 kilometre, after which it decreases slowly up to a height of 40 kilometre and thereafter remains approximately constant. This latter information was obtained from instruments sent aloft in rockets and, for even greater altitudes, in satellites.

The work of Hess and Kolhörster was the forerunner of a large number of investigations of cosmic rays. The penetrating power of this new radiation was an obvious point to investigate, and this was done by taking detecting apparatus up in balloons, and also down mine-shafts. There were also experiments which aimed at elucidating such questions as the nature of cosmic rays, their interactions with the earth's atmosphere, their origin, and the variation of cosmic ray intensity over the surface of the earth. We shall here be content with a summary of the major pieces of information regarding cosmic rays.

Primary cosmic rays, that is, the radiation which is incident upon the top of the earth's atmosphere are high energy atomic nuclei, which probably originate in intergalactic space. The nuclei which compose the primary cosmic radiation are mostly protons, while about 10% are α-particles, and somewhat less than 1% are nuclei of atoms heavier than helium. Figure 17·1 shows the track of a 'heavy' primary cosmic ray particle in a nuclear emulsion which was flown to a height of about 100,000 feet. This heavy primary is estimated to carry a positive charge ten times the electronic charge. The track thins down towards its end because the primary is slowing down to such a degree that it picks up electrons and thus its net charge decreases as it approaches the end of its range. This behaviour may be expected from the discussion of the ranges of charged particles in Section 12·1.

The study of primary cosmic radiation is complicated to a very great degree by the presence of the earth's atmosphere, since virtually all of the primary particles have

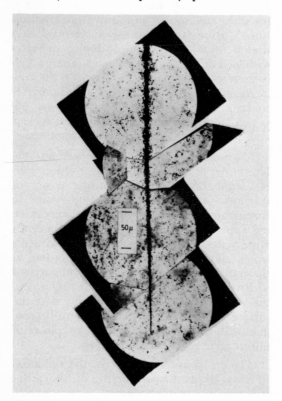

Fig. 17·1—*Track of a heavy primary cosmic ray (charge about ten times the electronic charge) in a nuclear emulsion*

been removed from the radiation, due to nuclear interactions in the atmosphere, before they reach the surface of the earth. The earlier experiments were carried out at or near the earth's surface, and therefore detected the *secondary* radiations, that is, the products of the interactions of the primary radiation with the atmosphere. Cosmic rays observed at sea level consist of two components: a 'soft' component (electrons and γ-rays) which is absorbed rapidly by a few inches of lead, and a 'hard' component which has a very great penetrating power and consists of charged particles of various kinds.

The energies of the primary particles are very high. Since they are charged particles, they will be affected by the earth's magnetic field, and more will spiral in toward the magnetic poles than are incident at the equator. This *latitude effect*, as it is known, gives a means of estimating the primary particle energy. A proton which approaches the earth with vertical incidence at the magnetic equator must have a minimum energy of about $1 \cdot 5 \times 10^{10}$ eV in order to enter the atmosphere, while at 45° latitude the minimum is one quarter of this. It is apparent, then, that the primary cosmic rays are extremely energetic particles. Some events which have been studied in nuclear emulsions were initiated by protons of 10^{15} eV kinetic energy. The magnitude of this figure is very impressive when it is remembered that the biggest particle accelerator yet made produces protons of nearly 3×10^{10} eV.

Figures 17·2 and 17·3 show events which are typical of those mentioned. In the first of these, a primary cosmic ray causes a nucleus to break up into many fragments, and further, one of these fragments has such high energy that it causes a second disintegration only a short distance from the first. Thus there are two *stars* produced. The fragments emitted in these stars are not always stable. Figure 17·3 shows a star in which an unstable particle is emitted. Its decay into two charged particles is shown a short distance from the main star at the bottom of the photograph.

The secondary cosmic radiation, which is

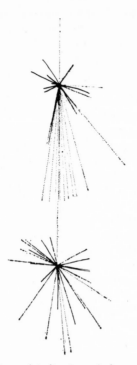

The mechanism of these showers is now well understood. Somewhere, perhaps high in the atmosphere, a primary particle produces a high energy photon. This has a large probability of producing an electron pair (see Section 17·2). These high energy electrons product photons of lower energy than the first one by the mechanism of X-ray production. These photons then produce more electron pairs, and so the process proceeds with the eventual result that one initiating particle may be multiplied into many thousands of shower particles. The electrons and photons that make up the cosmic ray showers form the soft component of the secondary radiation.

However, there is still the 'hard' component of the secondary cosmic radiation which has to be accounted for. As was mentioned earlier, many studies of cosmic radiation were made at relatively great depths below the earth's surface. Typical of the very careful measurements of the absorption of cosmic rays are those of Millikan and

Fig. 17·2—*A good indication of the extremely high energies of primary cosmic rays. Here a primary cosmic ray causes an "explosive" disintegration of a nucleus in the emulsion, and one of the emitted mesons has enough energy to cause a second disintegration a little further on*

produced as a result of the interaction of the primary radiation with the atmosphere, was studied quite intensively long before much attention was given to the primary radiation. As a result of these studies, many important discoveries were made.

In 1928, the Russian physicist Skobeltsyn photographed cosmic ray tracks in a Wilson cloud chamber. He discovered that the tracks appeared in groups and, further, that they all appeared to originate in some solid object above and close to the apparatus. Later work showed that Geiger counters separated by large horizontal distances recorded more coincident counts than could be accounted for purely by chance. These two pieces of data led to the discovery of *cosmic ray showers*. Some of the showers which have been studied extend over many acres at ground level.

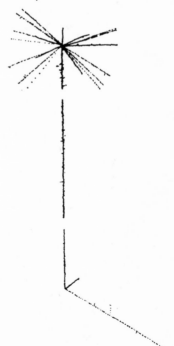

Fig. 17·3—*One fragment produced in this 'star' was unstable and decayed after travelling some distance in the emulsion*

Cameron, and of Wilson.[1] Wilson, for example, measured the intensity of the radiation down to a depth of 384 metre in a mine, or, in other terms, to a depth equivalent to over 1400 metre of water. Even at this great depth some cosmic radiation was recorded. Millikan and Cameron made careful studies of the cosmic ray intensity as a function of equivalent depth of water absorber. Their conclusions were, firstly, that the absorption of cosmic rays could not be characterised by one absorption coefficient,[2] but rather required two; and secondly, that these absorption coefficients indicated the presence of the soft and hard components. The hard component appeared to be about twenty times more penetrating than the hardest γ-rays known, and furthermore, its penetrating power increased quite markedly with depth.

Millikan was one of the first to put forward a hypothesis about the nature of the hard component. He presented quite a body of evidence mostly drawn from absorption data, in support of the idea that the hard component was composed of γ-rays of much shorter wavelengths than were currently known. This idea persisted until the completion of the very important work of Anderson, who, in cloud chamber studies of cosmic radiation at sea level, reported discoveries of two new fundamental particles.

17·2   The Positron

In the years following Skobeltsyn's detection of cosmic rays in a cloud chamber, many other investigators turned to this technique as a means of obtaining information about the charged particles present in the radiation. However, the mere photography of the tracks did not give a great deal of quantitative information. Anderson, at the California Institute of Technology, built a large cloud chamber and operated it between the poles of a very large and powerful electromagnet, and endeavoured to obtain information on the energies of the cosmic ray particles from the curvatures of their paths in the magnetic field. The magnetic flux density produced between the poles of the electromagnet was 2·4 weber metre^{-2} — much larger than any which had been used previously.

Soon after the completion of this powerful research tool, it produced results of far-reaching importance. Some cloud chamber photographs were obtained which showed two tracks apparently arising simultaneously at a common point. The curvatures of the two tracks were in opposite directions, and the densities of ionisation along them were approximately equal. Now the only charged sub-atomic particles known at the time were the proton and the electron. The ionisation produced in the cloud chamber indicated that the negatively charged particle was an electron. The positively charged particle could not have been a proton; the ionisation density was much too low for that to be true. There seemed no escape from the conclusion that this positively charged particle was a new fundamental particle — a positively charged electron. That is, it had the same mass and magnitude of charge as the ordinary electron, but a positive rather than a negative charge. These results were first announced by Anderson[3] in 1932.

The same author was soon to produce yet more conclusive evidence, and in this case it was not dependent upon the observation of a 'paired' track. Anderson next placed a sheet of lead, 6 mm thick, inside the cloud chamber, and in such a position that the track of a particle which passed through the lead could be photographed. By using the information gained from the direction of curvature of the track due to the magnetic field, and also the fact that particles *lose* energy in passing through an absorber, Anderson was in a position to determine the direction of motion, and consequently the charge, of single particles which passed through the chamber. It was no longer necessary to reject photographs of

[1] Millikan and Cameron, *Physical Review*, **28**, p851 (1926); **31**, p921 (1928); **37**, p235 (1931). Wilson, *Physical Review*, **53**, pp204, 337 (1938).

[2] The term 'absorption coefficient' has the same meaning in this context as that discussed in Section 4·11 in connection with the absorption of X-rays.

[3] Anderson, *Science*, **76**, p238 (1932).

single particle tracks, and wait for the appearance of paired tracks.

Figure 17·4 shows a very significant photograph which Anderson* obtained using this technique. This picture showed the track of a charged particle which had passed through the lead plate. In the lower part of the picture, below the lead plate, the trajectory is less curved than it is above the plate. This meant that the particle moved with greater speed in the lower half of the chamber than in the upper half, and therefore that the particle proceeded from the lower half to the upper. Knowing the direction of motion of the particle and the direction of the magnetic field, Anderson deduced that the particle was positively charged.

However, it was still possible that the track was that of a proton. Since the curvature of the track in the region above the plate was considerable, it was possible to measure its radius. From this, and the known strength of the magnetic field, Anderson found that, if the particle were a proton, its energy after traversal of the lead plate should be 3×10^5 eV. Now this energy was small enough to

* Anderson, *Physical Review*, **43**, p491 (1933).

make it immediately apparent that the track was not of a proton. Firstly, protons of this energy would have a range no more than 5 mm in the chamber, and the track length was more than 50 mm. Secondly, the ionising power of protons is great, and the track should have been thick, whereas it was, in fact, very similar to the tracks expected for electrons.

On the assumption that the particle was a positive electron, or *positron*, Anderson repeated the above computations, and from the radii of curvature which he measured, deduced that the initial energy of the particle was 63 MeV, while the final energy was 23 MeV. Further, this energy loss of 40 MeV is very close to the energy loss expected in the lead plate used, for a particle having the same charge to mass ratio as the electron. For this convincing evidence of the existence of the positron, Anderson was awarded the Nobel Prize for Physics in 1936.

17·3 Creation and Annihilation of Electron-Positron Pairs

Even after Anderson's discovery, it was still necessary to try to understand the mechanism

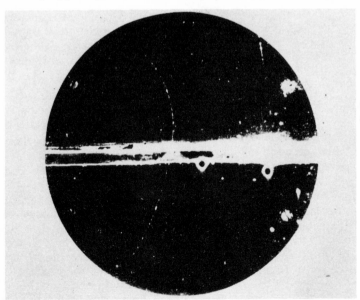

Fig. 17·4—*The cloud chamber photograph which gave the first definite evidence for the existence of the positron*

by which the 'paired' tracks were formed. A second, and related question was added to this one. What happens when a positron and an electron combine? The first clue to the answers to these questions had already been given. Scientists experimenting on the absorption co-efficients for hard X-rays in various materials had found anomalously large values for absorbers of high atomic number. Chao[1] found in 1930 that there was an unexplained secondary radiation present whenever anomalous values of absorption co-efficients were observed, and further, it was suspected that the energy going into these secondary radiations would account for the large absorption of the primary X-rays. By means of absorption measurements, Chao obtained the value of 0·55 MeV for the energy of the secondary radiations.

Further experiments brought to light more significant facts. The energy of the secondary radiation was independent, firstly, of the energy of the primary beam and secondly, of the material used for absorbing the primary beam. It could not be identified with any known characteristic X-rays, and its energy did not vary with change of its angle of emission with respect to the primary beam as had been found to be the case for a particular type of X-ray scattering known as Compton scattering. Also there were inaccurate and indirect determinations which suggested that the incident radiation had to be of energy between 1·5 and 2 MeV before this secondary radiation could be excited.

An explanation for all these facts was suggested in 1933 by Blackett and Occhialini,[2] and time has only served to verify the corectness of their suggestion. Electron-positron pairs are *created* by the action of γ-rays of energy above a certain minimum in passing through absorbers. Although sufficient quantitative evidence for the equivalence and interchangeability of mass and energy has already been given (Chapters 12 and 14), this

[1] Chao, *Physical Review*, **36**, p1519 (1930).
[2] Blackett and Occhialini, *Proceedings of the Royal Society*, **A 139**, p699 (1933).

process probably represents the most striking example of this equivalence. As is now known, a photon passing near an atomic nucleus may vanish and produce, in its place, an electron-positron pair. Now energy has to be transformed into mass for this process to take place.

An electron has mass of $9·1 \times 10^{-31}$ kgm and, according to Einstein's mass-energy equivalence relation, this represents an energy

$$E = mc^2 = 9·1 \times 10^{-31} \times (3 \times 10^8)^2 \text{ joule,}$$
$$= 8·19 \times 10^{-14} \text{ joule,}$$
$$= 0·511 \text{ MeV.}$$

Since *two* electrons (positive and negative) are formed in this *pair production*, the minimum energy of a γ-ray capable of initiating this process must be 1·022 MeV. This illustrates the reason for the existence of a minimum γ-ray energy for the appearance of this absorption process. In the terminology of nuclear reactions, the equation for pair production may be written

$$\gamma \rightarrow {}_{-1}e^0 + {}_{+1}e^0 - 1·02 \text{ MeV.} \qquad (17·1)$$

Note that charge is conserved in this reaction, as also are mass-energy and momentum. Figure 17·5 shows an excellent example of a cloud chamber photograph of the formation of a pair in the gas of the chamber. It should also be stated that any energy possessed by the incident γ-ray in excess of 1·02 MeV appears as kinetic energy shared between the positron and electron.

When an electron and a positron combine, one might expect that the reaction which is the reverse of that given in (17·1) would occur. This is true to a degree. Certainly, when the two particles combine, mass is transformed into energy; the two particles disappear, and the product is electromagnetic radiation. This then is the fate of the positrons *formed* in the 'anomalous absorption' experiments of Chao. However, we note that if a slow electron and positron combine, the energy released is, on the basis of the calculation above, expected to be 1·02 MeV. This is in contradiction to Chao's measurement of the energy of the

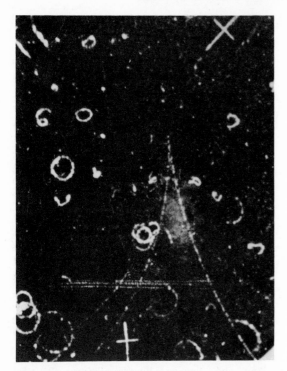

Fig. 17·5—An example of pair production in the gas of a cloud chamber which was placed in a magnetic field

secondary radiation, which gave a value just over 0·5 MeV.

The difficulty is resolved in the following way. Consider the combination of a slow electron with a slow positron. (This combination is observed to take place with far greater probability for slow positrons than for fast-moving ones.) Then application of the simple laws of conservation of energy and momentum, coupled with the assumption that the combination takes place in free space — away from any third particle — shows that it is only possible for the process to occur with the emission of *two* photons. A detailed theoretical treatment shows that by far the most probable distribution of energy between these photons is an equal one, and thus the occurrence of the secondary radiation of energy 0·5 MeV observed by Chao is explained, as are indeed all its observed properties.

The discovery of the positron revived interest in a paper published by Dirac some years earlier, which contained the implied proposal that, for every sub-atomic particle, there should exist an 'anti-particle', that is, a particle of the same mass and carrying charge of the same magnitude but of opposite sign. Anderson's discovery of the positron certainly supported this proposal in the case of the electron. It was then natural to ask whether there was an 'anti-proton'. This question remained unanswered for over twenty years, until, with the Berkeley Bevatron, Segré and others were able to produce anti-protons in the laboratory.

17·4   The μ-Meson

The paper by Dirac was not the only theoretical discussion which profoundly affected the progress of knowledge of elementary particles. In 1935, Yukawa* was seeking an explanation of the then, and still, unknown nature of nuclear forces. In the course of this search, he was led to predict that there existed a previously unobserved particle, which acted, as it were, as the 'glue' which held the nucleons together to form a stable nucleus. Of course, the properties of this 'glue' had to be made to fit in with those empirical facts about nuclear forces that were known (see Section 15·7), and this requirement led Yukawa to the following predictions. The 'meson', which was the name given to this particle, was to have a mass of about 200 times the mass of the electron. It was necessary to postulate the existence of three types of meson, positively charged, neutral and negatively charged, and in the case of the charged mesons, the magnitude of the charge was to be equal to that of the electron. Later, Yukawa estimated that the mesons, if isolated from nuclei, should undergo radioactive decay with a half-life of about 10^{-6} second. Further, the very reason for which the meson was predicted required that it interact strongly with atomic nuclei. Yukawa's work earned him the 1949 Nobel Prize for Physics.

* Yukawa, *Proceedings of the Physico-Mathematical Society of Japan*, **17**, p48 (1935).

In 1936, Anderson and Neddermeyer[1] discovered tracks in a cloud chamber which were tentatively interpreted as being due to protons, even though the range, the degree of ionisation, and the radius of curvature in the magnetic field were not really consistent with this hypothesis. Anderson and Neddermeyer expressed their view in these words:

. . . If the observed curvature (of the track) were produced entirely by magnetic deflection it would be necessary to conclude that this track represents a massive particle with an e/m much greater than that of a proton or any other known nucleus.

Further evidence for the existence of particles of the type discovered by Anderson and Neddermeyer was soon forthcoming from many other laboratories, all these observations being made on cosmic rays.

Since the intensity of cosmic radiation is very low, a large amount of tedious and painstaking work was necessary to establish the properties of this new particle, which has been called the *μ-meson* or *muon*. Eventually the properties of the μ-meson were established and may now be summarised. Both positively-charged and negatively-charged μ-mesons are found in cosmic radiation at sea-level. The charge carried by the μ-meson is equal in magnitude to the electronic charge, and its mass is $(207 \pm 1)m_e$, where m_e is the mass of the electron. Furthermore, the μ-meson was identified as the particle responsible for the hard component in cosmic ray showers. Its interaction with matter was extremely small.

The μ-meson was found to be a radioactive particle. The presently accepted equation representing its radioactive decay is

$$\mu^{\pm} \rightarrow e^{\pm} + 2\nu,$$

the $\pm$ denoting the two known possibilities for the signs of the charges of meson and electron. The postulate that *two* neutrinos are emitted is necessary, in order to retain the principles of conservation of energy and momentum for the decay process.

[1] Anderson and Neddermeyer, *Physical Review*, **50**, p263 (1936).

The characteristic time usually quoted for the μ-meson decay is the *mean* life, which is equal to $1/\lambda$, where λ is the disintegration constant. Rossi and Nereson[2] found $(2 \cdot 15 \pm 0 \cdot 07) \times 10^{-6}$ second for the mean life of the μ-meson. This short life-time was one factor which excluded the possibility that the μ-mesons were components of the primary cosmic rays. Figure 17·6 is a cloud chamber photograph which shows a μ-meson approaching an aluminium plate, emerging after being slowed down in it, and eventually coming to rest and decaying. The finer track of the electron is visible at the bottom of the photograph.

It will be noticed that most of the properties of the μ-meson fit in with the predictions of Yukawa for the 'nuclear force' mesons, and for several years they were regarded as identical with them. The disturbing feature, however, was the very small interaction of these μ-mesons with matter. It was pointed out that this was about 10^6 times too small for

[2] Rossi and Nereson, *Physical Review*, **62**, p417 (1942); **64**, p199 (1943).

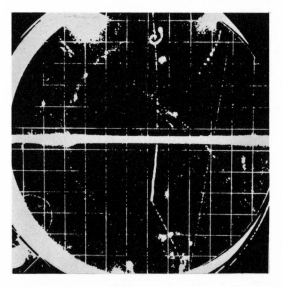

Fig. 17·6—*A cloud chamber photograph showing the slowing-down of a μ-meson in an aluminium plate, its subsequent coming to rest (heavy track) and the track of the electron resulting from its decay*

the identification just mentioned to be correct. Thus it was concluded that, if Yukawa's theory was correct, there remained another meson to be discovered.

17·5 The π-Meson

At about this same time, a group working under Powell[1] found that, in the emulsions which they exposed at high altitudes, there were some events in which mesons caused nuclear disruptions, and others in which they were themselves produced. This behaviour was completely contrary to the known behaviour of μ-mesons which had been observed at sea level. In addition, they observed tracks which terminated, indicating that the 'meson' had come to rest, and yet from this termination another high energy particle appeared to emerge. After much painstaking work, for which Powell was awarded the Nobel Prize for Physics in 1950, his group established the nature of the events they had observed, and reported the discovery of the *π-meson* or *pion*. This was heavier than the μ-meson and, on coming to rest, decayed into a μ-meson plus a neutrino. If this were so it should be possible to observe occasionally in emulsions decay processes of the type $\pi \to \mu \to e$. Such an event is shown in Figure 17·7, although the track of the electron is very faint.

Positively charged, negatively charged and neutral mesons were found in the years following 1948. This year was notable for the fact that π-mesons were first produced in the

[1] Lattes, Muirhead, Occhialini and Powell, *Nature*, **159**, p694 (1947).

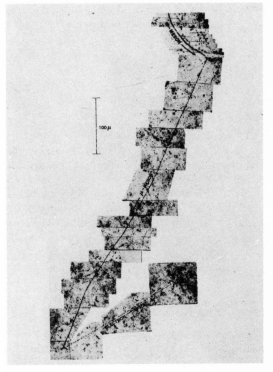

Fig. 17·7—*A nuclear emulsion photograph of the decay chain* $\pi \to \mu \to e$

laboratory[2] when a carbon target was bombarded with 380 MeV α-particles.

The properties of the π-mesons are summarised in Table 17·1. It has become possible to obtain the properties of these particles to a relatively high degree of accuracy, as a result of their production by accelerators. They can be made by bombardment of targets with nucleons or very high energy γ-rays. The latter method probably gives the greatest

[2] Gardner and Lattes, *Science*, **107**, p270 (1948).

Table 17·1 — *Summary of properties of π-Mesons*

Mass	Mean Life	Decay Equation
π^+ $(273 \cdot 4 \pm 0 \cdot 2)m_e$	$(2 \cdot 55 \pm 0 \cdot 19) \times 10^{-8}$ sec	$\pi^+ \to \mu^+ + \nu$
π^- $(272 \cdot 5 \pm 0 \cdot 3)m_e$	$(2 \cdot 44 \pm 0 \cdot 18) \times 10^{-8}$ sec	$\pi^- \to \mu^- + \nu$
π^0 $(263 \cdot 7 \pm 0 \cdot 9)m_e$	$\sim 10^{-14}$ sec	$\pi^0 \to 2\gamma$

insight into the production mechanisms, and the simplest possible production equations for the three π-mesons are (representing the proton, deuteron and neutron by p, d and n respectively)

$$p + \gamma \rightarrow \pi^+ + n,$$
$$p + \gamma \rightarrow \pi^0 + p,$$
and
$$d + \gamma \rightarrow \pi^- + 2p.$$

As was discovered by Powell, these π-mesons interact very strongly with nuclei. Figure 17·8 shows a 'star' event in a nuclear emulsion in which many mesons were produced. As a result of this strong interaction, the π-mesons were identified with the mesons predicted by Yukawa. However, the details of the Yukawa theory are fraught with difficulties which are as yet unsolved, so that a detailed insight into the nature of nuclear forces has not yet been obtained.

17·6   Other Mesons

The continuing cloud chamber studies of cosmic rays led to further discoveries of mesons even heavier than the π-meson. These studies were backed up by more work with

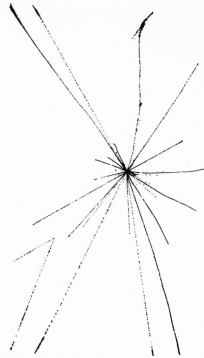

Fig. 17·9—*The V-shaped track in the lower left of the photograph is due to the formation of two charged particles in the decay of a neutral 'V-particle', which had been produced in the 'star' shown above it*

the high energy accelerators, so that such observations were quickly confirmed. There have been many more mesons discovered since 1950, and there are now no less than thirty 'fundamental' particles known. Today, these particles are not all known as mesons. Those heavier than nucleons are called *hyperons*, while the name *meson* is reserved for particles heavier than electrons but lighter than nucleons.

An example of the production, and subsequent decay of a heavy meson is shown in Figure 17·9. A neutral meson was produced in the 'star', and, after travelling a short distance, decayed into two charged particles which leave the V-shaped track in the lower half of the photograph. As a result of careful analysis of many hundreds of events such as this one, the very impressive list of fundamental particles shown in Table 17·2 has been compiled.

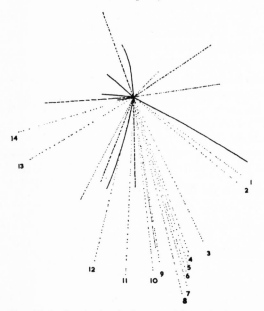

Fig. 17·8—*In the 'star' shown, a 'shower' of mesons has been produced. All the numbered tracks are due to mesons*

Table 17·2 – *Tabulation of the Known Fundamental Particles*

Family Name	Mass (in units of electron mass)	Particles				Anti-Particles		
		Positively Charged	Neutral	Negatively Charged	Particles which are their own anti-particles	Positively Charged	Neutral	Negatively Charged
Hyperons	2586		Xi Ξ^0	Xi Ξ^-		Xi Ξ^+	Xi $\bar{\Xi}^0$	
	2335	Sigma Σ^+	Sigma Σ^0	Sigma Σ^-		Sigma $\bar{\Sigma}^+$	Sigma $\bar{\Sigma}^0$	Sigma $\bar{\Sigma}^-$
	2182		Lambda Λ^0				Lambda $\bar{\Lambda}^0$	
Nucleons	1837	Proton p^+	Neutron n^0				Anti-neutron $\bar{n}^0$	Anti-proton $\bar{p}^-$
Mesons	966	K-meson K^+	K-meson K^0				K-meson $\bar{K}^0$	K-meson K^-
	270			Pi-meson π^-	Pi-meson π^0	Pi-meson π^+		
	207			Mu-meson μ^-		Mu-meson μ^+		
Leptons	1			Electron e^-		Positron e^+		
	0		Neutrino ν				Anti-neutrino $\bar{\nu}$	
	0				Photon γ			

The prediction of Yukawa which led to the π-meson being regarded as the 'nuclear force' meson must, in the light of these discoveries, be considered an inadequate picture. The obvious way to attempt to overcome this inadequacy is to try to understand the role played by these 'strange particles' (the more recently discovered mesons), since their very presence reveals a flaw somewhere in the theories which had been built up. The part played by the 'strange particles' is not understood at all at the present time.

17.7   The Anti-proton

It was mentioned earlier that the positron was the *anti-particle* of the electron, as had been predicted by Dirac. The arguments that he used were equally valid for protons, and so the existence of *anti-protons*, that is particles of the same mass as protons but carrying a negative charge, was suspected. The great difficulty which prevented the discovery of the anti-proton until 1955 was simply the very large amount of energy which is required to create a nucleon-antinucleon pair. Before the construction of the Bevatron at Berkeley, no accelerator could provide protons of a sufficiently high energy, and the only source of particles with enough energy was cosmic radiation.

In 1955,* it was shown quite definitely that anti-protons were produced by bombarding a copper target with the 6.4×10^9-eV proton beam of the Bevatron. The experimental difficulties which had to be overcome in order to demonstrate that anti-protons were formed as products were formidable. Bombardment of a target by the Bevatron proton beam gives rise mainly to π-mesons, K-mesons and hyperons (see Table 17·2). In fact these types of particles are produced so prolifically that only one anti-proton was counted for every 30,000 mesons recorded. This extremely small fraction of anti-protons was separated out in the

* Chamberlain, Segré, Wiegand and Ypsilantis, *Physical Review*, **100**, p947 (1955). The leaders of this group, Chamberlain and Segré, were awarded the Nobel Prize for Physics in 1959.

following way. Negatively charged particles which were produced in the reaction were analysed by passing them through a magnet system, which selected particles having a specified small range of momenta. In the experiment of Chamberlain *et al.*, the π-mesons selected had a velocity of 0·99 times that of light, while anti-protons of the same momentum had a speed of 0·78 times the speed of light. To separate these, counters which would respond only to particles whose speeds were between 0·75 and 0·79 times that of light were developed.

The identification of the anti-proton was made certain when its annihilation upon collision with a proton was observed. The products are not two γ-ray photons, but two mesons. The simplest processes are written

$$\bar{p} + p \rightarrow 2\pi^0$$

or
$$\bar{p} + p \rightarrow \pi^+ + \pi^-.$$

However, other processes are possible.

One further interesting fact has emerged. This is that the force of attraction between the anti-proton and nucleons is immensely stronger than that between protons and nucleons. This is not a result of electrostatic attraction (instead of repulsion), since the electrostatic force is much smaller than nuclear forces. It is expected that when this result is understood, it will open up new horizons in the studies of fundamental particles.

17·8   Retrospect and Prospect

In tracing the story of 'Modern Physics', we have seen how, in the main, the major contributions were made by scientists who had the insight to be able to visualise, in a mass of apparently unrelated data, an ordered picture, and who were thus led to some basic truth. In fact, the history of man's attempt to understand the nature of the atoms which make up the world in which he lives, may well be likened to the putting together of a jig-saw puzzle of which the pieces are the experimental facts which have been obtained.

More Fundamental Particles are Discovered

Let us now look at the progress in putting the jig-saw puzzle together, as we have it today. Around the outside edge of the puzzle are pieces which are concerned with the electronic structure of atoms. For instance, there are the facts about cathode rays which were put in order by J. J. Thomson's recognition that electrons are constituents of all types of atoms. There is the section on atomic structure which fell into place when Rutherford recognized the 'key piece' in the Geiger-Marsden experiments on the scattering of α-particles. Attached to it is the section which Bohr built, in which the data on atomic spectra were fitted together to a large degree. Out of these grew a further ordering which came with the development of wave mechanics.

Closer in towards the centre of the puzzle are the section which Chadwick set in order when he recognised the existence of the neutron, the section of which Hahn and Strassman built a part when they discovered fission and the part which Pauli set aright when he postulated the neutrino.

However, there are still many parts of this puzzle which are incomplete. A great deal of experimental information exists concerning the nuclear forces, but it has not yet been set in place. Much work has been done in studies of the release of energy when light nuclei combine, but no-one has been able to see the pattern in this section and so the fusion reaction has not been harnessed to provide power. As we have seen earlier in this chapter, there are about thirty fundamental particles known. Beyond the fact that these pieces belong near those labelled 'nuclear forces', we know nothing of how to put these together to make a coherent picture.

The outer regions of the puzzle have been set in order. What is needed above all in these next years is a group of scientists with the insight to complete the puzzle and the will to turn all the results of this vast amount of knowledge to the good of their fellow men.

APPENDICES

A: BIBLIOGRAPHY

B: TABLE OF MASSES AND ABUNDANCES OF
NATURALLY-OCCURRING ISOTOPES

C: TABLES OF NATURALLY-OCCURRING
RADIOACTIVE ISOTOPES

D: TABLE OF PHYSICAL CONSTANTS

APPENDIX A

Bibliography

1. General References

The following texts are suitable for general and more advanced reading in topics discussed in this book. These are not of a uniform standard; some are considerably more difficult than others.

Beyer, *Foundations of Nuclear Physics* (Dover Publications, 1949).

Born, *The Restless Universe* (Dover Publications, 1951).

Gamow, *Mr. Tompkins in Wonderland* (Macmillan, 1944).

Gamow, *Matter, Earth and Sky* (Macmillan, 1959).

Gentner, Maier-Leibnitz and Bothe, *An Atlas of Typical Expansion Chamber Photographs* (Pergamon, 1954).

Heathcote, *Nobel Prize Winners in Physics* (Henry Schuman, 1953).

Halliday, *Introductory Nuclear Physics* (Wiley, 1955).

Holton, *Introduction to Concepts and Theories in Physical Science* (Addison-Wesley, 1952).

Holton and Roller, *Foundations of Modern Physical Science* (Addison-Wesley, 1958).

Hughes, *The Neutron Story* (Doubleday, 1959).

Kaplan, *Nuclear Physics* (Addison-Wesley, 1955).

Leighton, *Principles of Modern Physics* (McGraw-Hill, 1959).

Richtmeyer, Kennard and Lauritsen, *Introduction to Modern Physics*. 5th ed. (McGraw-Hill, 1955).

Shamos, *Great Experiments in Physics* (Holt-Dryden, 1959).

Stranathan, *The 'Particles' of Modern Physics* (Blakiston, 1942).

Sullivan, *Trilinear Chart of Nuclides*, 2nd ed. (U.S. Government Printing Office, 1957).

Wehr and Richards, *Physics of the Atom* (Addison-Wesley, 1960).

2. Special References

The following references are appropriate to the specific chapters of this book indicated below. Once again, some references are considerably more advanced than others.

CHAPTER 1

Wightman, *The Growth of Scientific Ideas* (Oliver and Boyd, 1951).

CHAPTER 2

Millikan, *Electrons (+ and −), Protons, Photons, Neutrons and Cosmic Rays*, Chapters 3-5, revised edition (University of Chicago Press, 1947).

CHAPTER 3

Hughes and DuBridge, *Photoelectric Phenomena* (McGraw-Hill, 1932).

Weissler, 'Photoelectric Emission from Solids', *Handbuch der Physik*, **21**, p341 (Springer, 1956).

Zworykin and Ramberg, *Photoelectricity and its Applications* (Wiley, 1949).

CHAPTER 4

Glasser, *Wilhelm Conrad Röntgen* (Bale and Danielsson, 1933).

Worsnop and Chalklin, *X-rays*, 2nd ed. (Methuen, 1946).

CHAPTER 5

Eve Curie, *Madame Curie*; translator, Sheehan (Heinemann, 1938).

A. S. Eve, *Rutherford* (Cambridge University Press, 1939).

Rutherford, Chadwick and Ellis, *Radiations from Radioactive Substances* (Cambridge University Press, 1930).

Bibliography

CHAPTER 6

Constant, *Theoretical Physics — Electromagnetism*, Chapter 14 (Addison-Wesley, 1958).

Einstein, *Relativity*; translator, Lawson, 15th ed. (Methuen, 1954).

Ginzburg, 'Artificial Satellites and Relativity', *Scientific American*, **200**, No. 5, p149 (1959).

McCrea, *Relativity Physics* (Methuen, 1935).

CHAPTER 7

Fowler, *Report on Series in Line Spectra* (The Physical Society of London; Fleetway Press, 1922).

CHAPTER 8

Compton and Allison, *X-rays in Theory and Experiment*, Chapter 3, 2nd ed. (Van Nostrand, 1935).

CHAPTER 9

Andrade, 'The Birth of the Nuclear Atom', *Scientific American*, **195**, No. 5, p93 (1956).

Gamow, 'The Exclusion Principle', *Scientific American*, **201**, No. 1, p74 (1959).

Herzberg, *Atomic Spectra and Atomic Structure*, 2nd ed. (Dover Publications, 1944).

Johnson, *Atomic Spectra*, 2nd ed. (Methuen, 1950).

Pauling and Goudsmit, *The Structure of Line Spectra* (McGraw-Hill, 1930).

CHAPTER 10

Aston, *Mass Spectra and Isotopes* (Arnold, 1933).

Duckworth, *Mass Spectroscopy* (Cambridge University Press, 1958).

CHAPTER 11

Birks, *Scintillation Counters* (Pergamon, 1953)

Corson and Wilson, 'Particle and Quantum Counters', *Review of Scientific Instruments*, **19**, p207 (1948).

Fretter, 'Nuclear Particle Detection (Cloud Chambers and Bubble Chambers)', *Annual Review of Nuclear Science*, **5**, p145 (1955).

Jordan, 'Detection of Nuclear Particles', *Annual Review of Nuclear Science*, **1**, p207 (1952).

Jordan and Bell, 'Scintillation Counters', *Nucleonics*, **5**, p30 (Oct., 1949).

Rossi and Staub, *Ionization Chambers and Counters* (McGraw-Hill, 1949).

Swank, 'Characteristics of Scintillators', *Annual Review of Nuclear Science*, **4**, p111 (1954).

Wilkinson, *Ionization Chambers and Counters* (Cambridge University Press, 1950).

Yagoda, 'The Tracks of Nuclear Particles', *Scientific American*, **194**, No. 5, p40 (1956).

CHAPTER 12

Laura Fermi, *Atoms in the Family* (George Allen and Unwin, 1955).

CHAPTER 13

Fremlin and Gooden, 'Cyclic Accelerators', *Reports on Progress in Physics*, **13**, p295 (1950).

Institute of Physics, *The Acceleration of Particles to High Energies* (Institute of Physics, London, 1950).

Livingston, 'High Energy Accelerators — Standard Cyclotron, Synchrocyclotron, Proton Synchrotron', *Annual Review of Nuclear Science*, **1**, p157 (1952).

Slater, 'High Energy Accelerators — Linear Accelerators', *Annual Review of Nuclear Science*, **1**, p199 (1952).

Thomas, Kraushaar and Halpern, 'High Energy Accelerators — Synchrotons', *Annual Review of Nuclear Science*, **1**, p175 (1952).

Wilson, 'Particle Accelerators', *Scientific American*, **198**, No. 3, p64 (1958).

Bibliography

CHAPTER 14

Lapp and Andrews, *Nuclear Radiation Physics*, Chapter 13 (Prentice-Hall, 1948).

CHAPTER 15

Lapp and Andrews, *Nuclear Radiation Physics*, Chapters 6, 7, 12 (Prentice-Hall, 1948).

Marshak, 'The Nuclear Force', *Scientific American*, **202**, No. 3, p98 (1960).

Morrison, 'The Neutrino', *Scientific American*, **194**, No. 1, p58 (1956).

Peierls, 'The Atomic Nucleus', *Scientific American*, **200**, No. 1, p75 (1959).

Pollard and Davidson, *Applied Nuclear Physics*, Chapters 6 - 9 (Wiley, 1951).

CHAPTER 16

Gamow, *Atomic Energy* (Cambridge University Press, 1957).

Pollard and Davidson, *Applied Nuclear Physics*, Chapters 10, 11 (Wiley, 1951).

Post, 'Fusion Power', *Scientific American*, **197**, No. 6, p73 (1957).

Spitzer, 'The Stellarator', *Scientific American*, **199**, No. 4, p28 (1958).

Stephens, *Nuclear Fission and Atomic Energy* (Science Press, 1948).

CHAPTER 17

Gell-Mann and Rosenbaum, 'Elementary Particles', *Scientific American*, **197**, No. 1, p72 (1957).

Marshak, 'Pions', *Scientific American*, **196**, No. 1, p84 (1957).

Rochester and Wilson, *Cloud Chamber Photographs of the Cosmic Radiation* (Academic Press, 1952).

Rossi, 'High Energy Cosmic Rays', *Scientific American*, **201**, No. 5, p134 (1959).

Segré and Wiegand, 'The Anti-proton', *Scientific American*, **194**, No. 6, p37 (1956).

Shapiro, 'Table of Properties of the Elementary Particles', *Reviews of Modern Physics*, **28**, p164 (1956).

Thorndike, *Mesons, a Summary of Experimental Facts* (McGraw-Hill, 1952).

Treiman, 'The Weak Interactions', *Scientific American*, **200**, No. 3, p72 (1959).

APPENDIX B

Table of Masses and Abundances of Naturally Occurring Isotopes

The atomic masses given in this table have been taken, with permission, from Everling, König, and Mattauch, *Nuclear Physics*, **18**, p529 (1960) and are given in terms of the C^{12} mass standard. The values of the masses have been rounded off so that the quoted probable errors are no more than 5 in the last figure given.

The isotopic abundance values have been taken from the table of Strominger, Hollander and Seaborg, *Reviews of Modern Physics*, **30**, p585 (1958). The reader is referred to this tabulation for complete data on all known nuclei, both naturally-occurring and artificially produced.

Asterisks have been placed against the mass numbers of those isotopes which are known to be radioactive.

Element	Symbol	Z	A	Per cent Abundance	Atomic Mass (a.m.u.)
Neutron	n	0	1	—	1·008665
Hydrogen	H	1	1	99·99	1·007825
			2	0·01	2·014102
Helium	He	2	3	$1·3 \times 10^{-4}$	3·016030
			4	100	4·002604
Lithium	Li	3	6	7·4	6·015126
			7	92·6	7·016005
Beryllium	Be	4	9	100	9·012186
Boron	B	5	10	19·6	10·012939
			11	80·4	11·009305
Carbon	C	6	12	98·9	12·000000
			13	1·1	13·003354
Nitrogen	N	7	14	99·6	14·003074
			15	0·4	15·000108
Oxygen	O	8	16	99·76	15·994915
			17	0·04	16·999133
			18	0·20	17·999160
Fluorine	F	9	19	100	18·998405
Neon	Ne	10	20	90·9	19·992440
			21	0·3	20·993849
			22	8·8	21·991384
Sodium	Na	11	23	100	22·989773
Magnesium	Mg	12	24	78·8	23·985045
			25	10·2	24·985840
			26	11·1	25·982591

Table of Masses and Abundances of Naturally Occurring Isotopes

Element	Symbol	Z	A	Per cent Abundance	Atomic Mass (a.m.u.)
Aluminium	Al	13	27	100	26·981535
Silicon	Si	14	28	92·2	27·976927
			29	4·7	28·976491
			30	3·1	29·973761
Phosphorus	P	15	31	100	30·973763
Sulphur	S	16	32	95·0	31·972074
			33	0·8	32·971460
			34	4·2	33·967864
			36	0·01	35·967091
Chlorine	Cl	17	35	75·5	34·968854
			37	24·5	36·965896
Argon	A	18	36	0·34	35·967548
			38	0·06	37·962724
			40	99·6	39·962384
Potassium	K	19	39	93·1	38·963714
			40*	0·012	39·964008
			41	6·9	40·961835
Calcium	Ca	20	40	97·0	39·962589
			42	0·6	41·958628
			43	0·1	42·958780
			44	2·1	43·955490
			46	0·003	45·953689
			48	0·2	47·952519
Scandium	Sc	21	45	100	44·955919
Titanium	Ti	22	46	8·0	45·952633
			47	7·3	46·95176
			48	74·0	47·947948
			49	5·5	48·947867
			50	5·2	49·944789
Vanadium	V	23	50*	0·25	49·947165
			51	99·75	50·943978
Chromium	Cr	24	50	4·3	49·946051
			52	83·8	51·940514
			53	9·5	52·940651
			54	2·4	53·938879
Manganese	Mn	25	55	100	54·938054
Iron	Fe	26	54	5·8	53·93962
			56	91·7	55·93493
			57	2·2	56·93539
			58	0·3	57·93327
Cobalt	Co	27	59	100	58·933189
Nickel	Ni	28	58	67·8	57·93534
			60	26·2	59·93078
			61	1·2	60·93105
			62	3·7	61·92834
			64	1·1	63·92796

Table of Masses and Abundances of Naturally Occurring Isotopes

Element	Symbol	Z	A	Per cent Abundance	Atomic Mass (a.m.u.)
Copper	Cu	29	63	69·1	62·92959
			65	30·9	64·92779
Zinc	Zn	30	64	48·9	63·929145
			66	27·8	65·92605
			67	4·1	66·92715
			68	18·6	67·92486
			70	0·6	69·92535
Gallium	Ga	31	69	60·5	68·92568
			71	39·5	70·92484
Germanium	Ge	32	70	20·5	69·92428
			72	27·4	71·92174
			73	7·7	72·9234
			74	36·7	73·9211
			76	7·7	75·9214
Arsenic	As	33	75	100	74·92158
Selenium	Se	34	74	0·9	73·9224
			76	9·0	75·91923
			77	7·6	76·91993
			78	23·5	77·91735
			80	49·8	79·91651
			82	9·2	81·9167
Bromine	Br	35	79	50·6	78·91835
			81	49·4	80·91634
Krypton	Kr	36	78	0·3	77·920368
			80	2·3	79·91639
			82	11·6	81·91348
			83	11·5	82·91413
			84	56·9	83·911504
			86	17·4	85·91062
Rubidium	Rb	37	85	72·1	84·9117
			87*	27·9	86·9092
Strontium	Sr	38	84	0·6	83·91338
			86	9·9	85·9093
			87	7·0	86·9089
			88	82·5	87·9056
Yttrium	Y	39	89	100	88·9054
Zirconium	Zr	40	90	51·5	89·9043
			91	11·2	90·9052
			92	17·1	91·9046
			94	17·4	93·9061
			96	2·8	95·9082
Niobium	Nb	41	93	100	92·9060
Molybdenum	Mo	42	92	15·9	91·9063
			94	9·1	93·9047
			95	15·7	94·9057
			96	16·5	95·9045
			97	9·4	96·9057
			98	23·8	97·9055
			100	9·6	99·9076

Table of Masses and Abundances of Naturally Occurring Isotopes

Element	Symbol	Z	A	Per cent Abundance	Atomic Mass (a.m.u.)
Technetium	Tc	43	has no stable or naturally-occurring isotopes		
Ruthenium	Ru	44	96	5·6	95·9076
			98	1·9	97·905
			99	12·7	98·9061
			100	12·6	
			101	17·1	
			102	31·6	101·9037
			104	18·5	103·9055
Rhodium	Rh	45	103	100	102·9048
Palladium	Pd	46	102	1·0	101·9049
			104	11·0	103·9036
			105	22·2	104·9046
			106	27·3	105·9032
			108	26·7	107·9039
			110	11·8	109·9045
Silver	Ag	47	107	51·4	106·9050
			109	48·6	108·9047
Cadmium	Cd	48	106	1·2	105·9059
			108	0·9	107·9040
			110	12·4	109·9030
			111	12·7	110·9041
			112	24·1	111·9028
			113	12·3	112·9046
			114	28·8	113·9036
			116	7·6	115·9050
Indium	In	49	113	4·3	112·9043
			115*	95·7	114·9041
Tin	Sn	50	112	1·0	111·9049
			114	0·6	113·9030
			115	0·3	114·9035
			116	14·2	115·9021
			117	7·6	116·9031
			118	24·0	117·9018
			119	8·6	118·9034
			120	33·0	119·9021
			122	4·7	121·9034
			124	6·0	123·9052
Antimony	Sb	51	121	57·3	120·9037
			123	42·7	122·9041
Tellurium	Te	52	120	0·1	119·9045
			122	2·4	121·9030
			123	0·9	122·9042
			124	4·6	123·9028
			125	7·0	124·9044
			126	18·7	125·90324
			128	31·8	127·9047
			130	34·5	129·9067

Table of Masses and Abundances of Naturally Occurring Isotopes

Element	Symbol	Z	A	Per cent Abundance	Atomic Mass (a.m.u.)
Iodine	I	53	127	100	126·90435
Xenon	Xe	54	124	0·1	123·9061
			126	0·1	125·90417
			128	1·9	127·90354
			129	26·4	128·90478
			130	4·1	129·90351
			131	21·2	130·90509
			132	26·9	131·90416
			134	10·4	133·90540
			136	8·9	135·90722
Caesium	Cs	55	133	100	132·9051
Barium	Ba	56	130	0·1	129·90625
			132	0·2	131·9051
			134	2·6	133·9043
			135	6·7	134·9056
			136	8·1	135·9044
			137	11·9	136·9056
			138	70·4	137·9050
Lanthanum	La	57	138*	0·1	137·9068
			139	99·9	138·9061
Cerium	Ce	58	136	0·2	135·9071
			138	0·2	137·9057
			140	88·5	139·90528
			142*	11·1	141·9090
Praseodymium	Pr	59	141	100	140·90739
Neodymium	Nd	60	142	27·3	141·90748
			143	12·3	142·90962
			144*	23·8	143·90990
			145	8·3	144·9122
			146	17·1	145·9127
			148	5·7	147·9165
			150	5·5	149·9207
Promethium	Pm	61	has no stable or naturally-occurring isotopes.		
Samarium	Sm	62	144	3·1	143·9116
			147*	15·1	146·91462
			148	11·3	146·9146
			149	14·0	148·9169
			150	7·5	149·9170
			152	26·6	151·9193
			154	22·4	153·9217
Europium	Eu	63	151	47·8	150·9196
			153	52·2	152·9207
Gadolinium	Gd	64	152	0·2	151·9194
			154	2·2	153·9202
			155	15·1	154·9220
			156	20·6	155·9222
			157	15·7	156·9240
			158	24·5	157·9242
			160	21·7	159·9273

Table of Masses and Abundances of Naturally Occurring Isotopes

Element	Symbol	Z	A	Per cent Abundance	Atomic Mass (a.m.u.)
Terbium	Tb	65	159	100	158·924
Dysprosium	Dy	66	156	0·1	
			158	0·1	
			160	2·3	159·924
			161	19·0	160·926
			162	25·5	161·926
			163	24·9	162·928
			164	28·1	163·928
Holmium	Ho	67	165	100	164·930
Erbium	Er	68	162	0·1	
			164	1·6	163·929
			166	33·4	165·929
			167	22·9	166·931
			168	27·1	167·931
			170	14·9	169·935
Thulium	Tm	69	169	100	
Ytterbium	Yb	70	168	0·1	
			170	3·1	
			171	14·4	
			172	21·9	171·929
			173	16·2	
			174	31·7	173·926
			176	12·6	
Lutetium	Lu	71	175	97·4	
			176*	2·6	175·9414
Hafnium	Hf	72	174	0·2	
			176	5·2	175·9403
			177	18·6	176·9419
			178	27·1	177·9425
			179	13·7	178·9444
			180	35·2	179·9451
Tantalum	Ta	73	180	0·01	179·9457
			181	99·99	180·9462
Tungsten	W	74	180	0·2	179·9450
			182	26·4	181·9465
			183	14·4	182·9485
			184	30·6	183·9491
			186	28·4	185·951
Rhenium	Re	75	185	37·1	184·950
			187*	62·9	186·9550
Osmium	Os	76	184	0·02	
			186	1·6	185·9529
			187	1·6	186·9550
			188	13·3	187·9550
			189	16·1	188·9572
			190	26·4	189·9574
			192	41·0	191·9605

Table of Masses and Abundances of Naturally Occurring Isotopes

Element	Symbol	Z	A	Per Cent Abundance	Atomic Mass (a.m.u.)
Iridium	Ir	77	191	38·5	190·9599
			193	61·5	192·9623
Platinum	Pt	78	190*	0·01	189·9592
			192*	0·8	191·9605
			194	32·9	193·9624
			195	33·8	194·9645
			196	25·3	195·9646
			198	7·2	197·9675
Gold	Au	79	197	100	196·96655
Mercury	Hg	80	196	0·1	195·96582
			198	10·0	197·96677
			199	16·9	198·96826
			200	23·1	199·96834
			201	13·2	200·97031
			202	29·8	201·97063
			204	6·9	203·97348
Thallium	Tl	81	203	29·5	202·97233
			205	70·5	204·97446
			206*	—	205·97608
			207*	—	206·97745
			208*	—	207·98201
			210*	—	209·99000
Lead	Pb	82	204	1·4	203·97307
			206	25·2	205·97446
			207	21·7	206·97590
			208	51·7	207·97664
			210*	—	209·98418
			211*	—	210·98880
			212*	—	211·99190
			214*	—	213·99976
Bismuth	Bi	83	209	100	208·98042
			210*	—	209·98411
			211*	—	210·98729
			212*	—	211·99127
			214*	—	213·99863
Polonium	Po	84	210*	—	209·98287
			211*	—	210·98665
			212*	—	211·98886
			214*	—	213·99519
			215*	—	214·99947
			216*	—	216·00192
			218*	—	218·0089
Astatine	At	85	215*	—	214·99866
			218*	—	218·00855
Emanation	Em	86	219*	—	219·00952
			220*	—	220·01140
			222*	—	222·0175

Table of Masses and Abundances of Naturally Occurring Isotopes

Element	Symbol	Z		Per Cent Abundance	Atomic Mass (a.m.u.)
Francium	Fr	87	223*	—	223·01980
Radium	Ra	88	223*	—	223·01857
			224*	—	224·02022
			226*	—	226·0254
			228*	—	228·03123
Actinium	Ac	89	227*	—	227·02781
			228*	—	228·03117
Thorium	Th	90	227*	—	227·02777
			228*	—	228·02875
			230*	—	230·0331
			231*	—	231·03635
			232*	100	232·03821
			234*	—	234·0436
Protactinium	Pa	91	231*	—	231·03594
			234*	—	234·0434
Uranium	U	92	234*	0·006	234·04090
			235*	0·718	235·04393
			238*	99·276	238·0508

APPENDIX C

Tables of Naturally Occurring Radioactive Isotopes

The data in these tables are obtained, with permission, from the article 'Table of Isotopes', by Strominger, Hollander and Seaborg; *Reviews of Modern Physics*, **30**, p585 (1958).

1. ISOLATED ISOTOPES THROUGH THE PERIODIC TABLE

Element	Isotope	Isotopic 'bundance (Per Cent)	Half-Life	Mode of Decay* and Energies in MeV of Principal Particle Groups and γ-Rays
Potassium	$_{19}K^{40}$	0·01	$1\cdot3 \times 10^9$ y	β, 1·4; ϵ; γ, 1·5
Vanadium	$_{23}V^{50}$	0·3	4×10^{14} y	ϵ
Rubidium	$_{37}Rb^{87}$	28	5×10^{10} y	β, 0·3
Indium	$_{49}In^{115}$	96	6×10^{14} y	β, 0·6
Lanthanum	$_{57}La^{138}$	0·09	10^{11} y	β, 1·0; ϵ; γ, 1·4, 0·8
Neodymium	$_{60}Nd^{144}$	24	5×10^{15} y	α, 1·9
Neodymium	$_{60}Nd^{150}$	5·6	$>10^{16}$ y	β ?†
Samarium	$_{62}Sm^{147}$	15	$1\cdot3 \times 10^{11}$ y	α, 2·2
Lutetium	$_{71}Lu^{176}$	2·6	4×10^{10} y	β, 0·4; γ, 0·3, 0·2, 0·09
Tantalum	$_{73}Ta^{180}$	0·01	$>10^{12}$ y	β ?
Rhenium	$_{75}Re^{187}$	63	$>10^{10}$ y	β ?
Platinum	$_{78}Pt^{190}$	0·01	6×10^{11} y	α, 3·3
Platinum	$_{78}Pt^{192}$	0·8	10^{15} y	α, 2·6
Bismuth	$_{83}Bi^{209}$	100	$>2 \times 10^{18}$ y	α ?

* The following symbols are used:

   β : negative β-decay

   α : α-decay

   ϵ : electron capture.

† The isotopes with a query (?) against their mode of decay *should* be radioactive, according to their measured atomic masses. However, there is some doubt as to whether any radiations from them have actually been observed.

2. THE NATURAL RADIOACTIVE SERIES

THE URANIUM (4n + 2) SERIES

Element	Isotope	Original Name	Mode of Decay	Half-Life	Energies in MeV of Principal Particle Groups and γ-Rays
Uranium	$_{92}U^{238}$	Uranium I (UI)	α → β →	4.5×10^9 y	α, 4·2; γ, 0·05
Thorium	$_{90}Th^{234}$	Uranium X₁ (UX₁)	β →	24 d	β, 0·19, 0·10; γ, 0·09, 0·06, 0·03
Protactinium	$_{91}Pa^{234}$	Uranium X₂ (UX₂)	β, → / γ* →	1·2 m	β, 2·3; γ, 1·0
Protactinium	$_{91}Pa^{234}$	Uranium Z (UZ)	β →	6·7 h	β, 0·45; γ, 1·7–0·04
Uranium	$_{92}U^{234}$	Uranium II (UII)	α →	2.5×10^5 y	α, 4·8, 4·7; γ, 0·05
Thorium	$_{90}Th^{230}$	Ionium (Io)	α →	8.0×10^4 y	α, 4·7, 4·6; γ, 0·07
Radium	$_{88}Ra^{226}$	Radium (Ra)	α →	1620 y	α, 4·8; γ, 0·19
Emanation	$_{86}Em^{222}$	Radon (Rn)	α →	3·8 d	α, 5·5
Polonium	$_{84}Po^{218}$	Radium A (RaA)	α → / β (0·02%) →	3·1 m	α, 6·0; β, not measured
Lead	$_{82}Pb^{214}$	Radium B (RaB)	β →	27 m	β, 0·6; γ, 0·35–0·05
Astatine	$_{85}At^{218}$	—	α (0·04%) / β →	2 s	α, 6·6
Bismuth	$_{83}Bi^{214}$	Radium C (RaC)	α → / β →	20 m	α, 5·5, 5·4; β, 3·2–0·4; γ, 2·4–0·6
Polonium	$_{84}Po^{214}$	Radium C′ (RaC′)	α →	1.6×10^{-4} s	α, 7·7
Thallium	$_{81}Tl^{210}$	Radium C″ (RaC″)	β →	1·5 m	β, 2·0; γ, 2·4–0·3
Lead	$_{82}Pb^{210}$	Radium D (RaD)	β →	19 y	β, 0·02; γ, 0·05

Bismuth	$_{83}Bi^{210}$	Radium E (RaE)	$\overset{\alpha}{\underset{(0\cdot0004\%)}{\longrightarrow}}$ $\overset{\beta}{\longrightarrow}$	$\overset{\beta}{\rightarrow}$ 5·0 d	α, 4·8; β, 1·2
Polonium	$_{84}Po^{210}$	Radium F (RaF)	$\overset{\beta}{\longrightarrow}$	$\overset{\alpha}{\longrightarrow}$ 138 d	α, 5·3
Thallium	$_{81}Tl^{206}$	—		$\longrightarrow$ 4·2 m	β, 1·5
Lead	$_{82}Pb^{206}$	Radium G (RaG)	Stable		

* $_{90}Th^{234}$ decays both to an excited state of $_{91}Pa^{234}$ and to its ground state. When formed in this excited state, the $_{91}Pa^{234}$ nucleus may either decay by γ-emission to the ground state or by direct β-emission to $_{92}U^{234}$. The combination of these two processes results in $_{91}Pa^{234}$, when in this state, having a half-life of 1·2 minute. The $_{91}Pa^{234}$ when in its ground state, on the other hand, decays with a different half-life, 6·7 hour.

THE ACTINIUM (4n + 3) SERIES

Element	Isotope	Original Name	Mode of Decay	Half-Life	Energies in MeV of Principal Particle Groups and γ-Rays
Uranium	$_{92}U^{235}$	Actinouranium (AcU)	α →	7.1×10^8 y	α, 4.4; γ, 0.18
Thorium	$_{90}Th^{231}$	Uranium Y (UY)	β →	25 h	β, 0.30–0.09; γ, 0.23–0.02
Protactinium	$_{91}Pa^{231}$	Protoactinium (Pa)	α →	3.4×10^4 y	α, 5.0; γ, 0.36–0.03
Actinium	$_{89}Ac^{227}$	Actinium (Ac)	α (1.2%) → / β →	22 y	α, 4.9; β, 0.05
Thorium	$_{90}Th^{227}$	Radioactinium (RaAc)	β → / α →	18 d	α, 6.0; γ, 0.33–0.03
Francium	$_{87}Fr^{223}$	Actinium K (AcK)	β →	22 m	β, 1.2; γ, 0.08, 0.05
Radium	$_{88}Ra^{223}$	Actinium X (AcX)	α →	11 d	α, 5.7; γ, 0.45–0.03
Emanation	$_{86}Em^{219}$	Actinon (An)	α →	3.9 s	α, 6.8; γ, 0.40, 0.27
Polonium	$_{84}Po^{215}$	Actinium A (AcA)	α → / β (0.0005%) →	1.8×10^{-3} s	α, 7.4; β, not measured
Lead	$_{82}Pb^{211}$	Actinium B (AcB)	β →	36 m	β, 1.4; γ, 0.83–0.07
Astatine	$_{85}At^{215}$	—	α →	10^{-4} s	α, 8.0
Bismuth	$_{83}Bi^{211}$	Actinium C (AcC)	α → / β (0.32%) →	2.2 m	α, 6.6, 6.3; β, not measured; γ, 0.35
Thallium	$_{81}Tl^{207}$	Actinium C" (AcC")	β →	4.8 m	β, 1.5; γ, 0.87
Polonium	$_{84}Po^{211}$	Actinium C' (AcC')	α →	0.52 s	α, 7.4
Lead	$_{82}Pb^{207}$	Actinium D (AcD)	Stable		

THE THORIUM (4n) SERIES

Element	Isotope	Original Name	Mode of Decay	Half-Life	Energies in MeV of Principal Particle Groups and γ-Rays
Thorium	$_{90}Th^{232}$	Thorium (Th)	α →	$1\cdot4 \times 10^{10}$ y	α, 4·0; γ, 0·06
Radium	$_{88}Ra^{228}$	Mesothorium 1 (MsTh 1)	β →	6·7 y	β, 0·01
Actinium	$_{89}Ac^{228}$	Mesothorium 2 (MsTh 2)	β →	6·1 h	β, 2·2–0·45; γ, 1·6–0·06
Thorium	$_{90}Th^{228}$	Radiothorium (RdTh)	α →	1·9 y	α, 5·4, 5·3; γ, 0·08
Radium	$_{88}Ra^{224}$	Thorium X (ThX)	α →	3·6 d	α, 5·7; γ, 0·24
Emanation	$_{86}Em^{220}$	Thoron (Tn)	α →	52 s	α, 6·3
Polonium	$_{84}Po^{216}$	Thorium A (ThA)	α →	0·16 s	α, 6·8
Lead	$_{82}Pb^{212}$	Thorium B (ThB)	β →	10·6 h	β, 0·59, 0·36; γ, 0·41–0·11
Bismuth	$_{83}Bi^{212}$	Thorium C (ThC)	α (36%) → β →	61 m	α, 6·1, 6·0; β, 2·3; γ, 2·2–0·04
Polonium	$_{84}Po^{212}$	Thorium C′ (ThC′)	β → α →	3×10^{-7} s	α, 8·8
Thallium	$_{81}Tl^{208}$	Thorium C″ (ThC″)	β →	3·1 m	β, 1·3–2·4; γ, 2·62–0·28
Lead	$_{82}Pb^{208}$	Thorium D (ThD)	Stable		

APPENDIX D

Table of Physical Constants

The data for this table have been adapted from Cohen, Crowe and Du Mond, *Fundamental Constants of Physics*, Tables 8·6 and 8·7 (Inter-science, 1957), with permission. The accuracy of these values is such that the error in each case is two or less in the last quoted figure.

Avogadro's number	$N_0 = 6 \cdot 0230 \times 10^{26} (\text{kgm-mole})^{-1}$
Velocity of light in vacuum	$c = 2 \cdot 99793 \times 10^8 \text{ m sec}^{-1}$
Planck's constant	$h = 6 \cdot 6252 \times 10^{-34} \text{ joule sec}$
Boltzmann's constant	$k = 1 \cdot 3804 \times 10^{-23} \text{ joule deg K}^{-1}$
Electronic charge	$e = 1 \cdot 6021 \times 10^{-19} \text{ coulomb}$
Specific charge of electron	$e/m_0 = 1 \cdot 75890 \times 10^{11} \text{ coulomb kgm}^{-1}$
Faraday's constant	$F = N_0 e$
	$= 9 \cdot 6494 \times 10^7 \text{coulomb (kgm-mole)}^{-1}$
Electron volt	$1 \text{ eV} = 1 \cdot 6021 \times 10^{-19} \text{ joule}$
Atomic mass unit ($\frac{1}{12}$ mass of C^{12})	$1 \text{ a.m.u.} = 1 \cdot 6603 \times 10^{-27} \text{ kgm}$
Mass-energy conversion factors	$1 \text{ a.m.u.} = 931 \cdot 44 \text{ MeV}$
	$1 \text{ kgm} = 5 \cdot 6100 \times 10^{29} \text{ MeV}$

Masses of particles at rest

Electron
$$m_0 = 5 \cdot 4859 \times 10^{-4} \text{ a.m.u.}$$
$$= 9 \cdot 108 \times 10^{-31} \text{ kgm}$$
$$= 0 \cdot 51098 \text{ MeV}$$

Neutron
$$m_n = 1 \cdot 00866 \text{ a.m.u.}$$
$$= 1 \cdot 6747 \times 10^{-27} \text{ kgm}$$
$$= 939 \cdot 51 \text{ MeV}$$

Proton
$$m_p = 1 \cdot 00728 \text{ a.m.u.}$$
$$= 1 \cdot 6724 \times 10^{-27} \text{ kgm}$$
$$= 938 \cdot 21 \text{ MeV}$$

Hydrogen atom
$$m_H = 1 \cdot 00783 \text{ a.m.u.}$$
$$= 1 \cdot 6733 \times 10^{-27} \text{ kgm}$$
$$= 938 \cdot 72 \text{ MeV}$$

Ratio proton mass to electron mass $\quad m_p/m_0 = 1836 \cdot 12$

INDEX

Index

Index

Length contraction, 67
Leucippus, 2
Limit of spectral series, 73, 74
Line spectra, 71, 84, 85
  series in, 71 *et seq.*, 74
Linear Accelerator, 141
Lines, spectral, 71
Liveing, 73
Livingston, 144
Lorentz, 66
Lorentz transformation, 66
Lyman, 90
Lyman series, 75, 90, 96

MAGNETIC quantum number, 95
Malus, 62
Marsden, 77, 80, 81, 82, 124
Marshall, 116
Mass, variation with velocity, 68
Mass-energy equivalence, 68
Mass excess, 166
Mass number, 110
Mass scale, atomic, 110
Mass spectrograph, 105, 109
  Aston, 105 *et seq.*
  Bainbridge, 109
Mass spectrometer, 108
  Dempster, 107 *et seq.*
Mass spectrum, 105
Mass unit, atomic, 110
Mattauch, 129, 151, 166, 201
Matter, early ideas of nature of, 2
Maxwell, 6, 22, 62
Mayer, 6
McMillan, 145
Mean life, 190
Meitner, 174
Mesons, 172, 189 *et seq.*
Meyer, 48
Michelson, 64
Michelson and Morley experiment, 64
Microtron, 149
Millikan, 15, 25, 186
Millikan's measurement of *e*, 15 *et seq.*
Millikan's verification of Einstein's equation, 25 *et seq.*
Moderator, 177

Molecular weight, 5
Morley, 64
Moseley, 96, 97
Moseley's law, 97
M-shell, 96
μ-meson, 189 *et seq.*, 193
Muirhead, 191
Müller, 115
Muon, 190
Murphy, 89

NATURAL leak of electroscopes, 183
Neddermeyer, 190
Negative glow, 10
Neptunium, 178
Neptunium series, 165, 167
Nereson, 190
Neutrino, 163, 193
  detection of, 163
Neutrons
  detection of, 122, 163
  fast and slow, 157
  fission produced by, 173 *et seq.*
  identification of, 131 *et seq.*
  mass of, 132 *et seq.*
  nuclear disintegrations produced by, 156, 176
  prediction of, 101
  radioactive decay of, 171
  thermal, 176
Neutron number, 169
Neutron-proton structure of nuclei, 152
Newton, 62, 70
Newtonian transformation, 65
Nomenclature of reactions, 154
Nuclear atom, 77 *et seq.*
Nuclear binding, 166 *et seq.*, 173
Nuclear emulsion, 122
Nuclear forces, 171, 189 *et seq.*
Nuclear reaction, 127 *et seq.*, 150 *et seq.*
Nuclear stability, 169 *et seq.*
Nucleon, 152
Nucleus, 78
  charge of, 78, 82, 90, 99, 100
  radius of, 78
  structure of, 100
Nuttall, 161